MW00783083

Monstrous Compendium®

Appendix III: Creatures of Darkness

Principal Designers: **Kirk Botulla, Shane Hensley, Nicky Rea,** and **Teeuwynn Woodruff**
Additional Designers: **Anne Brown, William W. Connors, Andria Hayday, Colin McComb, Bruce Nesmith,** and **David Wise**
Editor: **William W. Connors**
Cover Artist: **Jeff Easley**
Primary Interior Artist: **Mark Nelson**
Additional Interior Artists: **Tom Baxa** and **Stephan Fabian**
Graphic Design: **Dawn Murin**
Typesetting: **Nancy J. Kerkstra**

This product is dedicated to:

Jacob Boss
and
Jim & Lisa Parks

Who praise us when we do things right
and point it out when we don't.

TSR, Inc.
P.O. Box 756
Lake Geneva
Wisconsin 53147
USA

TSR Ltd.
120 Church End
Cherry Hinton
Cambridge CB1 3LB
United Kingdom

Introduction

As I write this it's been almost exactly five years since Bruce Nesmith and Andria Hayday started working on the *RAVENLOFT® Realm of Terror* boxed set. How do I know that? They started writing on the same day that I was hired by TSR, Incorporated. Of course, most people would say that this was nothing more than coincidence, but I know better.

It wasn't long before I found myself captivated by the notion of the RAVENLOFT campaign's unique blend of horror and fantasy. Luckily, I wasn't the only one. RAVENLOFT quickly became TSR's most successful game line. I'm very proud to have been a part of that, and I hope that I'll be a part of the Demiplane of Dread for years to come.

One of the first design projects I had at TSR was the *RAVENLOFT Appendix* to the MONSTROUS COMPENDIUM® product line (MC). At first, I thought that writing an MC would be pretty dull. After all, you crank out a monster, clear your brain, and start again. Not exactly gripping from an author's point of view.

Well, I'm very happy to say that I was wrong. The more of Ravenloft's inhabitants I created, the more I thought of. Before long, I found that I was being overwhelmed with ideas for the nightmarish citizens of Ravenloft. Indeed, I still have notes around describing monsters that I wanted to put in that book but didn't have space to. You'll find several of them lurking within the pages of this very book.

A year or so after the first RAVENLOFT MC came out, we decided to put out another. As it sold well and the comments we received on it were generally very favorable, it seemed like a sound decision. Once again, the mists stepped in and I mysteriously found that I was the one selected to design it. Unfortunately, as is always the case in Ravenloft, the road took an unexpected bend just ahead.

For one reason or another, I don't remember exactly what it was, we had to change our schedules around. The 128-page book you're holding in your hands had to be bumped back a year and replaced with a smaller MONSTROUS COMPENDIUM appendix. This time, however, I was going to write the smaller one and all the notes I had made for the larger one were going to be passed on to a team of freelance designers. I was right (or is it "write?") back at the beginning.

I asked for permission from the powers that be to do a MONSTROUS COMPENDIUM with a twist. Why not do an MC that featured only unique villains? After all, we stress that point frequently in our RAVENLOFT campaign writings and seminars. This would show people that we meant what we said. The boss agreed, I burned the negatives, and work began on *Children of the Night,* the second RAVENLOFT MONSTROUS COMPENDIUM Appendix.

With that done, I turned my attention back to the 128-page volume. You see, the mists had risen again and I was now slated to do the editing and development work on the material turned over by the freelance team. Ravenloft monsters and I seemed to still be on intimate terms. I'm not entirely sure whether that's a good thing or not, but what the heck. As the Vistani say, *You go where the mists take you.*

Like all the members of the Kargat (as our cadre of RAVENLOFT game designers and editors is known), I have pretty high standards for the line. In addition, I'd written the first MONSTROUS COMPENDIUM as well as *Children of the Night* and was openly prejudiced by my opinion of how the third one should be done. As luck would have it, this seemed to have spilled over onto the freelance designers as well. The more I read of their work, the better I liked it. It's not often that you get to have as much fun on a project as I did on this one.

So here it is, the third *RAVENLOFT Appendix* to the MONSTROUS COMPENDIUM line. A great many people have put a lot of time and effort into the creation of this product. I hope that you're as happy with it as I am. I look forward to hearing your comments about it at conventions and through the mail.

The only problem that I have now is what to do with all these notes for monsters that didn't make it into *this* book?

William W. Connors

Welcome to the third Monstrous Compendium volume detailing the horrible creatures of TSR's Ravenloft campaign setting. Between the covers of this book lurks a collection of creatures so vile and loathsome that any Dungeon Master will delight in haunting his players with them.

As with most volumes in the Monstrous Compendium series, the reader is reminded that the monsters included here are typical for their type. Variations of your own design are encouraged. Because of the special nature of Ravenloft adventures, no encounter tables are included in this book. Each entry includes the following information:

CLIMATE/TERRAIN defines where the creature is most often found. Normally, climates include things such as arctic, subarctic, temperate, and tropical, and terrain would include plain/scrub, forest, rough/hill, mountain, swamp, and desert. Many of the entries in this book will include the name of the domain(s) where they are found.

FREQUENCY is the likelihood of encountering a creature in an area. Very rare is a 4% chance, rare is 11%, uncommon is 20%, and common is a 65% chance. Chances can be adjusted for special areas. As the traditional random encounters used in other campaigns are not generally found in Ravenloft, this entry can be taken as a guideline for adventure design.

ORGANIZATION describes the general social structure that the monster adopts. Common types are solitary, clan, pack, herd, flock, and such. In many cases, "solitary" includes small familial groups like mated pairs.

ACTIVITY CYCLE is the time of day when the monster is most animated. Those who tend to be busy at night may be active at any time in subterranean or similar settings. It is worth remembering that the "activity cycle" entry is a general guide and exceptions are fairly common.

DIET tells what the creature generally eats. Carnivores eat meat, herbivores eat plants, omnivores eat either, and scavengers dine mainly on carrion. Unusual entries, like *life energy* or *emotions,* will be listed from time to time and explained more fully in the text.

INTELLIGENCE is the equivalent of the Ability Score of the same name. Certain unintelligent monsters are instinctively cunning hunters and these are noted in the monster descriptions. Ratings correspond roughly to the following Intelligence Ability Scores:

0	Non-intelligent or not ratable
1	Animal intelligence
2–4	Semi-intelligent
5–7	Low intelligence
8–10	Average (human) intelligence
11–12	Very intelligent
13–14	Highly intelligent
15–16	Exceptionally intelligent
17–18	Genius
19–20	Supra-genius
21+	Godlike intelligence

TREASURE refers to the treasure tables in the *Dungeon Master® Guide* and indicates the type of wealth likely to be found on an individual monster. Treasure should be adjusted downward if few monsters are encountered. This may be further increased or decreased at the DM's discretion. These tables should not be used to place dungeon treasure, as numbers encountered underground will be much smaller. Intelligent monsters will use magical items present and try to carry off their most valuable treasures if hard pressed.

Major treasures are usually found in the monster's lair and will be enclosed in parentheses. As a rule, these should not be determined randomly but ought to be designed and placed by the DM. If the Dungeon Master does decide to assign such treasure randomly, he should roll for each type possible: if all rolls fail, no treasure of any type is found.

Unusually large or small treasures are noted by a parenthetical multiplier (×10, etc.), These should not be confused with treasure type X.

ALIGNMENT shows the general behavior of the average monster of that type. Exceptions, though uncommon, may be encountered, especially within the misty confines of Ravenloft.

NO. APPEARING indicates an average number of creatures that will be encountered in the wild. The DM should alter this to fit the circumstances as the need arises. In many cases, additional information on this topic will be presented in the **Habitat/Society** or **Ecology** section.

ARMOR CLASS is a rating of the monster's resistance to damage in combat. In many cases this will be due to the creature's natural defenses, but it can also indicate armor worn by humanoids or other creatures. In some cases, high speed, natural agility, or magical protection may play a part in the determination of a creature's Armor Class rating. Humans and humanoids of roughly man-size that wear armor will have an unarmored rating in parentheses. Listed ACs do not include any situational bonuses noted in the description.

MOVEMENT shows the relative speed of the creature with an unencumbered man having a rating of 12. Higher speeds may be possible for short periods. Human, demihuman, and humanoid movement rates are often determined by armor type (unarmored rates are given in parentheses). Movement through common media are abbreviated as follows:

Br	Burrowing
Fl	Flying
Sw	Swimming
Wb	Moving in a web

Flying creatures also have a Maneuverability Class from A to E that is indicated in parentheses. Complete information on Maneuverability Classes and their use can be found in the Aerial Combat rules in the *Dungeon Master® Guide.*

How to Use this Book

HIT DICE indicates the number of dice rolled to generate the creature's hit points. Unless otherwise stated, Hit Dice are 8-sided. The Hit Dice are rolled and the numbers shown are added to determine the monster's hit points.

Some monsters will have additional points added to the total rolled on the Hit Dice. Thus, a creature with a rating of 4+4 has between 8 and 36 hit points. Monsters with a bonus of +3 or more to their rolled hit points are considered to have an extra Hit Die for the purposes of attack rolls and saving throws. Thus, a creature with 4+4 Hit Dice attacks and saves as if it had 5 Hit Dice.

In rare cases, a monster will have a hit point spread without a Hit Dice rating. In order to determine the number of Hit Dice that such creatures have for Attack and Saving Throws, divide the listed hit points by 4. Round the Hit Die rating up with remainders of .5 or greater and drop all other fractions.

THAC0 is the base roll that the monster needs to hit an enemy with an Armor Class of 0. This is a function of Hit Dice as described in the Combat section of the *DUNGEON MASTER® Guide*. Modifiers to the creature's attack roll will be presented in the **Combat** section of the entry, but the listed THAC0 does not include any special bonuses.

NO. OF ATTACKS indicates the number of times that the monster can attack in a single round. Multiple attacks can usually be taken to indicate several attacking arms, raking paws, multiple heads, etc. In some cases, this does not include special attacks listed in the **Combat** section, but the text will make that clear. This number may be modified by hits that sever members, magic such as *haste* or *slow* spells, and so forth.

DAMAGE/ATTACK shows the severity of a given attack and is expressed as a spread of damage points. The number and type of dice rolled to determine the total number of hit points lost by the target of the attack will be listed in parentheses. If the monster uses weapons, the damage listed is for its favored weapon. Damage bonuses due to high strength, special abilities, and the like are listed in the **Combat** section of the entry.

SPECIAL ATTACKS details any unusual attack modes possessed by the creature such as breath weapons, spell use, poison, and the like. These are fully explained in the monster description.

SPECIAL DEFENSES provides information detailing any unusual resistances to harm that the monster might have. These commonly include an immunity to certain forms of attack or an invulnerability to non-magical weapons. These are fully detailed in the monster description.

MAGIC RESISTANCE is the percentage chance that magic cast upon the creature will fail to affect it, even if other creatures nearby are affected. If the spell penetrates this resistance, the creature is still entitled to any normal saving throws allowed. A creature may drop its magic resistance at any time and allow a spell to affect it normally if it so chooses.

SIZE is an indication of the overall dimensions of the creature. In the case of humanoids, it indicates the height of the monster. For other creatures (snakes and dragons, for example), it refers to the animal's length. Other measurements are possible and will be explained in the text.

T = tiny	under 2 feet tall
S = small	over 2 feet to 4 feet tall
M = man-sized	over 4 feet to 7 feet tall
L = large	over 7 feet to 12 feet tall
H = huge	over 12 feet to 25 feet tall
G = gargantuan	over 25 feet tall

MORALE is a general rating of how likely the monster is to persevere in the face of adversity or armed opposition. This guideline may be adjusted for individual circumstances. Morale ratings correspond to the following range:

2–4	Unreliable
5–7	Unsteady
8–10	Average
11–12	Steady
13–14	Elite
15–16	Champion
17–18	Fanatic
19–20	Fearless

XP VALUE is the number of experience points awarded for defeating (not necessarily killing) the monster. This value is a guideline that may be modified by the DM for the degree of challenge, encounter situation, and overall campaign balance.

PSIONICS gives a complete breakdown of the creature's innate psionic abilities, including sciences or devotions known and PSPs available. A complete understanding of this section requires the *Complete Psionics Handbook*. This entry is included only for those creatures that have psionic powers.

COMBAT provides all of the information that a DM will need to resolve a battle with the monster. Among other things, it details special combat abilities, arms or armor, and unusual tactics employed by the creature.

HABITAT/SOCIETY outlines the monster's general behavior, nature, social structure, and goals. Where the previous section provided the information needed for resolving skirmishes involving the creature, this entry provides information useful for role-playing encounters.

ECOLOGY describes how the monster fits into the campaign world, gives useful products or byproducts of the creature, and presents other miscellaneous information. This information can help the Dungeon Master to decide exactly when and where to best introduce the monster to his campaign.

CLOSE VARIATIONS of a monster are given in a special section after the main monster entry. For example, the *akikage* entry also includes a brief discussion of the *ansasshia,* a closely related creature.

One of the things that game designers love to do is change things. As of this writing, it has been about five years since the final touches were put on the ADVANCED DUNGEONS & DRAGONS® 2nd Edition game rules. In that time, a number of major and minor changes have been made to the game system.

One of the more important revisions is a change to the formula used to calculate experience point rewards for defeating the various monsters encountered during an adventure. This revision was introduced in the *MONSTROUS MANUAL*™ hardbound and has become the new standard for the calculation of experience points.

The experience point values for the monsters in this *MONSTROUS COMPENDIUM* Appendix have all been calculated using the new, revised rules. The table to the right, updating the one printed in the AD&D® 2nd Edition *DUNGEON MASTER Guide*, is provided in order to make the Dungeon Master's task easier when designing his own monsters.

It is worth noting that there are cases where DMs will want to deviate from the values given here. Some monsters are so powerful that the experience point rewards generated with these tables will be far less than a party might deserve. Some good examples of such creatures are the denizens of the Abyss and similar realms described in the *PLANESCAPE*™ campaign setting or the various lords of Ravenloft's domains.

What Has Changed?

None of these changes affect the general way in which experience points are calculated. A DM still begins by noting the number of Hit Dice that a monster has (Table 31) and then applying some modifiers based on the general powers and abilities of that creature. Only the modifiers (Table 32) have changed, although both tables have been printed here for easy reference.

Two new entries for psionic abilities have been added to the table. Thus, the possibility that a monster might have psionic disciplines or sciences (as detailed in *The Complete Psionics Handbook)* available to it has now been taken into account. Dungeon Masters who are not using psionic powers in their campaigns can simply ignore these additions.

Both the **magic resistance** and **breath weapon** entries have been split into two categories, reflecting the great range of possibilities within these classifications.

The bonus normally awarded for flight has been expanded to include other special forms of movement. Thus, a monster like a bulette or xorn, which can travel through the earth at great speed, would receive the same adjustment to its experience point value as a flying creature.

Of course, exceptions and unusual cases will still crop up. When this happens, Dungeon Masters will simply have to use a little common sense in the awarding of experience points.

Table 31: Creature Experience Point Values

HD or Level	XP Value
Less than 1–1	7
1–1 to 1	15
1+1 to 2	35
2+1 to 3	65
3+1 to 4	120
4+1 to 5	175
5+1 to 6	270
6+1 to 7	420
7+1 to 8	650
8+1 to 9	975
9+1 to 10+	1,400
11 to 12+	2,000
13 or higher	2,000 + 1,000 per additional Hit Die

Table 32: Hit Dice Value Modifiers

Modifier	Ability
+1	Armor Class 0 or lower
+1	Blood drain
+1	Breath weapon (up to 20 hp maximum damage)
+1	Can fly or has other special movement power
+1	Cause disease
+1	Employs psionic devotions
+1	Greater than normal hit points (over 6 hp/HD)
+1	Has and uses magical items or weapons
+1	High (13–14) or better Intelligence
+1	Hit only by magic or silver weapons
+1	Immunity to a spell
+1	Immunity to or half-damage from any weapon type
+1	Invisible at will
+1	Magic resistance (less than 50%)
+1	Missile weapons or ranged attack ability
+1	Multiple (four or more) attacks per round
+1	Regeneration
+1	Spell casting (level 2 or less)
+1	Unlisted special defense mode
+1	Unlisted non-magical special attack mode
+2	Breath weapon (over 20 hp maximum damage)
+2	Causes weakness or fear
+2	Employs psionic sciences
+2	Magic resistance (50% or better)
+2	Multiple attacks inflicting over 30 points of damage
+2	Paralysis
+2	Poison
+2	Single attack inflicting over 20 points of damage
+2	Spell casting (level 3 or greater)
+2	Swallows whole
+2	Unlisted special magical attack mode
+3	Energy drain (level or ability draining)
+3	Petrification

Monsters From Other Sources

As of this writing, the MONSTROUS COMPENDIUM series includes 15 volumes. Many creatures appearing in appendices for other campaign worlds can enhance a RAVENLOFT campaign, too. In order to help satisfy the seemingly endless desire of Dungeon Masters and players for new monsters, a master list of such terrifying and haunting creatures appears below.

MC1 & MC2: AD&D Monsters (For All Campaigns)
Bat (all)
Carrion Crawler
Doppleganger
Elf, Drow
Gargoyle
Ghost
Ghoul (all)
Golem (all)
Groaning Spirit (Banshee)
Guardian Daemon (all)
Hag (all)
Haunt
Hell Hound
Heucuva
Homonculous
Imp
Jackalwere
Lich
Lycanthrope (all)
Mind Flayer
Mummy
Poltergeist
Rakshasa
Rat (all)
Shadow
Skeleton (all)
Spectre
Vampire
Wight
Will O'Wisp
Wolf (all)
Wolfwere
Wraith
Zombie (all)

MC3: FORGOTTEN REALMS® Appendix
Claw, Crawling
Cloaker
Darkenbeast
Death, Crimson
Revenant
Web, Living

MC4: DRAGONLANCE® Appendix
Beast, Undead (all)
Dreamshadow
Dreamwraith
Fetch
Fire Minion
Fire Shadow
Haunt, Knight
Imp, Blood Sea
Knight, Death
Spectral Minion
Skeleton Warrior
Witchlin
Yaggol

MC5: GREYHAWK® Appendix
Crypt Thing
Hound, Yeth
Kyuss, Son of
Necrophidius
Raven (all)
Scarecrow
Shadow, Slow
Wraith (all)
Zombie, Sea

MC6: KARA-TUR Appendix
Buso (all)
Chu-u
Con-tinh
Gaki (all)
Goblin Rat
Goblin Spider
Hannya
Hengeyokai (all)
Hu Hsien
Ikiryo
Kaluk
Krakentua
Kuei
Memedi
Oni (all)
P'oh Gohei
Spirit, Stone
Yuki-on-na

MC7: SPELLJAMMER® Appendix
Ancient Mariner
Spiritjam

MC8: Outer Planes Appendix
Baatezu (all)
Bebilith
Bodak
Gehreleth
Githyanki
Githzerai
Hordling
Larva
Night Hag
Nightmare
Tanar'ri (all)
Vaporighu
Yugoloth (all)

MC9: SPELLJAMMER® Appendix II
Allura
Dreamslayer
Dweomerborn
Firelich
Skullbird
Spirit Warrior
Undead, Stellar

MC11: FORGOTTEN REALMS® Appendix II
Bat, Deep
Cat (all)
Harrla
Inquisitor
Lhiannan Shee
Manni
Naga, Dark
Orpsu
Phantom
Plant, Carnivorous (Black Willow)
Skuz
Tempest

MC12: DARK SUN® Appendix
Banshee, Dwarf
Beetle, Agony
Bog Wader
Dune Runner
Elemental (all)
Golem (all)
Id Fiend
Plant, Carnivorous (all)
Sand Bride
Thrax
Zhackal
Zombie Plant

MC13: AL-QADIM® Appendix
Ammut
Black Cloud of Vengeance
Copper Automaton
Ghost Mount
Ghul, Great
Heway
Living Idol (all)
Lycanthrope, Werehyena
Lycanthrope, Werelion
Rom
Serpent, Winged
Silats

MC14: FIEND FOLIO® Appendix
Apparition
Coffer Corpse
Dark Creeper
Dark Stalker
Grimlock
Hellcat
Iron Cobra
Mephit (all)
Penangglan
Phantom Stalker
Sheet Ghoul/Sheet Phantom

Akikage

Climate/Terrain:	Rokushima
Frequency:	Very rare
Organization:	Solitary
Activity Cycle:	Night
Diet:	Nil
Intelligence:	High (13–14)
Treasure:	Nil
Alignment:	Lawful evil
No. Appearing:	1
Armor Class:	1
Movement:	12
Hit Dice:	6+3
THAC0:	13
No. of Attacks:	4
Damage/Attack:	1d6 (×4)
Special Attacks:	Death blow
Special Defenses:	+2 or better weapon; spell immunity
Magic Resistance:	Nil
Size:	M (6′ tall)
Morale:	Fanatic (17–18)
XP Value:	3,000

The akikage (ah-ki-ka-gee), or shadow ninja, is the spirit of an oriental assassin who died while stalking an important victim. In life, the akikage was obsessed with duty and discipline. Now it cannot rest in its grave until it has successfully completed its final mission.

The akikage is an incorporeal spirit that is rarely visible. When seen, the creature is dressed all in black. It wears tight gloves and boots as well as a mask and hood that hide all traces of its former humanity.

The akikage cannot speak but seems to understand the words of those around it regardless of the language in which they are spoken. Even a *speak with dead* spell will elicit no response from the spirit assassin.

Combat: The akikage is a stealthy and ruthless killer. Because it is incorporeal, the shadow ninja cannot manipulate objects as it did in life, but it can move unhindered through solid matter. It can become *invisible* at will, imposing a –4 penalty on opponents' attack rolls.

In battle, the akikage strikes with murderous ferocity. While it does not use weapons, its skill in unarmed combat allows it four attacks per round. Each blow that lands inflicts 1d6 points of damage due to the creature's essence of absolute cold.

The akikage's most devastating power is its ability to instantly slay a victim with its death blow. To do this, the akikage must become visible for one combat round. During this time, it channels all its supernatural power into one devastating strike (forfeiting its other three attacks). As the akikage drives its fist forward, its chilling power pierces the victim's body, inflicting 3d6 points of cold damage. Further, if the victim of this piercing blow fails a save vs. death magic, he dies immediately (regardless of hit points). A prompt autopsy on the corpse reveals that the victim's heart has been frozen solid.

The shadow ninja can only be struck with magical weapons of +2 or greater enchantment. It is immune to *sleep, fear, charm,* and *hold* spells and is unaffected by all poisons or diseases. All manner of mental or cold-based attacks have no effect upon the creature. Holy water inflicts 1d8 points of damage per vial splashed upon the shadow ninja. An akikage can be turned by a cleric as if it were a spectre or destroyed with a *raise dead* or *dispel evil* spell.

Habitat/Society: This grim spirit seeks no company save that of the person it is destined to destroy. If the akikage successfully completes the mission that it failed in life its spirit is released from its curse of undeath. At this point, the spectral menace dissipates and vanishes for good.

Ecology: As an undead creature, the akikage requires neither food nor rest. Because of its spectral nature, however, it cannot escape the notice of animals. Whether domesticated or wild, all the beasts of the world become jittery and nervous when a shadow ninja is within 50 feet.

Ansasshia

Tales are told of ansasshia, akikage that are captured and forced to serve a living master. This enslavement usually occurs when an evil cleric uses his ability to command undead or someone casts a *control undead* spell. It is also possible to gain control of a shadow ninja by discovering who the intended victim of the spirit assassin is and killing him before the creature can strike. If this is done and a *control undead* spell is promptly cast upon the body of the akikage's target, the shadow ninja will become an ansasshia, doomed henceforth to obey the caster of the spell.

While under the influence of another, these assassins carry out their orders promptly and efficiently. While they might yearn to be free of their master's will, their devotion to duty and honor makes it impossible for them to disobey or betray him in any way.

Animator, General Information

Animators are evil, violent spirits that can enter an object and imbue it with a life force. They vary widely in capabilities, but all are mischievous and dangerous.

Powerful and dark emotions attract an animator—emotions like hate, anger, and fear. It seems likely that the creature draws some manner of sustenance from these karmic vibrations. In most cases, these emotions radiate from a living person, but in rare instances they may be residual energies emanating from a corpse.

Upon discovering the source of such dark emotion, the creature finds an object that is of special importance to the subject and then merges with it. Animators are unable to invade magical objects or those currently under the effects of a magical spell. Once an object is controlled by an animator it is not forced to flee if a spell is cast upon its host. It takes some time for an animator to take control of an object (1d4 hours), during which time the item radiates a faint glow. If the object is moved during this period, the process is disrupted and the animator must find another item or begin again.

Wards: Once it has assumed control of an object, the animator will act to protect the source of the emotions that summoned it. For this reason, that person is generally referred to as the animator's ward. While this might seem a benevolent action on the part of the creature, it is important to remember that the ward and animator may have very different ideas about the best way to do this.

All animators have a crude form of telepathy that allows them to sense the sources of their ward's distress. An animator will often act upon this information and attempt to harm or destroy the cause. Because they are such willful creatures, animators do not generally obey the desires or spoken commands of their wards.

Animators display the volatile disposition of angry children. They are extremely jealous and may become hostile toward anyone or anything that draws the ward's attention away from them. For example, an animator that occupies the house of an embittered widow may attempt to prevent the woman's attempts to leave the house or block the entry of a suitor.

Movement: An animator can freely operate the working parts of any object it inhabits. Thus, a door might be made to unlatch and swing open or a loaded crossbow might fire without any pull of the trigger.

Animators cannot cause solid matter to flex or bend. Thus, an animator might cause a pair of scissors to open and close unexpectedly but could not cause the blades to warp or curl.

Thrice per day, all animators can impart a motive force to the object that they reside in. The strength of this force varies with the power of the animator as does its duration. This force will not have any effect upon an object that is anchored to the ground unless it is sufficient to break the host free of its bonds.

A minor animator can impart a force similar to that of a human with a Strength of 8 for one round. For example, a minor animator that has entered a dagger could cause its host object to fly through the air as if it had been thrown. There would be enough force propelling the dagger to enable it to stick into a wooden surface or impale a surprised spectator. In the latter case, an Attack Roll would be required with results based upon the effective strength of the creature.

The strength of the common animator is much greater. When it applies motive force to its host object, it moves as if propelled by a person with a Strength score of 18. In addition, the animator can sustain this effort for a full turn. Should the object be used to make an attack of some sort, the attack and damage rolls are modified by this greater Strength score.

The greater animator can exert the power of a hill giant (Strength 19) through the object it inhabits. This force can be maintained for a full hour. As these creatures tend to possess large structures this ability is seldom manifested.

Combat: Every animator has different combat abilities depending upon the nature of the object it occupies. An animator possessing a dagger is likely to be much more lethal than one inhabiting a milk pail. By their nature, animators seldom enter an object that does not have some potential for violence.

Armor Class: Damaging the object that houses an animator ranges in difficulty depending upon the composition of that item. While other factors might contribute to the final AC of the animator, its base AC can be determined using the following table:

AC	Composition	AC	Composition
10	Glass	5	Hardwood
9	Cloth	4	Soft metal
8	Soft leather	3	Banded wood
7	Softwood	2	Hard metal
6	Hard leather	1	Cast iron

Hit Dice: The amount of damage that an animator can sustain before being destroyed is based upon its size and the material from which it is made. The base HD value for an object possessed by an animator is 1 per 10 pounds of weight (rounded up). Thus, an animator controlling a heavy crossbow (14 pounds) has 2 HD.

Hit Points: The number of hit points that an animated object has (per Hit Die) is based upon its composition. Simply subtract the object's base AC (as indicated above) from 11 to determine how many hit points an object has per die. Thus, an item made of glass has 1 hit point per die while something fashioned from cast iron has 10. Simply multiply this by the number of Hit Dice that the object has and you'll know how many hit points it has. The crossbow mentioned in the previous example is made of hardwood and would have 6 points per HD for a total of 12 hit points.

Battling an Animator: There are three basic ways to combat an animator. The first (and generally the easiest) is to disable the object that it inhabits. Once this is done, an attempt can be made to drive the creature out of its host or even destroy it.

An animator can often be rendered harmless by anchoring the object that it has possessed in some way. The aforementioned crossbow might simply be locked in a safe. This is only a temporary solution for the spirit will simply abandon the object and seek out another one.

Powerful magical spells such as *dispel evil* or *wish* can be used to drive the spirit from its home. This does not prevent the animator from returning to the object later, but that process is quite time-consuming.

The destruction of the object in which an animator resides does not actually harm the creature. However, it does drive it out of the item and forces the creature to seek a new home.

Just as some spells can force the creature to flee the object in which it resides, others can trap it there for a period of time. Only by doing this and then destroying the object that holds the spirit of the animator is it possible to finally kill the creature. The animator can be contained with either a *quest* or *geas* spell, although others might suffice, at the DM's option.

CLIMATE/TERRAIN:	Ravenloft
FREQUENCY:	Very rare
ORGANIZATION:	Solitary
ACTIVITY CYCLE:	Any
DIET:	Karmic resonances
INTELLIGENCE:	Exceptional (15–16)
TREASURE:	Nil
ALIGNMENT:	Chaotic evil
NO. APPEARING:	1
ARMOR CLASS:	Varies
MOVEMENT:	9
HIT DICE:	Varies
THAC0:	Varies
NO. OF ATTACKS:	1
DAMAGE/ATTACK:	1d4
SPECIAL ATTACKS:	Nil
SPECIAL DEFENSES:	Spell immunity
MAGIC RESISTANCE:	Nil
SIZE:	T to S (1 inch to 4 feet)
MORALE:	Average (8–10)
XP VALUE:	Varies

As the weakest of its kind, a minor animator can only take control of small objects. Thus, a minor animator might possess a clay mug and cause it to topple over, spilling the hot coffee within onto its target. This type of creature is seldom deadly, but can be menacing if it gains control of a weapon or other dangerous object. Objects controlled by a minor animator gain no special abilities.

The true appearance of animators remains a mystery. When these creatures are not in control of a physical object, they are utterly insubstantial and invisible. It is probable that they would seem vaporous to someone able to detect invisible things when forced out of their host object.

Minor animators have no language, and any magical attempt to communicate with them is doomed to failure. Those who attempt to achieve some manner of telepathic contact with the animator will find that its mind is utterly unlike that of a human or demihuman, thus forcing the psionicist to make a madness check.

Combat: Minor animators can only possess objects of tiny or small size. This greatly limits the amount of damage the creatures can inflict in combat. Thus, they tend to inhabit things that are inherently very dangerous. Examples include a dagger, shaving razor, leather garotte, or knitting needle.

Minor animators are seldom engaged in direct combat. Their limited motive powers force them to be more subtle. Thus, a length of rope controlled by an animator might coil itself around the neck of a sleeping victim or a kitchen knife might topple off a counter and impale someone's foot.

Animators vary wildly in their capacity to inflict harm on their targets. As a rule, minor animators are unable to inflict more than 1d4 points of damage from any attack they make. There are exceptions, of course, but this is a good guideline. For example, an animated rope might trip someone and cause him to tumble down a flight of stairs. This could cause much more damage and might even require the victim to make a saving throw to escape serious injury.

Animators of all types are immune to any form of mind- or biology-affecting spells and attacks. Thus, they cannot be *charmed, held,* or poisoned. The nature of the object in which the animator resides dictates its vulnerability to other forms of attack.

Habitat/Society: Minor animators can possess any type of ordinary object. A rope, a bucket, a dagger, or a pillow may become the home of one of these impulsive spirits. Because of its evil nature, the animator will generally attempt to take control of items that can cause injury.

Minor animators are the most volatile and least predictable of their kind, making up for their limited power by being exceptionally evil and terribly cunning. Well aware of the fact that they can seldom make effective direct attacks, they strike at their victims obliquely. A thief adventurer whose dagger has been possessed by an animator may awake one morning to discover that his weapon is buried in the back of a rival party member. Since the weapon doesn't appear to be enchanted, even with the casting of a *detect magic* spell, the innocent rogue is likely to come under suspicion for the crime.

Minor animators are also intelligent enough to play dumb when it is appropriate. Since it is unlikely to be detected until it chooses to act, the creature knows that it can simply lie in wait for a perfect opportunity to strike.

Ecology: The common animator seems to thrive on existing and residual emotions generated by other creatures. Exactly how it derives nourishment from these vibrations is unknown to even the wisest of sages.

Almost nothing is known about whether these creatures interact with one another or have any sort of social structure. It seems unlikely that they do. As they are not undead, it seems likely that they must reproduce in some way, although no evidence exists to suggest what that might be.

Animator, Common

Climate/Terrain:	Ravenloft
Frequency:	Very rare
Organization:	Solitary
Activity Cycle:	Any
Diet:	Karmic resonances
Intelligence:	Exceptional (15–16)
Treasure:	Nil
Alignment:	Chaotic evil
No. Appearing:	1
Armor Class:	Varies
Movement:	12
Hit Dice:	Varies
THAC0:	Varies
No. of Attacks:	1
Damage/Attack:	1d8
Special Attacks:	Varies
Special Defenses:	Varies
Magic Resistance:	Nil
Size:	M to L (4′–12′ tall)
Morale:	Average (8–10)
XP Value:	Varies

More powerful than the minor animator, this creature can enter larger objects such as coaches or stoves and bring them to life. The power of the common animator is such that it can bestow an unusual power upon its host object. This power can range from annoying to deadly. For example, an animator that has taken control of a cast-iron stove might cause it to spew forth a jet of flame when its door is opened.

The common animator has no direct ability to communicate. From time to time, however, these creatures might deliver messages to their wards by scratching words into a wooden surface, tapping in code, or some similar manner. This is strictly one-sided, however, as all efforts to speak with or instruct the animator will fail. This includes the use of magical or psionic abilities. Any direct attempt to touch the mind of an animator may well require a madness check at the DM's discretion.

Combat: A common animator may activate all of the moving parts of the object that it occupies. For example, a coach may roll around on its own volition, a piano might play itself at will, and the drawers of a dresser could open and shut without warning.

When it is not controlling a weapon of some type, the animator must employ some indirect manner of attack to harm its victims. An attack roll is required with the creature's THAC0 being determined by its weight and composition (see *Animator, General Information*). In most cases, the damage from such an attack is limited to 1d8 points. If the attack has some unusual side effect, a saving throw might be required to avoid more severe injury. For example, an animated coach might attempt to pitch its driver from his seat, probably requiring him to make a Dexterity Check to avoid being dismounted. If the poor fellow were thrown under the wheels of a passing wagon, he might then be required to make a saving throw vs. paralyzation to avoid being crushed to death.

In addition to such physical attacks, a common animator enables the object it possesses to deliver a magical attack of some sort. The effects of such powers range dramatically and are based upon the object in which the creature resides. A large cast-iron stove may have the ability to breathe fire, a piano may have the power to cast an *Otto's irresistible dance* spell on those who hear it play, and a small fishing boat might be able to *entangle* its occupants in lines and nets. Whatever the nature of the magical effect, it generally mirrors the effects of a wizard or priest spell of up to 4th level. The spell-like power of an animator is normally one that inflicts harm, they never have healing or beneficial powers.

Animators of all types are immune to any form of mind- or biology-affecting spells and attacks. Thus, they cannot be *charmed, held,* or poisoned. The nature of the object in which the animator resides dictates its vulnerability to other forms of attack.

Habitat/Society: When not in possession of an object, animators are assumed to drift like insubstantial vapors through the world. When they sense strong negative emotions, they move in and feed. In this state, there seems to be no barrier that the creature cannot pass in its pursuit of a home.

Ecology: Common animators, like other animators, thrive on existing and residual emotions of the living. Some creatures inhabit places associated with a particularly emotional death, and are often mistaken for ghosts or other forms of incorporeal undead.

Animator, Greater

Climate/Terrain:	Ravenloft
Frequency:	Very rare
Organization:	Solitary
Activity Cycle:	Any
Diet:	Karmic resonances
Intelligence:	Exceptional (15–16)
Treasure:	Nil
Alignment:	Chaotic evil
No. Appearing:	1
Armor Class:	Varies
Movement:	Nil (with exceptions)
Hit Dice:	Varies
THAC0:	Varies
No. of Attacks:	1
Damage/Attack:	1d12
Special Attacks:	Spell ability
Special Defenses:	Spell immunity
Magic Resistance:	Nil
Size:	L+ (12′ tall or larger)
Morale:	Average (8–10)
XP Value:	Varies

The strongest of its kind, a greater animator can inhabit entire buildings or great sailing ships, turning them into vast, living death traps. The terrific power of these creatures enables them to manifest a bizarre array of unusual abilities with which to torment those trapped within their walls. In addition, these mighty animators are able to manifest a wide variety of powerful spell-like abilities that make them particularly deadly and unpredictable.

Unlike others of its ilk, the greater animator has the power to communicate once per day. It generally does this in some unusual and shocking manner. For example, an animated house might have walls that bleed and form words or messages. The animator will not converse and its messages are limited to one word per Hit Die. These messages are never real efforts to communicate; rather they are threats or other expressions of the negative emotions upon which the creature feeds.

Any magical or psionic attempt to communicate directly with the mind of an animator fails and requires a madness check. Because of the power of these creatures, however, such attempts also require the person attempting such communication to make a saving throw vs. spell or fall under the effects of a *domination* spell.

Combat: The greater animator occupies objects of large or better size. It can operate all of the moving parts of the object it occupies and does so as if it had the strength of a hill giant (19). Thus, a house occupied by an animator could deliver a crushing blow by slamming someone in a door, and an animated ship could probably turn the wheel to go where it wanted despite the best efforts of the helmsman to hold a steady course.

When an animator is capable of making a direct attack on someone, a typical blow will cause 1d12 points of damage. Under special circumstances, the damage might be more or a saving throw might be required to avoid additional injury. A sailor in the crow's-nest of a ship might find himself struck by part of the mast and forced to make a saving throw or ability check to avoid falling to the deck.

In addition, the greater animator has a large number of spell-like abilities that it can use at its will. Every greater animator may use the following spell-like abilities twice per day as if cast by a 12th level spell wizard or priest: *animate dead, animate object, weather summoning, control temperature 10′ radius, control winds, cantrip, summon swarm, summon insects.* The use of the *animate object* spell by these creatures is limited to items that are native to the space it has inhabited. Thus, a greater animator could mobilize any of the furniture or utensils in the house but could not affect objects brought into the house by adventurers. The greater animator may use *animate dead* to mobilize skeletons and corpses that lie buried beneath it or die on its premises.

Animators of all types are immune to any form of mind- or biology-affecting spells and attacks. Thus, they cannot be *charmed, held,* or poisoned. The nature of the object in which the animator resides dictates its vulnerability to other forms of attack.

Habitat/Society: Greater animators display the same emotional volatility as their minor and common cousins. They tend to be less cunning and deceptive in their evil deeds, however, employing their great strength and spell abilities simply to crush and devastate their enemies.

Ecology: Like all animators, the greater animator thrives upon the powerful emotions of the living. Because of its more pronounced hunger, this creature will often go to great lengths to induce fear in its victims before killing them.

Bakhna Rakhna

CLIMATE/TERRAIN:	Temperate woodlands
FREQUENCY:	Uncommon
ORGANIZATION:	Tribal
ACTIVITY CYCLE:	Night
DIET:	Omnivore
INTELLIGENCE:	Low (5–7)
TREASURE:	C (K)
ALIGNMENT:	Neutral evil
NO. APPEARING:	4–24 (4d6)
ARMOR CLASS:	7
MOVEMENT:	6
HIT DICE:	1
THAC0:	19
NO. OF ATTACKS:	1
DAMAGE/ATTACK:	1d4 (by weapon)
SPECIAL ATTACKS:	Poison weapons
SPECIAL DEFENSES:	Nil
MAGIC RESISTANCE:	Nil
SIZE:	S (3′ tall)
MORALE:	Average (8–10)
XP VALUE:	175

These small jungle creatures look somewhat like albino goblins. They are mischievous beings who make a habit of stealing food from the farms and settlements near their lairs. While it is possible to accommodate the bakhna rakhna, any efforts to thwart their depredations can result in disaster.

The bakhna rakhna are small humanoids with flat faces and sloping foreheads. They have broad noses and pointed ears as well as wide mouths filled with small sharp fangs. They walk upright and have long arms that hang to their knees. Their skin is white to pearl gray in color and their ratty hair sometimes has a pale yellow cast to it.

The bakhna rakhna speak their own language and some can communicate in halting common. Their vocabulary is fairly simple and tends to revolve around concepts like pain, pleasure, food, and naps.

Combat: These small creatures avoid direct physical confrontations whenever possible. They prefer to retreat to the brush where they can ambush their enemies if pursued.

Each bakhna rakhna carries a small bow as well as 1d6 pointed sticks that are coated with a paralytic poison. The sticks cause 1d4 points of damage and can be wielded as daggers or fired from the bows. Anyone struck by one of these sticks must make a saving throw vs. poison with a –3 penalty or be immediately paralyzed for 1d4 turns.

The bakhna rakhna generally will not kill opponents who have fallen in combat if the victims might serve as a future source of food to raid. If, however, any of their own are harmed, the bakhna rakhna's retribution can be quite ruthless. They will use their sticks to poke a single hole in the neck of a fallen paralyzed victim and allow his blood to drain away while he is fully conscious. A victim bleeding to death will lose 1 hit point per round but will die in 2d8 +15 rounds even if he has hit points remaining. The bakhna rakhna never leave injured or dead comrades behind.

Bakhna rakhna are sensitive to sunlight and have infravision out to 180 feet. A *light* spell cast on a bakhna rakhna will cause it to have a fit that effectively paralyzes it for 1d4 turns if it fails its saving throw vs. spell.

The bakhna rakhna are extremely stealthy and have a 70% chance of hiding in shadows or moving silently. They also have the ability to *passwall* four times per day. A bakhna rakhna may cast *silence, 15′ radius* twice per day. They are immune to all poisons.

Habitat/Society: Bakhna rakhna have an insatiable curiosity and prefer taking other people's food to hunting for their own. They use their ability to move through walls to gain entrance to homes and conduct their raids under the cover of their *silence* spells. Their raids are undertaken at night and they are rarely caught in the act. Unless food is set out for them, bakhna rakhna always manage to leave an extraordinary mess behind. If a raid is interrupted, the bakhna rakhna will flee through the walls.

The nuisance of this pillaging can be avoided if food is left out for the bakhna rakhna. If efforts are made to prevent their nocturnal visits, the bakhna rakhna will poison the food they have left behind with type G poison (ingested; 2d6 hours; 20/10). Additional attempts to stop these vermin can cause them to become a deadly menace.

Bakhna rakhna live in small clans of ten, but have been found in groups of as many as 30 creatures. They usually dwell in small underground burrows but may take up residence beneath the floor or porch of a human dwelling that has become a source of food.

Ecology: These small creatures live in forested areas and, while they can hunt and forage for food, do so only when in danger of starvation. They much prefer to live as scavengers, raiding neighboring settlements for the food and supplies they need to survive.

Baobhan Sith

Climate/Terrain:	Temperate forest
Frequency:	Rare
Organization:	Band
Activity Cycle:	Night
Diet:	Omnivore
Intelligence:	Average to very (8–12)
Treasure:	(X)
Alignment:	Chaotic evil
No. Appearing:	5–30 (5d6)
Armor Class:	6
Movement:	6, Fl 12 (B)
Hit Dice:	1
THAC0:	19
No. of Attacks:	1
Damage/Attack:	1d4 (by weapon)
Special Attacks:	Laughter
Special Defenses:	See below
Magic Resistance:	25%
Size:	S (2′ tall)
Morale:	Average (8–10)
XP Value:	270

The Vistani swear these desperate and bitter creatures are the descendants of a cursed pixie clan captured by the mists of Ravenloft for the unspeakable acts they committed in a distant land. They are cruel creatures who take their greatest pleasure from the suffering of the weak and helpless.

The baobhan sith (or *black sprites*) stand two feet tall and have large transparent wings like those of a cicada. They have sharp elven features with long, almost bat-like ears. Even druids have difficulty distinguishing the baobhan sith from pixies, and it is only the dull luster of their wings and their distinctive ears that identify them. They favor garish clothing and wear colorful caps.

The baobhan sith speak common and it is believed that they may also know the languages of other sprites and woodland animals.

Combat: Unless confident of victory, the baobhan sith will flee any direct confrontation in favor of returning at a later time to torment their opponent through cruel tricks that appeal to their particularly dark sense of humor. If forced to do battle, these creatures can become *invisible* at will and carry small daggerlike spears that inflict 1d4 points of damage in combat.

The baobhan sith have infravision out to 180 feet and hearing that is far more sensitive than that of a normal human. They are able to employ the following magical spells once per round at the 5th level of ability: *ventriloquism*, *trip*, and *change self.*

Perhaps the most bizarre characteristic of these twisted creatures is their infectious (and magical) laughter. Anyone within 15 feet of a laughing baobhan sith must make a saving throw vs. spell or suffer the effects of *Tasha's uncontrollable hideous laughter.* The baobhan sith cannot use this power at will but must be genuinely amused by something. They generally burst into laughter at the sight of human suffering or an opponent's mishap in combat.

Habitat/Society: There is something dark and desperate about the baobhan sith that drives them to ever greater acts of cruelty. They spend their waking hours in a frenzy of evil, fearful that even a moment's rest will cause them to reflect on the dark crime of their ancestors and lead to madness.

The greatest love of the baobhan sith is to cause misfortune for others. They will select a family or community to terrorize and torment them in a manner that will cause the most prolonged suffering. Pets are often captured and then returned dead after the family has had a week or more to search, or a family's sole workhorse may be spooked until it breaks a leg. The baobhan sith rarely kill someone through direct combat, but prefer instead to destroy the people and things about which their victims care most.

The baobhan sith prefer to prey upon the weak and helpless. Nothing is quite as satisfying to these creatures as pushing an elderly victim down a flight of stairs and then bursting into hysterical laughter that quickly spreads to the shocked onlookers.

Baobhan sith dwell in caverns beneath the twisted roots of trees in dark forest glades. They live in loose tribal structures and select leaders for their cruelty and deviousness. While the leader of a tribe is generally the most intelligent of the pack, there are constant power struggles and only the truly barbarous can maintain control for any period of time. While the baobhan sith place no value on magic objects, they will sometimes collect them in their lair to be used later as bait in their tricks.

Ecology: Baobhan sith live primarily on roots and insects. They occasionally fall prey to predators who mistake them for birds. Baobhan sith can live up to 200 years. The wings of the baobhan sith can be crushed to create *dust of disappearance.* Twenty-five wings can make one dose that must be used within 1d4 weeks or else it will lose its potency.

Beetle, Scarab

	Grave	Giant	Monstrous
CLIMATE/TERRAIN:	Temperate lands & subterranean		
FREQUENCY:	Common	Rare	Rare
ORGANIZATION:	Swarm	Swarm	Solitary
ACTIVITY CYCLE:	Night	Night	Any
DIET:	Scavenger	Scavenger	Scavenger
INTELLIGENCE:	Non- (0)	Non- (0)	Non- (0)
TREASURE:	(Z)	(Z)	(C,R,S,T)
ALIGNMENT:	Neutral	Neutral	Neutral
NO. APPEARING:	1d4 swarms	1d6 swarms	1d6
ARMOR CLASS:	4	4	2
MOVEMENT:	6, Br 3	6, Br 3	9, Br 3
HIT DICE:	5 per swarm	6 per swarm	8
THAC0:	15	15	13
NO. OF ATTACKS:	1	1	1
DAMAGE/ATTACK:	Special	Special	4d6
SPECIAL ATTACKS:	Nil	Disease	Nil
SPECIAL DEFENSES:	Nil	Nil	Nil
MAGIC RESISTANCE:	Nil	Nil	Nil
SIZE:	T (3″ long)	T (6″ long)	L (11′ long)
MORALE:	Elite (13–14)	Elite (13–14)	Elite (13–14)
XP VALUE:	420	975	1,400

These flesh-eating beetles line the walls of tombs and underground passageways. They attack in horrifying swarms and leave very little in their wake.

There are three types of scarab beetles. The most common, and in many ways the deadliest, is the swarming grave scarab. The larger giant scarab is somewhat less insidious than its smaller cousin but carries a terrible disease. The monstrous scarab is a solitary nightmare that dwells in remote caverns and tunnels.

None of these creatures is able to communicate with others, although the grave and giant beetles have a rudimentary language that serves to exchange information within the swarm.

Combat: Scarab beetles are often passive, feeding primarily on decomposing flesh and detritus. However, there is a 50% chance that a person will be bitten as he passes through an infested area, setting off a feeding frenzy among the beetles who will swarm over the victim.

A swarm of grave scarabs is treated as a single monster. Each swarm covers a 10′ × 10′ area and has 5 Hit Dice. Any victim caught in this area will automatically take damage equal to half the hit points of the swarm plus his base Armor Class each round. If a victim manages to escape the infested area 25% of the remaining beetles will cling to him and continue to deliver damage until destroyed.

Melee weapons have almost no effect on a swarm of scarab beetles. Each successful attack roll delivers 1 point of damage to the writhing mass. If the beetles being attacked have crawled onto someone, the person under the swarm suffers normal damage from the attack. Victims of the attack who are of at least small size can attempt to battle the swarm by falling to the ground and rolling back and forth. A small creature inflicts 1d4 points of damage to the swarm, a man-sized victim inflicts 1d6 points, large creatures inflict 1d8, and huge or gargantuan creatures inflict 1d10.

Area effect weapons such as flaming oil or magical spells do normal damage to scarab beetles, as well as to the persons who are being attacked by them.

Habitat/Society: Scarab beetles dig holes and tunnels near piles of offal and decomposing organic material. They are good burrowers and unwary travelers are often horrified to find a clear stretch of ground suddenly swarming with ravenous beetles.

Ecology: Through their consumption of carrion and the like, scarab beetles speed the reintroduction of decaying organic material into the environment. Gems and other inedible items of value are sometimes found among their food caches.

Giant Scarab

The giant scarab is a slightly larger member of the scarab family and grows to lengths of up to 6 inches. They are treated like grave beetles in combat except that each 10′ × 10′ area has 6 Hit Dice. Each round that a victim loses hit points to a swarm of giant scarab beetles he must make a saving throw vs. poison or contract a disease similar to that created by the *cause disease* spell. A single failed saving throw indicates a *debilitating* disease. A second failed roll makes this a *fatal* disease.

Monstrous Scarab

These solitary creatures are enormous monsters of tremendous proportions. In combat, they strike with keen, powerful pincers that deliver an incredible 4d6 points of damage. These beasts have been known to bury still-living victims in their lairs for later consumption.

Boneless

Climate/Terrain:	Darkon or Hazlan
Frequency:	Very rare
Organization:	Nil
Activity Cycle:	Any
Diet:	Nil
Intelligence:	Non- (0)
Treasure:	Nil
Alignment:	Neutral
No. Appearing:	3–30 (3d10)
Armor Class:	8
Movement:	6, 12 on all fours
Hit Dice:	3
THAC0:	17
No. of Attacks:	2
Damage/Attack:	1d4/1d4
Special Attacks:	Constriction
Special Defenses:	Spell immunity
Magic Resistance:	Nil
Size:	M (6′ tall)
Morale:	Fearless (19–20)
XP Value:	270

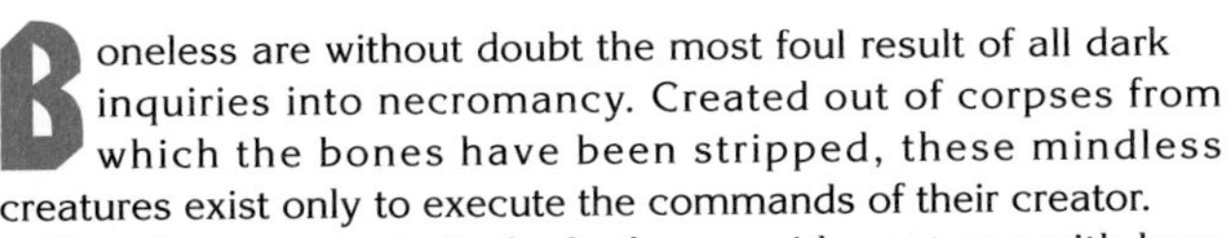

Boneless are without doubt the most foul result of all dark inquiries into necromancy. Created out of corpses from which the bones have been stripped, these mindless creatures exist only to execute the commands of their creator.

Boneless appear to be lanky humanoid creatures with long withered limbs and small wrinkled ball-like heads atop a flexible cord of a neck. The creases and folds of their puckered, fetid skin have a translucent reddish-brown hue. They are sometimes clothed in loose-fitting rags that are often stitched directly to their flesh. They move with a lurching uncertainty, sometimes dropping to all fours for a burst of speed or added stability.

These abominations have no ability to communicate but will follow the simple verbal commands of their creator.

Combat: Boneless are astonishingly flexible and strong. They can wield melee weapons doing normal damage, but are often instructed to grapple and constrict their victims instead. A boneless may slap with both of its withered hands in one round to deliver 1–4 points of damage for each hit.

If a boneless manages to hit a target with both hands in one round the victim has been grappled. On each succeeding round, the boneless automatically constricts its victim for an additional 2d4 points of damage. While caught in the embrace of these creatures, a victim may not cast spells requiring semantic components, make any sort of physical attack, or initiate any action other than trying to free himself. A successful bend bars/lift gates roll (by either the victim or a rescuer) will allow someone to break free of the boneless's vile grip. There is a 40% chance that anyone attempting to strike a boneless's while it is grappling a victim will hit the victim instead.

Blunt weapons do half damage to the boneless while edged and piercing ones have their normal effects. A vial of holy water inflicts 1d8 points of damage to them, as does the touch of a holy symbol. Boneless can be turned normally.

Boneless are immune to *fear, sleep, charm,* or *hold* spells. Death magic, poisons, and all telepathic psionic sciences and devotions are similarly useless against them. Unless instructed otherwise, boneless will fight until destroyed.

The pliability of the boneless gives it several special abilities that make it particularly useful. For example, a boneless can work its way under a door with only a one-inch gap or be folded and fit into a space of one cubic foot.

Habitat/Society: These creatures are the result of dark experiments conducted by the wizard Faylorn while staying as a guest of the lich lord Azalin at his keep in Darkon. He found that, under the right conditions, he could animate the bones and body of a corpse quite independently. Since that time, Faylorn's methodology has spread and others have learned how to create these foul things.

Boneless have no social structure. They require neither food nor sleep, but must be periodically moistened to maintain its flexibility. Consequently, a boneless must be saturated with water once per week. Boneless who are left in at least two inches of water or an airtight compartment will require no maintenance.

Boneless who are not able to maintain their moisture lose all grappling and special movement abilities and will behave as common zombies in combat, attacking only once each round for 1d4 points of damage or by weapon. Fire-based attacks, of either a magical or mundane nature, will do double damage to a dehydrated boneless.

Ecology: Boneless have no role in nature and are purely the result of dark magic. It is said that the magic by which they are created is similar in many ways to the well-known *animate dead* spell, but that its material components are somewhat different. There is much evidence to support the belief that this spell functions only within on the Demiplane of Dread.

Boowray

Climate/Terrain:	Temperate forest
Frequency:	Rare
Organization:	Solitary
Activity Cycle:	Any
Diet:	Nil
Intelligence:	Very (11–12)
Treasure:	Nil
Alignment:	Lawful evil
No. Appearing:	1
Armor Class:	2
Movement:	12, Fl 24 (B)
Hit Dice:	4
THAC0:	17
No. of Attacks:	1
Damage/Attack:	1d4
Special Attacks:	See below
Special Defenses:	+1 or better weapon to hit
Magic Resistance:	Nil
Size:	T (2′ tall)
Morale:	Champion (15–16)
XP Value:	1,400

This whispering spirit delights in corrupting the innocent and inspiring good folk to evil actions. Once it attaches itself to a victim, it provides a constant stream of wicked advice. Over time even the most stalwart souls may find themselves seduced by the sinister allure of evil.

The boowray is a non-corporeal spirit that is normally invisible. When it chooses to become visible, it appears as a tiny, semi-transparent humanoid with greenish skin, bright yellow eyes, and mint leaves instead of hair. It dresses in a leafy jerkin tied off at the waist. Its innocent, harmless appearance gives no indication of its malign intent.

Boowrays seem to speak the common languages of the domain in which they are encountered. As others in proximity to the boowray and its victim seem unable to hear the creature, it appears to be somewhat telepathic.

Combat: The boowray is an elusive foe and the greatest difficulty in fighting one is simply finding him. They are usually invisible, but can become visible at will. Those who strike at the creature when it is invisible suffer a –4 penalty to their attack rolls. This, in addition to the creature's minute size, can enable it to escape almost any search.

If forced to engage in physical combat, the boowray can bite once per round for 1d4 points of damage. It constantly keeps an eye out for some means of escape and will make the most of its ability to fly and turn invisible. Boowrays can only be struck by magic weapons of a +1 or better nature.

The boowray is immune to all spells that affect its thoughts. Thus, they cannot be *charmed,* given a *command,* or placed under any similar spell.

The boowray is completely and utterly devoted to the spiritual collapse of its victims. While it has the power to use a *suggestion* spell once per day, it finds that the satisfaction caused by such magically inspired trouble is only fleeting. Real pleasure comes from an actual shift in the alignment of the chosen victim.

Any time a victim takes an evil action at the prompting of a boowray a Ravenloft powers check must be made. No check is required if the character acted under the influence of the creature's *suggestion* spell. The seductive charm of the boowray imposes a 5% penalty to the check.

A boowray may be driven off through the casting of a *dispel evil* spell. A victim may gain temporary relief from the whispering with any manner of *silence* spell. A victim may also use wax, cotton, or the like to block out the sound of the boowray, but will also be unable to hear anything else while in this state.

Habitat/Society: When a boowray first selects a target, it whispers helpful advice and warnings into the victim's ear. Claiming to be a guardian spirit or other helpful magical entity, the wicked creature quickly earns the trust of its prey. Having secured itself as a faithful friend, the boowray begins to prey upon the victim's natural weaknesses and character flaws. It will sow discord by feeding any petty resentment, jealousy, anger, greed, or prideful thoughts the victim may harbor, no matter how well hidden. The boowray is diabolical and will pursue its goals with great subtlety.

Boowrays are solitary creatures, but they occasionally meet for festive gatherings in dark clearings where they exchange tales of their accomplishments.

Ecology: The Vistani word for the boowray, *terrepopolo,* translates roughly as people of the land, apparently in reference to their seemingly close bond to the Demiplane of Dread. They do not appear to eat or sleep, and only serve to spread the evil on which the land itself seems to thrive.

Climate/Terrain:	Any Ravenloft but Tepest
Frequency:	Very rare
Organization:	Solitary
Activity Cycle:	Day
Diet:	Omnivore
Intelligence:	Very (11–12)
Treasure:	(D)
Alignment:	Chaotic good
No. Appearing:	1
Armor Class:	0
Movement:	15
Hit Dice:	8
THAC0:	13
No. of Attacks:	2
Damage/Attack:	1d6+6/1d6+6
Special Attacks:	See below
Special Defenses:	See below
Magic Resistance:	25%
Size:	M (5'–6' tall)
Morale:	Champion (15–16)
XP Value:	2,000

The bruja are melancholy, haglike creatures that, despite their frightening countenances, are in fact kind and helpful. Cursed with foreknowledge of their own deaths, these sad creatures work in modest ways to stem the tide of evil throughout the lands of Ravenloft.

Bruja look like wretched crones with long, ratty, black hair and gnarled faces. Their skin varies in color from chalky white to ash gray and their skin has the texture of a hard forest fungus. Warts and sores mar their flesh and rotten yellow teeth fill their mouths. The eyes of a bruja are usually milky and dull, giving the appearance of blindness. They wear simple peasant dresses that are usually devoid of patterns and decorations. Although frail in appearance, bruja are extremely strong and quick.

The bruja speak no languages of their own but have learned those of the communities and peoples of Ravenloft. They are able to converse freely with any type of wild animal that dwells near their home.

Combat: All bruja have a Strength of 18/00, the ability to *change self* at will, and an innate magic resistance. They often use their ability to *change self* in order to collect information and to provide assistance to travelers without revealing their true nature. Bruja have infravision (60-foot range) and their powerful senses make them impossible to surprise. Further, their stealth results in a –3 penalty to the surprise roll of any opponents when in a forest. The tremendous tracking abilities of the bruja result in a 100% chance of picking up a trail that is up to 24 hours old. For each hour past that time the likelihood of success drops by 10%.

While bruja generally use their spells to avoid direct combat, they can make use of their talonlike fingernails to deliver a violent attack that inflicts 1d6 points of damage. They gain a +3 adjustment to their attack rolls and a +6 adjustment to damage rolls because of their extraordinary strength.

Bruja can cast the following spells at will: *bless, change self, invisibility to undead, invisibility, know alignment, pass without trace,* and *speak with animals.* Once per day the bruja can cast *dispel evil, heal, remove curse, sunray* and *protection from evil, 10' radius.*

Habitat/Society: Because of their reclusive nature very little is known about these pensive creatures. Some say there are only three and that they once formed a dark covey like the sisters of Tepest. As a punishment for peering into forbidden aspects of the future they were cursed with a vision of their own terrible deaths. This drove them apart and slowly filled them with a disconsolate compassion for all things mortal. Whether such tales are true, no one can say.

Whatever their origins, the bruja tend to live in small houses in remote areas far from large communities. At home a bruja will generally be found in the company of 1d8 woodland and domestic animals not exceeding an accumulated total of 20 Hit Dice. Bruja use woodland animals as spies to inform them of the comings and goings within the domain where they live.

While a bruja will attempt to conceal her true identity in most encounters with others, she is susceptible to the arrogance to which all hags are prone. She is also used to dealing primarily with animals who do her bidding without question. Any long exposure to people is likely to bring out an impulsive display of power that can result in the inadvertent compromising of her disguise.

Ecology: Bruja have ravenous appetites and devour their food with gluttonous abandon. While they particularly enjoy raw meat, a holdover from their tainted pasts, they have acquired a taste for the nuts and berries that they gather in the forest. Bruja sometimes feast upon the flesh of intelligent creatures, but only those who have wronged them.

Carrion Stalker

Climate/Terrain:	Any subterranean
Frequency:	Uncommon
Organization:	Solitary
Activity Cycle:	Any
Diet:	Carnivorous
Intelligence:	Non- (0)
Treasure:	(B)
Alignment:	Neutral
No. Appearing:	1d6
Armor Class:	2
Movement:	9
Hit Dice:	4
THAC0:	17
No. of Attacks:	1 or 1d4 +5
Damage/Attack:	1d6 or special
Special Attacks:	Paralysis, spawning
Special Defenses:	Nil
Magic Resistance:	Nil
Size:	T (12″ long)
Morale:	Average (9–10)
XP Value:	650

An encounter with a carrion stalker may well be the most horrifying experience a traveler can have. These ghastly creatures actually live within decaying bodies and lie in wait for a bypasser to serve as a new nest for their disgusting larvae.

The carrion stalker looks something like a horseshoe crab but also sports the tentacles of a jellyfish. They are occasionally seen scuttling about dank mausoleums and moldering cemeteries with their vile tendrils trailing behind them. Carrion stalkers grow to 1′ in length at maturity. Their fine but strong tendrils can grow to lengths of 15 feet. They range in color from glossy black to bone white, but are most commonly a putrid combination of gray and pink.

Carrion stalkers are not intelligent and act only upon their instinctive needs to feed and reproduce. As such, they have no language, although they do produce a piercing squeal when attacking unwary travelers.

Combat: Carrion stalkers spend most of their wretched lives lurking within the decaying bodies of the dead. When a warm-blooded creature comes within 15 feet of these havens, however, they attack with blinding speed. Because of their speed and the difficulty in spotting them, stalkers impose a –2 penalty on their victims' surprise and initiative rolls.

A carrion stalker's attack begins when it lashes out with a storm of eight slender tendrils. Each of these makes a separate Attack Roll and is covered with painful stingers that inflict 1d4 points of damage. If even a single tendril scores a hit, the victim must make a saving throw vs. paralysis or become entangled. A –1 penalty is imposed on this roll for every tentacle that succeeded in hitting the target.

Once caught by these leathery cords, the victim (or a would-be rescuer) must make a bend bars/lift gates roll to escape. While caught in the painful embrace of these stinging members, the victim will suffer an additional point of damage per tendril each round. Tentacles that failed to grapple the target in previous rounds will continue to strike at the victim until either all eight are secured or the prey has broken free.

Once grappled, the helpless victim is dragged toward the corpse at a rate of 3 feet per round. As soon as the prey is within 3 feet, a cloud of larvae bursts from the stalker. Between 4 and 9 (1d6+3) of the disgusting grubs will land on the victim and begin to burrow into his flesh on the next round. The young carrion stalkers are AC 8, have 1 hit point, and do 1 point of damage per round to the victim until they are destroyed. Anyone working to free an entangled victim must make a saving throw vs. breath weapon or be infested with 1d4 grubs himself.

Adult and larval carrion stalkers are immune to all manner of poisons or disease, but can be injured or destroyed by most other forms of attack. It is worth noting, however, that the nature of these creatures makes it hard to attack them without injuring their victim. Because of this, damage from most attacks is divided evenly between the carrion stalker and its victim.

Habitat/Society: Carrion stalkers appear to have no social order although they are often found nesting near one another. The larva that infest a host body will ultimately kill each other in competition for food. Thus, only two or three will grow to maturity within the corpse. Carrion stalkers are sexless and any adult is capable of generating offspring every 2d4 weeks.

Ecology: Carrion stalkers are parasites who survive by devouring the bodies of their hosts, even after its death. They breed and die rapidly, surviving just long enough to spawn a few times.

CLIMATE/TERRAIN:	Odiare
FREQUENCY:	Very rare
ORGANIZATION:	Solitary or pack
ACTIVITY CYCLE:	Any
DIET:	Nil
INTELLIGENCE:	Average (8–10)
TREASURE:	Nil
ALIGNMENT:	Chaotic evil
NO. APPEARING:	1 or 2d4
ARMOR CLASS:	6
MOVEMENT:	6
HIT DICE:	2
THAC0:	19
NO. OF ATTACKS:	1
DAMAGE/ATTACK:	1 point
SPECIAL ATTACKS:	Paralyzation and domination
SPECIAL DEFENSES:	See below
MAGIC RESISTANCE:	Nil
SIZE:	T (6″ to 2′ tall)
MORALE:	Fearless (19–20)
XP VALUE:	975

Easily mistaken for a common toy, the carrionette is as foul and sinister a creature as one will find in the Demiplane of Dread. Its sharp needles literally paralyze men with fear.

Carrionettes are living, animated puppets or marionettes. They are essentially wooden dolls, painted and clothed, which have come to life. All of their limbs are jointed and have small holes for a puppeteer's strings. Carrionettes vary in height from 6 inches to 2 feet. They can look like anything, from clowns and knights to farm animals or monsters. Most, however, look like people.

Carrionettes can speak the favored language of their creator as well as any tongue appropriate to their shape. For example, a carrionette in the image of a drow would be able to speak the language of those sinister elves. The voice of a carrionette is hollow and shrill.

Combat: Carrionettes must have miniature, sharp weapons to attack with and cause damage; they cannot use blunt weapons. They can only do 1 point of damage per attack and the nature of its weapon does not affect how much damage the carrionette does. Typical weapons for carrionettes are large sewing needles, small kitchen knives, razor blades, and the like.

Each carrionette carries a small quiver of ten silver needles. They can throw these needles like spears, aiming at a leg or an arm. The needle has a maximum range of 15 feet and trails a magical silver cord attached to the carrionette's hand. A hit by the needle does no damage but requires the victim to make a saving throw vs. paralyzation. If the roll fails, that limb becomes paralyzed and the silver cord becomes invisible. A character who has a single paralyzed leg moves at half speed. The needle itself is not magical. The magical energy cord is created by the carrionette itself. If the character can remove the needle, he regains use of that limb in 1d4 rounds.

An immobilized character, whether paralyzed, asleep, or unconscious, is particularly vulnerable to the carrionette. The evil puppet can drive a needle into the base of the character's neck, which has the effect of transferring the essence of the carrionette into the person and vice versa. The person inhabiting the doll's body is inanimate for a full hour after the transferral. The carrionette in the person's body is unconscious for only a round, after which it can remove any and all needles stuck in its new body.

The carrionette has two other special abilities. It can climb walls like a thief, with an 85% chance of success. This chance increases to 95% if the puppet can use a string and needle or other aid. Secondly, the carrionette is able to employ a *ventriloquism* spell at will.

As one might expect, carrionettes are immune to poison cold, electricity, and all mind-affecting spells. A *warp wood* spell instantly destroys one of these creatures.

The person in the carrionette's body need not give up all hope of rescue, for he can recover his normal body with effort. The carrionette cannot destroy the doll body, for that would kill its own essence as well as the spirit of the person trapped in it. Therefore, the carrionette tends to lock up its former body or send it far away. To return things to normal, a silver needle must be driven into the live body (it does no damage). The doll body must hold either the needle or a silver wire no more than 15 feet long attached to the needle. When this is done, the doll's essence is instantly returned to its body, which remains inert for an hour. The person's essence is returned to his body and is active again in a single round.

Habitat/Society: Carrionettes are parasites that live off humans and human society. They tend to hide in plain sight, such as in children's toy rooms, toy shops, theaters, or other places where marionettes and puppets are not unusual. They can remain inanimate for extremely long periods of time, until they find a reason to exert themselves.

Carrionettes are driven by a single desire: to get a host. They desperately want to have a living body. Usually they operate in packs to drag down the bodies of the living, but they are known to operate alone. Carrionettes have no social structure. They do not interact with each other except when in a pack. Once a carrionette has a human body, it ignores other carrionettes, though it is capable of detecting their presence.

Ecology: A carrionette can be made of almost anything. Among the most common materials used are wood, straw, ceramic, cloth, and tin. For game purposes they are all treated the same. It takes a month to craft the carrionette body, something only a dedicated craftsman can do.

Cat, Midnight

Climate/Terrain:	Any non-arctic urban
Frequency:	Very rare
Organization:	Solitary
Activity Cycle:	Night
Diet:	Life force
Intelligence:	Average (8–10)
Treasure:	Nil
Alignment:	Lawful evil
No. Appearing:	1
Armor Class:	4
Movement:	18
Hit Dice:	3+6
THAC0:	17
No. of Attacks:	3
Damage/Attack:	1d2/1d2; rake 1d2/1d2
Special Attacks:	Spirit drain, curse
Special Defenses:	Nil
Magic Resistance:	25%
Size:	T (1′ tall)
Morale:	Very steady
XP Value:	1,400

Little is known about these brooding creatures save that they are found most frequently in the company of evil spellcasters. While they are often sought out for their rumored ability to lift curses, they are greatly feared for their ability to bestow the same. The most dreadful and least understood power of these ebon felines, however, is their ability to consume the very spirit of a living being, leaving behind a drained and empty shell.

Midnight cats are easily mistaken for ordinary house cats with lustrous coats of soft, ink-black fur. A closer examination, however, will reveal that their luminous yellow-green eyes are utterly pupilless and glow with an inner light in even the darkest of places.

Midnight cats can speak a crude form of common but generally choose to do so only when laying a curse upon an enemy. When they wish to, these creatures can converse freely with non-magical felines, although they have no power to command them in any way.

Combat: Midnight cats share all of the predatory skill of their more common cousins. In addition, their powerful eyes enable them to see perfectly well in anything but absolute darkness (such as that created by the spell of that name). Their natural stealth imposes a –3 penalty on the surprise rolls of their opponents and they themselves are surprised only on a roll of 1 on 1d10. Midnight cats have a 99% chance of moving silently and an 85% chance of hiding in shadows. They are good climbers and can scale trees or similar objects at half their normal movement rate without any die roll. They can make a standing jump of 10 feet and easily leap up to 20′ with a running start.

The midnight cat can use its claws to defend itself, striking with both of its front claws for 1d2 points of damage each. If it hits with both of these, it can automatically rake with its rear claws for an additional 1d2 points of damage each.

A midnight cat is quick to take offense and will cast embarrassing and frustrating curses at the least infraction. Troublesome curses may be cast on opponents that a cat is especially displeased with. Dangerous or lethal curses can be laid by a midnight cat only when it is gravely threatened (reduced to fewer than 5 hit points).

A midnight cat can lift troublesome, embarrassing, or frustrating curses at will. It is very difficult to persuade them to lift any curse, however, unless they are paid for their efforts. Generally, this recompense takes the form of evil deeds done on behalf of the sinister feline.

The midnight cat sustains itself by devouring the spirits of the living. As this ability can only be used upon sleeping victims, it is seldom effective in combat. To satisfy its hunger, the beast crawls onto its victim's chest and inhales sharply near the victim's lips. If a saving throw vs. breath weapon fails, a thin trail of vapor issues from the lips of the victim and courses into the mouth of the cat. A victim of this attack cannot heal new or existing damage by magical or natural means, cannot be cured or a disease, and loses the ability to employ any form of magical spells or turn undead. These symptoms persist until either the victim dies or the midnight cat is killed.

Habitat/Society: These coy, epicurean creatures insist on being waited upon by others and will only hunt for their food when forced to do so. Midnight cats usually adopt a "master" upon whom they rely for these creature comforts. As a rule, they choose spellcasters as companions. They seem to be able to detect when a *find familiar* spell has been cast by such people and are able to make themselves the subject of the spell.

Ecology: The midnight cat was first discovered in the domain of Tepest and is believed to be a dark strain of the elven cat.

Cat, Skeletal

CLIMATE/TERRAIN:	Any
FREQUENCY:	Uncommon
ORGANIZATION:	Pack
ACTIVITY CYCLE:	Night
DIET:	Nil
INTELLIGENCE:	Non- (0)
TREASURE:	Nil
ALIGNMENT:	Neutral
NO. APPEARING:	4–40 (4d10)
ARMOR CLASS:	6
MOVEMENT:	18
HIT DICE:	1
THAC0:	19
NO. OF ATTACKS:	3
DAMAGE/ATTACK:	1d2/1d2; rake 1d2/1d2
SPECIAL ATTACKS:	Cling
SPECIAL DEFENSES:	Spell immunity
MAGIC RESISTANCE:	Nil
SIZE:	T (1′ tall)
MORALE:	Fearless
XP VALUE:	65

Skeletal cats are the ambulatory remains of pets who have clawed their way back from the grave to avenge themselves upon masters who treated them poorly or ended their lives. These creatures are not terribly dangerous by themselves, but often form packs that are nearly unstoppable.

Skeletal cats appear to be animated feline skeletons. Unlike the skeletons summoned by spellcasters, these self-willed creatures often have tatters of fur and desiccated flesh clinging to their bones. Until the flesh of the creature completely rots away, it exudes the odor of rotting carrion.

Skeletal cats have no language, but are known for the ominous caterwauling that often fills the night prior to an attack.

Combat: Skeletal cats are agile hunters. They move with surprising grace causing opponents to suffer a –3 penalty on surprise rolls. Because their naturally sharp senses have been heightened in death, a skeletal cat can never be surprised.

Skeletal cats can attack as their living counterparts with claws and teeth. Each attack delivers 1d2 points of damage to their victim. If they hit with both claws they can use their rear claws to rake their victim, doing an additional 1d2 points with each rear claw. Anyone bitten by a skeletal cat has a 10% chance of contracting a debilitating disease (as per the *cause disease* spell) that can only be treated with a *cure disease* spell.

If a skeletal cat successfully rakes its victim, it will cling to him. One cat can cling to a person per foot of height, so that six may attach themselves to the average man. A victim suffers a –1 penalty on its Attack or Damage Rolls and a –2 to his Movement Rate for each such creature clinging to it. A clinging cat may rake again on the next round.

Skeletal cats are immune to all *sleep, charm, fear,* and *hold* spells. Cold-based, poison, or paralyzation attacks do them no harm and edged or piercing weapons inflict only half damage. Blunt weapons and fire do normal damage to them. These creatures are never required to make morale checks.

Skeletal cats retain the aversion to water that they had in life. As such, water-based attacks will cause a skeletal cat to flee if there is an open escape route. If the cat is cornered, however, it will fight with renewed vigor resulting in a +2 bonus to its Attack Rolls. Water can never drive a skeletal cat away from the specific target of its vengeance (see **Habitat/Society**). Holy water does no damage to skeletal cats but can still be used to drive them off.

Habitat/Society: It can scarce be argued that cats are the most noble and majestic of household pets. When one of these stately creatures suffers and dies from the abuse of a cruel master, it sometimes returns in the form of a skeletal cat. The first objective of these undead creatures is to hunt down and destroy the person who caused their suffering in life.

Once a skeletal cat has slain its former master, it will be released from its compulsion for vengeance, but not from the curse of undeath. Such a creature will wander about by night, eventually joining with others of its kind to form a drifting pack of evil hunters.

Skeletal cats are occasionally seen undertaking pathetic mockeries of their habits from life. One might be seen playing with a ball of yarn or trying futilely to drink milk from a saucer. These creatures may even jump into the lap of a human and appear docile in every way.

Ecology: Skeletal cats have no natural role in the world and serve no purpose other than to avenge themselves upon the living. They require no nourishment, although they sometimes kill small rodents and birds out of habit.

Cloaker, Shadow

Climate/Terrain:	Ravenloft
Frequency:	Very rare
Organization:	Solitary
Activity Cycle:	Any
Diet:	Special
Intelligence:	High (13–14)
Treasure:	Nil
Alignment:	Chaotic neutral
No. Appearing:	1
Armor Class:	7
Movement:	12, Fl 15 (D)
Hit Dice:	6
THAC0:	15
No. of Attacks:	2
Damage/Attack:	1d6/1d6
Special Attacks:	Constitution drain
Special Defenses:	See below
Magic Resistance:	Nil
Size:	M (7′ long)
Morale:	Elite (13–14)
XP Value:	2,000

The shadow cloaker is an unusual parasite that is believed to have been spawned on the Demiplane of Shadow. Once it attaches itself to someone, it uses them as a conduit through which it can drain the Constitution of other creatures. If unable to satisfy its hunger in this fashion, it begins to feed directly on the Constitution of its host.

When seen in bright light the shadow cloaker appears to be a black void in the shape of a great cape. Because of its ability to blend naturally into shadows, the cloaker is rarely seen except when it has already attached itself to a host.

It is believed that shadow cloakers are intelligent and may have their own language but every attempt to communicate with them has resulted in failure. Attempts to establish direct mental contact with any form of cloaker often require a madness check.

Combat: This sinister creature stalks its prey silently, gliding along the ground or along walls as gently as a passing shadow. Because of its absolute lack of color, a shadow cloaker has a 90% chance of hiding in shadows. If it is successfully hidden, the shadow cloaker always gains surprise when it attacks.

The shadow cloaker's whiplike tail is a dangerous weapon. In a single round it may strike twice, doing 1d6 points of damage each time.

When it is without a human counterpart, the cloaker will attempt to attach itself to a potential host's shadow by making a successful Attack Roll. A successful hit on the part of the shadow cloaker does no damage to the victim, but allows the creature to affix itself to its target's shoulders.

Once a shadow cloaker has attached itself to a new host it will attempt to feed by imbuing its companion with the ability to drain Constitution points by touch. Any time the host makes physical contact with another living creature, the shadow cloaker will drain a point of Constitution from him. The shadow cloaker will drain only one point per day so that subsequent touches will do no harm to anyone.

If a full day passes without the cloaker feeding, it will draw the point directly from its host instead. If a host's Constitution reaches 0, he dies. When this happens, the shadow cloaker will leave to seek another host. Twenty-four hours later, the drained host will rise again as an undead shadow.

The shadow cloaker's Constitution draining ability is difficult to detect because of a strange anesthetizing quality of its attack that causes the weakening effects of the touch to be unfelt for 2d8 rounds. The intentional use of a shadow cloaker's draining touch by a host is an evil action and requires a powers check.

A shadow cloaker can only be struck by magical weapons. If attacked when it is attached to someone, the creature will engulf its host and use its tail to ward off would-be rescuers. While engulfed, the host may use no melee weapons, psionics, or spells that require verbal or somatic components. The host absorbs half of any normal damage delivered to a shadow cloaker while engulfed. Area effect weapons and spells do full damage to both the creature and its host.

A *continual light* or *light* spell cast directly at a shadow cloaker will force it to release its hold on a host and flee. These creatures are immune to *sleep*, *charm*, and *hold* spells. Shadow cloakers are not undead and cannot be turned or harmed by holy water.

Habitat/Society: What little is known (or assumed) about these solitary creatures has been almost impossible to verify. The first known shadow cloaker returned almost unnoticed with the sole survivor of a party of Dark Delvers exploring a series of underground caverns in Arak. Since then, other creatures of this type have appeared in Ravenloft, seemingly without cause.

Ecology: Shadow cloakers are parasites that depend upon a host to employ their energy-draining powers. Without a host to help it feed, the shadow cloaker loses 1 Hit Die per week until it dies.

Cloaker, Resplendent

CLIMATE/TERRAIN:	Ravenloft
FREQUENCY:	Very rare
ORGANIZATION:	Solitary
ACTIVITY CYCLE:	Day
DIET:	Special
INTELLIGENCE:	High (13–14)
TREASURE:	Nil
ALIGNMENT:	Chaotic neutral
NO. APPEARING:	1
ARMOR CLASS:	5
MOVEMENT:	12, Fl 15 (D)
HIT DICE:	6
THAC0:	15
NO. OF ATTACKS:	None
DAMAGE/ATTACK:	Nil
SPECIAL ATTACKS:	See below
SPECIAL DEFENSES:	See below
MAGIC RESISTANCE:	Nil
SIZE:	M (7′ long)
MORALE:	Unsteady (5–7)
XP VALUE:	2,000

Shunned by many as an ill omen, the resplendent cloaker is a mournful creature that must alleviate the suffering of others in order to survive. This benign symbiont attaches itself to the nape of a host's neck and feeds by healing his wounds. While this can be a very valuable service, there is a drawback. The resplendent cloaker gives off a dazzling glow that makes it and its host highly visible.

The resplendent cloaker appears to be a large cloak with a scintillating dorsal surface and a bright white underside. Its claws appear to be gold clasps and what passes for a collar of burning, multi-colored jewels serve as the creature's eyes.

It is thought that resplendent cloakers may communicate with one another by varying the intensity of their glow. Attempts to make direct mental contact with a cloaker require a madness check.

Combat: The resplendent cloaker often lies in wait by draping itself on the floor or across a piece of furniture. When a potential host comes near, it attacks by emitting a sudden blinding burst of light that acts like the *color spray* of a 6th level wizard. This power can be used three times per day.

Once its victim has been dazzled by its *color spray*, the cloaker flies at its target and attempts to attach itself to the target's neck. A successful Attack Roll does no damage but allows it to affix itself to the victim. Once in place, the resplendent cloaker acts a *ring of regeneration*.

The resplendent cloaker also has the ability to engulf its victims. Each round the victim is affected as if by a *color spray* spell. An engulfed victim can make no attacks and may not employ spells or powers that have a somatic or verbal component. While a victim is engulfed, any damage done to the cloaker is divided evenly between the creature and the trapped victim. Area effect spells such as *fireball* do full damage to both the cloaker and its victim.

If the resplendent cloaker takes damage, it will immediately (in the same round) replenish the lost hit points by draining them from its host. When it heals itself, it must absorb 2 points for every 1 that it is regaining. If it kills its host by fully draining it of life the resplendent cloaker will then disengage itself and seek a new host.

If a cloaker is forcibly removed torn from its host, a feat that requires a bend bars/lift gates roll, both the cloaker and host must make a system shock roll or die instantly. A successful roll still leaves the host stunned and paralyzed until treated with a *heal* spell.

Attempts to smother the glow of the cloaker with heavy robes or by casting *darkness* on it will cause it to lose 1 hit point each round. It will replenish each lost hit point by immediately draining 2 from its host if possible.

A resplendent cloaker must heal at least 1 hit point each day in order to sustain itself. After 4 days without healing, it will leave the host in search of better feeding grounds. Any magical healing applied to a resplendent cloaker's host will immediately drive the creature away and do damage to equal to the number of points that would normally have been healed. This damage is applied to both the host and the cloaker.

Habitat/Society: Because of their attraction to suffering and bloodshed, these creatures are believed to have a prescient awareness of impending misfortune. Consequently, the appearance of a resplendent cloaker is believed to portend ill for the coming days.

Despite their somber significance, some prize these creatures for their symbiotic healing abilities. Others despise them for their tendency to draw attention to a host. More than one host has been murdered by thieves believing they had found an enchanted cloak. A greater number have fallen prey to predatory animals drawn to the resplendent cloaker's bright glow.

Ecology: The resplendent cloaker is a symbiotic creature that manages to sustain itself by healing the wounds of others. Exactly how it derives nourishment from this action is unknown.

Cloaker, Undead

CLIMATE/TERRAIN:	Ravenloft
FREQUENCY:	Very rare
ORGANIZATION:	Solitary
ACTIVITY CYCLE:	Night
DIET:	Special
INTELLIGENCE:	High (13–14)
TREASURE:	C
ALIGNMENT:	Chaotic evil
NO. APPEARING:	1
ARMOR CLASS:	3
MOVEMENT:	3, Fl 15 (D)
HIT DICE:	6
THAC0:	15
NO. OF ATTACKS:	2
DAMAGE/ATTACK:	1d6/1d6
SPECIAL ATTACKS:	Level drain, laceration
SPECIAL DEFENSES:	See below
MAGIC RESISTANCE:	Nil
SIZE:	M (7′ long)
MORALE:	Elite (13–14)
XP VALUE:	2,000

The undead cloaker is a foul and dangerous creature that is believed to be the earthly remains of a resplendent cloaker that has had its life drained away by the living dead. The creature actually imbues its host with the power to drain life energy. If the host fails to do this, the undead cloaker will drain his life energy instead.

The undead cloaker appears to be a large decaying cloak. What might seem to be tattered cloth from a distance is clearly composed of rotting flesh when viewed at closer range.

While it is not known if these creatures can communicate, they are believed to have a dim telepathic ability to direct the actions of a mindless undead host. Direct mental contact with an undead cloaker requires any living being to make a madness check.

Combat: When the undead cloaker assaults a new host, it flies quickly at the victim and engulfs it in its rotting folds. If its attack is successful, it will have attached itself to its victim's neck, doing 1d4 points of damage. If the attack is unsuccessful, it will continue to attempt to attach itself in succeeding rounds.

A victim who is engulfed by an undead cloaker is unable to take any physical actions, cast spells with somatic or material components, or use psionics of any kind. The undead cloaker will keep its new host engulfed until he stops struggling. Once a new host is subdued, the undead cloaker will retain its grip at the victim's neck, but allow its host free movement. The undead cloaker may engulf its host at any time without an attack roll if the host attempts to free itself. An engulfed host will take half of any physical damage inflicted upon the undead cloaker. Area effect weapons and spells will do full damage to both the undead cloaker and its host.

Once the undead cloaker has secured a new host, it will drain a life level from any living creature that the host touches. If the host fails to feed the undead cloaker in this manner at least once per day, the creature will drain a life level from the host. Any creature that is drained to zero level by an undead cloaker or its host will return from the grave in 1d4 days as a common zombie.

The undead cloaker can also use its tail to deliver two lacerating attacks per round to any opponents who attempt to harm it or remove it from its host. Each time the tail strikes a victim, it delivers 1d6 points of damage and creates a long, bloody gash that will continue to bleed (1d6 points per round) until the wound is bound or some form of healing magic is employed. It requires one full round and the use of both hands for an individual to bind one of these wounds.

Physically removing an undead cloaker from its host requires a bend bars/lift gates roll. If the cloaker is successfully torn from its wearer, the creature will be instantly killed and drain 1d4 life levels from the host.

An undead cloaker will not select a host who is under the effects of a *negative plane protection* spell. Casting this spell on an undead cloaker's host will cause the creature to break free and seek a new quarry. A cloaker can also be turned by a priest as a 6-HD creature, in which case it will detach from its host and flee.

Undead cloakers are immune to all *sleep, charm, hold, fear,* and cold-based attacks. They are not harmed by diseases, poisons, or paralyzation attacks. They are also immune to the level draining touch of their hosts or other undead creatures. A *raise dead* spell cast upon an undead cloaker will destroy it if a saving throw vs. spell fails. Holy water will inflict 1d6+2 points of damage to an undead cloaker.

Habitat/Society: Undead cloakers are solitary and chaotic creatures who have never been known to cooperate with one another or with other creatures. They are, however, occasionally found attached to zombies they have created. An undead cloaker seems to have the ability to direct the actions of a mindless undead host that it has destroyed. In these cases, the creature will continue to use the newly-created zombie as a conduit for its life-draining power.

The willful use of an undead cloaker by a host to drain life energy levels is an evil act and requires a powers check.

Ecology: As undead creatures, these cloakers have no place in the natural order. If it is true that they were once resplendent cloakers, then their conversion to unlife is somewhat tragic.

Corpse Candle

CLIMATE/TERRAIN:	Ravenloft
FREQUENCY:	Very rare
ORGANIZATION:	Solitary
ACTIVITY CYCLE:	Any
DIET:	Nil
INTELLIGENCE:	Average (8)
TREASURE:	Nil
ALIGNMENT:	Chaotic neutral
NO. APPEARING:	1
ARMOR CLASS:	4
MOVEMENT:	12, Fl 24 (B)
HIT DICE:	6
THAC0:	15
NO. OF ATTACKS:	1
DAMAGE/ATTACK:	1–6
SPECIAL ATTACKS:	See below
SPECIAL DEFENSES:	Spell immunity, +1 or better weapon to hit
MAGIC RESISTANCE:	Nil
SIZE:	M (6′ tall)
MORALE:	Steady (13–14)
XP VALUE:	1,400

The corpse candle is the undead spirit of a murdered man or woman that coerces the living into bringing its killer to justice. Its name comes from the flamelike light that flickers in the eyes of its corpse while the spirit waits for a champion to avenge it.

Corpse candles are both ethereal and invisible creatures. Those who can see such things describe them as vaporous wisps of mist or fog.

The corpse candle cannot speak and can only communicate its desire to have its killer brought to justice by means of a weak mental suggestion that it employs when it selects a champion.

Combat: When a corpse candle is first encountered, it appears as a ghostly flame flickering in the eyes of a murdered man or woman. Anyone looking into the eyes of a body that houses a corpse candle must make a saving throw vs. spell at a –3 penalty. Those making their saving throw simply see the flame dim. A failed roll indicates that the adventurer sees the face of the corpse's killer in its flickering eyes.

The sight of this countenance carries with it a terrific spiritual message. The adventurer will suddenly find himself reliving the last few seconds of the corpse's life. He will experience everything that led to the death, but cannot affect this traumatic chain of events in any way. Those accompanying the adventurer will see him toss and turn in agony, howl in rage, or take other actions dictated by the nature of his hallucination.

When this nightmarish experience has passed, the adventurer will remember vividly all that occurred. The face of the killer will be burned into his mind so that it is visible in any open flame, campfire, torch, or lantern. Even smoke will carry the eerie vision of the murderer. These haunting images, while clear to the champion, will be seen by no one else.

If the champion brings the murderer to justice by either tracking him down and killing him or by seeing him judged for his crime, the corpse candle will be set to rest.

If, however, the champion chooses to ignore the visions for more than 1d4 days, the corpse candle will use its power to *affect normal fires* to harry the champion to action. This ability is similar to the 1st level wizard spell, except that the corpse candle can cause small flames to leap distances of up to 10′. It can also enable flames to take on any shape as long as it does not require greatly increasing the size of the original fire. A small candle flame might take the form of a spider and leap onto a drape or bedsheet, setting it aflame. A large bonfire could take the form of a man and momentarily envelop the champion. The corpse candle can only hold such forms for one round and flames cause only 1d6 points of damage. Such flames may, however, set flammable material alight.

Casting *true seeing* will reveal a ghostly image of the dead person sitting astride the champion's shoulders. A *protection from evil* or *negative plane protection* will force the corpse candle away from the champion for the duration of the spell. During such times, the corpse candle cannot cause the champion to see the killer's face, but can use its ability to *affect normal fires* outside the range of the protective spells. A corpse candle can be directly attacked with magic weapons and will retaliate in such situations by using *burning hands* as if cast by a 6th level spellcaster.

Corpse candles can be driven off permanently with spells such as *dispel magic, dismissal, banishment, holy word,* and *wish.* Also, if at any time the corpse candle's killer should die, even accidentally, the spirit will rest in peace. Corpse candles are immune to *sleep, charm, hold,* and *death* spells as well as cold-based spells, poison, and paralyzation. They can be turned as 6th level undead, but will return to their champion as soon as possible. If at any time a *speak with dead* spell is used to communicate with a corpse candle, the spirit can only repeat the name of its killer.

Habitat/Society: Corpse candles are found only with their earthly remains. Consequently, they can be encountered in places as varied as tombs and public alleyways.

Ecology: Corpse candles fill no natural role in the world. They do, however, satisfy an emotional need so great that it defies even the grave.

Death's Head Tree

CLIMATE/TERRAIN:	Forlorn
FREQUENCY:	Rare
ORGANIZATION:	Solitary
ACTIVITY CYCLE:	Any
DIET:	Special
INTELLIGENCE:	Semi- (2–4)
TREASURE:	Special
ALIGNMENT:	Neutral evil
NO. APPEARING:	1
ARMOR CLASS:	10: trunk 7: branches & heads
MOVEMENT:	Nil: tree Fl 6 (E): heads
HIT DICE:	10 + 6 hp/head
THAC0:	11
NO. OF ATTACKS:	1 per head
DAMAGE/ATTACK:	1d4 (bite)
SPECIAL ATTACKS:	Spit seeds
SPECIAL DEFENSES:	Immune to fire
MAGIC RESISTANCE:	10%
SIZE:	H (15′–20′ tall)
MORALE:	Fearless (19–20)
XP VALUE:	1,400

A death's head tree looks much like a 15- to 20-foot-tall weeping willow, except that its branches are thicker. Its seeds need blood to germinate, so it grows most commonly in places where a great deal of blood has been spilled. Thus, battlefields and places of sacrifice are two areas where death's head trees thrive. In fact, these trees often mark places where ancient battles have been fought or where evil temples once stood.

A mature tree bears a strange and terrible fruit: 4d4 rotten-smelling "death's heads." Each of these appears to be the severed head of any of the standard human and demihuman races, except for the fact that each head grows from a branch of the tree and is attached to the branch at the neck. In time, these heads ripen and fall from the tree, actually floating away on organic gases, seeking the bodies of warm-blooded creatures in which to plant their seeds.

Neither the death's head tree nor its sinister fruit can communicate normally. Although the death's heads themselves are able to moan for help and otherwise attempt to attract the attention of potential victims, most sages agree that they are only mimicking speech and are not truly able to communicate.

Combat: Like most carnivorous plants, the death's head tree engages in combat primarily when potential victims come within its reach, but this plant has a unique lure: It grows heads that are distinctly humanoid in appearance and then, with its very limited intelligence, animates them just enough to enable the heads to softly call "help." While those who investigate the source of the pleas have few problems identifying the heads as monstrous, a sense of curiosity or repugnance (and a resulting urge to destroy the tree) frequently draws them in close enough for the tree to attack.

When physically attacked, the death's head tree uses its "fruit" to defend itself. Each head is capable of biting once per melee round, inflicting 1d4 points of damage and simultaneously inserting a seed into the wound (see below). While the death's head tree itself is not capable of locomotion, it can move its branches. Hence, the trunk has an Armor Class of 10, but the branches and heads have an effective Armor Class of 7.

Due to its magical nature, a mature death's head tree has a limited amount of magical resistance. It is also immune to fire and fire-based magical attacks.

Due to this mobility and the flexibility of its branches, the tree is capable of making as many attacks against a target as it has death's heads. Each head will die upon sustaining 6 points of damage, and the branches may be hacked off upon sustaining 10 points of damage (from a slashing weapon only).

Each of the 4d4 death's heads on a mature tree contains 1d6 needlelike seeds that inflict minimal damage (just 1 point per seed) upon a successful hit. Each head is capable of spitting one seed per melee round at any warm-blooded creature who ventures within 30 feet of the tree.

The seeds can be removed within 24 hours, in much the same way as one would remove a sliver (inflicting another point of damage in the process). However, the points of the seeds excrete a low-grade natural anesthetic, which means that they don't bother the victim after the initial sting of penetration. Therefore, many victims forget about them after the battle is over, allowing the seeds to take root. If left in place for longer than a day, the seeds germinate and begin to grow, causing an ever-increasing amount of damage as sprouts spread through the victim's body. The shoots inflict 1d4 points of damage on day one, 2d4 on day two, 3d4 on day three, and so on, to a maximum of 10d4 points of damage per day.

Forcibly removing or cutting these new shoots out of a victim's body, once they have rooted, inflicts damage equal to half of what would otherwise be the growth damage for that day, and doing so has only a 50% chance to be completely effective. A slip of the plant may remain inside the victim's body and continue to grow. Any spell that will kill a plant, however, will immediately kill the growths (which at this stage have no immunity to magic or fire).

While most carnivorous plant life is largely anchored to a single spot, the fruit of the death's head tree becomes fully mobile once it has ripened and broken from the branch. Buoyed by gases produced by their own rot, the fallen heads float off, seeking a warm-blooded creature in which to plant their seeds. The smell of blood can attract a death's head from as far away as a mile, and it can travel up to 20 miles in search of a warm-blooded host. Once a potential victim is located, the death's head spits until all of its 1d6 seeds are gone. Once its seeds are exhausted, it will continue to attack by biting for 2d4 rounds, at which point it falls to the ground, dead.

Although the fruit of a death's head tree has the appearance of a waxy, slack-jawed corpse, a head is not considered undead as long as it is still attached to the tree. Only when it has fully matured and broken from the tree does it assume the characteristics of undead. At this point, it can be turned as a zombie. Once fallen from the tree, the head is also vulnerable to fire, but it retains its magic resistance.

Habitat/Society: There is only one limit to the number of death's head trees that can grow in a given area, and that is how much blood has been spilled. Theoretically, there could be one tree for every corpse. In fact, it is not uncommon to see an entire forest of tiny saplings springing up a few days after a large battle. Of course, until these reach maturity, they can be killed or uprooted as easily as any other plant. Also, they tend to sink their roots into each other, attempting to steal extra life's blood and grow stronger, and eventually only one tree is left within 50 or more feet. Thus, the fully mature death's head tree is a rare find.

Ecology: The average death's head tree takes 50+1d10 years to mature to the point where it can grow a crop of death's heads. Until the time when its branches thicken enough to bear the weight of its ghastly fruit, it looks much like a weeping willow. Only a knowledgeable observer can tell the difference.

Once it reaches maturity, a death's head tree is capable of living for thousands of years. A few sages have speculated that cutting down a specimen and counting its rings can establish the number of years that have passed since a battle was fought or a place of sacrifice was abandoned. The theory is a sound one, but few people who are aware of the tree's nature will volunteer to chop one down and prove it.

Once a death's head tree matures, it produces a crop of ghastly fruit every other year. Within 1d6 days of budding, the death's heads grow from the size of walnuts to the size of normal humanoid heads. Having reached their full size, the heads take on a distinctive appearance and then begin to softly call out the word "help" in a language appropriate to the race of the head. Within another 3d6 days, they ripen and begin to fall.

Aside from its need for blood to germinate its seeds, the death's head tree takes its daily sustenance from the sun and soil like any other plant. It does not require any more blood to survive, once it has successfully germinated and rooted itself in the ground. Because there is no limit to the type of terrain on which blood is spilled, the death's head tree grows virtually anywhere. One may be found growing among the stones of a ruined temple or on an ancient battlefield that is littered with rusted weapons and the bleached bones of the soldiers who once fought there.

Since the fruit of a death's head tree is always humanoid in appearance, it is largely believed that the seeds can be germinated only in humanoid blood. A few experiments attempting to sprout a seed in animal blood have thus far been unsuccessful, but sages theorize that this should be possible, since the death's heads are known to spit their seeds at warm-blooded animals, as well as humanoids.

Some say that the fruit of a death's head tree resembles the face of the person whose blood nurtured it. Indeed, since the death's head fruit has been heard to whisper in many languages, some sages believe that each is an undead manifestation of a particular individual. Others insist that this is no more than mere mimicry, that there is no connection between those who have died and the fruit of a death's head tree.

The wood of a mature death's head tree is prized for its natural magical resistance and immunity to fire, and it is an essential part of many magical devices, especially fire-resistant shields. It is also used as a component in spells designed to protect against flame and heat.

While a death's head tree has no treasure of its own, those it kills often carry treasure. There is a 15% chance that a corpse lies at the foot of a death's head tree. If so, it will have Treasure Type U, plus 1d10 of each type of coin. The body also will (90% of the time) have a death's head tree sapling growing out of it.

Doppleganger, Ravenloft

Climate/Terrain:	Any
Frequency:	Rare
Organization:	Clan
Activity Cycle:	Any
Diet:	Omnivore
Intelligence:	High (13–14)
Treasure:	E
Alignment:	Neutral evil
No. Appearing:	3–12
Armor Class:	5
Movement:	12
Hit Dice:	5
THAC0:	15
No. of Attacks:	1
Damage/Attack:	1–12 (fist) or by weapon
Special Attacks:	Surprise
Special Defenses:	See below
Magic Resistance:	See below
Size:	M (5′ tall)
Morale:	Elite (13–14)
XP Value:	650

The Ravenloft doppleganger is a master of mimicry that survives by taking the shapes of humans, demihumans, and humanoids.

In its natural form, the Ravenloft doppleganger is a bipedal sexless humanoid with a monstrous face. It has a hairless head, ash-gray complexion, and pointed ears that bend out from the head rather than lying against the skull. The space between the mouth and nose is far too large—several inches at least—while the eyes are too high up on the face. The skin is thick and folded (giving the doppleganger a natural Armor Class of 5), and the fingers and toes have no nails.

A doppleganger is rarely seen in its natural form, however; usually it is mimicking the form of another humanoid. When a doppleganger dies, it reverts to its true form. Sometimes (particularly if the doppleganger takes a long time to expire), it first shifts through one or two of the other forms it has mimicked recently before reverting at last to its true form.

Combat: This monster is able to assume the shape of any humanoid creature between 4 feet and 8 feet high. The doppleganger seeks out a solitary victim, makes the kill, then uses its mimicry ability to assume that creature's form. The doppleganger can then insinuate itself into a group, using its *ESP* ability to behave as others expect it to behave, thus lulling its future victims into believing the doppleganger is their companion.

A Ravenloft doppleganger is immune to *sleep* and *charm* spells. It rolls all saving throws as a 10th level fighter.

Unlike its weaker cousin (who is only 90% effective in its mimicry), the Ravenloft doppleganger can make its new shape authentic to the touch. Anyone touching a Ravenloft doppleganger in its new form will be unable to tell it from the real thing. The actual process of taking the victim's shape takes a full round to complete.

While the doppleganger can change its outer shape, it cannot alter its true nature. No matter what form it takes on, the doppleganger retains all of its original combat values and attributes. It could, for example, make itself look incredibly muscular, but it would in fact be no stronger.

Before it can mimic someone with any degree of accuracy, a doppleganger must get a good look at its target. (This usually means the doppleganger must approach to within 30 feet.) However, bad lighting can reduce this distance, and magic, such as a *crystal ball,* can increase the distance, as can certain items of mundane equipment. (It is amazing how much detail a spyglass can pick up.)

A Ravenloft doppleganger is able to alter the shape of any equipment it carries. However, this ability functions only between items of similar function and material. For example, the doppleganger could change a sword into an axe, or clothing into leather armor—even ragged clothing into an elegant gown. But it could *not* change normal clothes into plate mail.

While in its new form, the object functions normally. An axe changed into a sword, for example, does damage as a sword.

Equipment and belongings are held in their new shape by the will of the doppleganger. If a doppleganger's clothing or equipment is separated from the creature by a distance of 5 feet or more, the objects revert to their true form.

The doppleganger knows full well the limitations of its mimicry. For this reason, it is rare to find a doppleganger that is not carrying a little bit of everything. The Ravenloft doppleganger usually wears normal clothes and carries a medium-sized metal weapon, small metal pieces such as daggers and tools, and wooden objects like figurines and lutes. (It never knows what it will have to imitate.) The doppleganger prefers, however, to use real items whenever possible. Victims will always be stripped of their belongings.

The doppleganger's *ESP* ability operates exactly like the spell. The only exception is that it can attempt to read a creature's mind as often as it wants. For the Dungeon Master, this means that there is normally no point in rolling saving throws for the PCs involved, since they are bound to fail sooner or later. Rolling a saving throw is necessary only in time-critical situations.

The ability to read minds serves the doppleganger in preparing for the murder of a victim and in maintaining its mimicry after making the switch. Initially, it reads the minds of a group of characters to learn their habits and abilities. This gives the doppleganger an idea of who would make the best victim and when would be the best time to strike.

Before it actually kills its chosen victim, the doppleganger spends several days reading that person's mind to familiarize itself with the victim's personality and way of doing things. Once the doppleganger is in place, it uses its *ESP* ability to continually read the minds of the people around it. From their thoughts, the doppleganger learns to do exactly what they expect the person it is mimicking to do. In this way, the doppleganger is never surprised and rarely acts in a suspicious manner.

One of the trickier situations that a doppleganger must handle is skilled labor. The person that has been replaced doubtlessly had talents that the doppleganger is unable to imitate (spellcasting, high level thieving abilities, or special proficiencies, for example). The doppleganger uses its *ESP* to forewarn itself of these situations, attempting to weasel out of performing tasks that it is incapable of doing.

Habitat/Society: Doppleganger clans are structured hierarchically. There is a leader (usually the oldest doppleganger) and a pecking order that tends to place the youngest at the bottom. The age of a doppleganger can be determined only when it is in its true form. The more creases it has under its eyes, the older it is.

When planning an infiltration, the youngest dopplegangers get the most dangerous jobs and the lowest-ranking victims of any target group. The highest-ranking victim will be replaced by the head of the clan.

Because dopplegangers are asexual, they care little for distinctions based on gender. When mimicking a person of a particular gender, a doppleganger will often ignore or even rebel against the limitations placed on that gender by society, but will readily comply with these limitations for self-preservation.

The doppleganger's inability to imitate skills means that it will try to pick a victim whose daily life does not involve skilled labor or unique abilities. (Wizards are probably the most avoided class for dopplegangers.)

Unlike their weaker cousins, Ravenloft dopplegangers can learn certain very specific skills. They may learn any of the thieving skills up to the equivalent of a thief of 7th level. These skills can be used only when the doppleganger is in the form in which the skills were learned; they cannot be used in any of the doppleganger's other human shapes.

Although these skills allow a doppleganger to mimic a thief with ease, a doppleganger rarely picks a thief when looking for a victim to replace. Dopplegangers prefer to mimic law-abiding citizens.

Dopplegangers are both greedy and cowardly. They tend to favor rich targets but frivolously spend the wealth they embezzle. When confronted or in times of true danger, they flee. It is rare for a doppleganger to accept any significant risk once it has achieved a new shape.

Dopplegangers rarely work alone. Each doppleganger belongs to a small, tightly knit clan of three to twelve members and no children. Clan members work together to murder a victim and set one of their number up in that person's place. Once one doppleganger has insinuated itself into a new life, it can work from the inside to help its clan members claim other victims.

Usually dopplegangers work from the bottom up. (It is difficult to replace a wealthy noble without inside help.) First, the dopplegangers replace a guard or servant in the noble's home. From there, they take over a high-ranking servant such as the captain of the guard or the head butler. With the captain or butler replaced, they aim for a family member. When several dopplegangers are established inside the noble's estate, it is relatively easy to replace the noble himself.

Ecology: The single most limiting aspect of doppleganger ecology is that they cannot reproduce among themselves; they must mate with humanoids of other races to produce offspring. In its natural form, the doppleganger is sexless, but it can imitate a member of either sex.

Doppleganger genes are always dominant. A newborn child who has one doppleganger parent and one humanoid parent appears to be of the same race as its humanoid parent. It is indistinguishable from any other child of that race.

The child's doppleganger heritage is not revealed until it reaches puberty. Gradually, the child's appearance begins to change, shifting more and more toward that of the doppleganger's true form. When this begins to happen, a member of the doppleganger clan approaches the child and reveals the child's true nature.

Normally, it is the doppleganger parent who reveals this fact to the child (if it is still masquerading as the husband or wife of the humanoid parent). Because a dozen years or more elapse from the conception of the child until it is ready to be brought into the clan, sometimes the doppleganger parent's true nature will have been discovered. The doppleganger parent may have been driven away or destroyed by the time the child reaches puberty. In these cases, another member of the clan will attempt to make contact with the child when the time is right. However, this is not always possible.

If the child doppleganger is not taught about its true heritage, it is likely to be caught and killed.

Furies

Climate/Terrain:	Ravenloft
Frequency:	Unique
Organization:	Triune
Activity Cycle:	Day
Diet:	Nil
Intelligence:	Exceptional (15–16)
Treasure:	Nil
Alignment:	Lawful evil
No. Appearing:	3
Armor Class:	7
Movement:	6, Fl 15 (C)
Hit Dice:	7
THAC0:	13
No. of Attacks:	3
Damage/Attack:	1–4/1–4/1–6; rake 1–4/1–4
Special Attacks:	Attribute drain
Special Defenses:	See below
Magic Resistance:	Nil
Size:	M (6′ tall)
Morale:	Fearless (19–20)
XP Value:	5,000 per sister

The Furies are three malicious creatures who strive to prevent the redemption of Ravenloft's evil denizens. These foul sisters wander the Demiplane of Dread seeking those who would turn away from the path of evil. When they find such a person, the trio descends upon him and attempts to force him to continue his depravity and commit greater and greater crimes.

The Furies always appear together and take the form of harpy-like creatures. They have the clawed legs of vultures and the black leathery wings of enormous bats. Their torsos and heads are those of beautiful, unclad women with coal black skin and raven hair. They have teeth as long and sharp as needles and long talons of bone capping their fingers. Their eyes glow dusky red and their breath carries the smell of rotting meat.

The Furies seem unhindered by the many languages of humans and demihumans, for they always taunt their victim in his native language. Magical or psionic attempts to *silence* them or force them to speak when they do not wish to will always fail.

Combat: The Furies have an innate ability to locate their victim, making it impossible for him to hide from them even with magical means. It may well be that one is safe from the sisters beyond the domains of Ravenloft.

When possible, they begin any skirmish by diving down on their prey from trees, high cliffs, or other perches. When they are able to attack in this manner they gain a +2 bonus to their Attack and Damage Rolls. Once in melee combat, the Furies do not generally seek to pull back and arrange a second such ambush.

The dark sisters attack with their deadly talons, slashing twice in each round for 1d4 points of damage each. In addition, they can bite a victim for 1d6 points. If both of their talons hit, they are assumed to have gotten a grip on their victim and are able to rake with their vultures' legs. A successful attack with these keen claws inflicts 1d4 points of damage each.

While all five of a Fury's physical attacks must be directed at a single target, the creatures have a special attack that can be employed upon any single target within 5 feet of them. Thrice per day, each of the sisters can exhale a breath of putrid air that has the same effects as a *stinking cloud* spell but affects only one person.

While the Furies will employ these tactics in most battles, they carry magical *scourges +3* they save for their primary victim. During any round that the Furies do not make their normal melee attacks they may strike once with these barbed whips, inflicting 1d4 points of damage with each hit. In addition to their normal damage, the lashes of the Furies have the ability to drain Ability Score points from their targets. Alecto's scourge destroys 1 point of Wisdom, Tisiphone's drains Strength, and Megarea's reduces the victim's Intelligence. Unless the target is slain, lost Ability Score points are regained at a rate of 1 per day. A Fury **can** employ her stinking breath in the same round that she uses her scourge.

The sisters can also *change self* at will, taking the form of old crones. They use this ability when they must act without revealing their true natures.

Although they are not undead, the Furies can be turned by a cleric of good alignment as if they were vampires. However, this attempt requires one round for each of the sisters and will only succeed if the priest invokes their names individually. Turning the sisters will only drive them off until their next visitation and they cannot be destroyed or commanded in this fashion.

When a victim dies at the hands (or scourges) of the Furies, spells such as *raise dead*, *resurrection*, *reincarnate*, or *wish* cast with the intent of bringing the victim back to life will serve only as an *animate dead* spell. The target of the spell will rise from the grave as a zombielike creature with half the Hit Dice it had in life. Such an undead creature will obey the caster of the spell.

The dark sisters cannot intentionally harm creatures of good alignment, although they may direct their fetid breath at them. They may strike at neutral and evil characters freely, but prefer to attack the latter over the former if given a choice.

Only the attacks of good aligned characters do full damage to one of the Furies. They take only half damage from any attack made by a neutral creature and are entirely immune to harm by any evil being.

The furies are immune to all spells and psionics that attempt to control the mind or body. They are further immune to all spells from the school of Enchantment/Charm or the sphere of Charm.

In addition to these powers, each of the three sisters has unique abilities that affect how she conducts combat. Complete information about these wretched creatures will be found at the end of this entry.

Habitat/Society: The three sisters are always found together. It is not known where their lair is, if one exists at all. They appear to move freely between all the domains of Ravenloft and even a domain lord cannot prevent their entry or exit from his lands.

Known to the Vistani as Alecto, Tisiphone, and Megarea, these creatures are said to have originated amid the Gray Wastes. How they came to be trapped in the Demiplane of Dread and what relationship they might have to macabre powers behind the swirling Mists of Ravenloft is unknown.

The furies seem to have an uncanny sense that tells them when someone who has begun to travel down the seductive road of evil is attempting to atone for his wrongs and return his spirit to a state of grace. Exactly how this ability functions, or what its parameters might be, is unknown. It is clear from past experience that the furies have no interest in those who are trapped in the first or second stages of corruption, known to the Vistani as *the enticement* and *the invitation*. Only those who have progressed to the third and fourth stages, *the touch of darkness* and *the embrace* are of interest to this foul triad. It is worth mentioning that those lamentable few who have moved beyond the fourth stage, becoming *creatures of Ravenloft* or *lords of a domain* are beyond salvation and thus of no interest to the furies.

When a repentant creature comes to the attention of the furies, they swoop out of the mists and make a lair in some out of the way place. If possible, this will be an area that is often visited by the person who has captured their interest. If no such place is available, they will nest where they must and then arrange to lure their victim to them.

In the shape of crones, they will contact the one who seeks atonement and befriend him. Using every bit of their considerable guile and wit, they will seek to persuade the poor dupe to undertake additional acts of evil. It is their hope to lure him beyond the fourth stage of corruption to a point where redemption is no longer possible. Once this is done, the furies lose all interest in their victim and abandon him to his fate, no matter what promises they might have made to him previously.

If their victim resists, they will recount his crimes and assure him of his doom. Taunting him mercilessly, they will say whatever they must to cajole the tortured spirit to violent outbursts or evil reactions.

The sisters will attempt to halt the redemption of an individual only three times. If they have not been successful after this, they will decide to simply destroy him. The sisters always select a public setting for their attack and strike with the intention of torturing their victim to death. Thus, they will do everything in their power to make his demise as painful as possible. It is their belief that this will be a lesson to other evildoers who might wish to renounce their malevolent ways. The furies will quickly kill any creature that attempts to stand in the way of their dark purpose.

Any time one of the furies is reduced to 0 hit points, she will dissipate with her scourge in a vaporous black cloud. If any of the furies are destroyed in this manner, the remaining sisters will continue to fight. The next time the furies return to torment their victim, any fallen sister will appear fully restored to health.

If all three of the furies are slain in a single battle or if the victim has not been slain after three attacks, the sisters will abandon their quest. They will not return and the taint of evil, including any curses or maledictions under which the victim suffers, will be lifted.

Ecology: The furies thrive on the flesh of intelligent creatures. Between the three of them, they will consume an average man or similar creature each day. They are careful to conceal their hunting, however, for fear that the location of their lair will be given away and their mission interfered with.

Alecto

Also called *the Implacable* and *She Who Must Not Be Named* by the Vistani, this sister has the spell-casting powers of a 10th level priest and normally enters combat with a full complement of spells. She has access to the All, Animal, Combat, Creation, Divination, Elemental, Necromantic, Plant, Protection, Summoning, and Weather spheres. When rolling saving throws, Alecto may use the more favorable number of the fighter or priest classes.

Alecto's preferred spells include *call lightning, cause light wounds, charm person, continual light, dispel good, dispel magic, endure heat/endure cold, entangle, faerie fire, hold person, protection from good (10' radius), silence (15' radius), spell immunity, trip,* and *true seeing.*

Tisiphone

Also known as *the Avenger* by the Vistani, Tisiphone has the prowess of a 10th level warrior. This gives her a THAC0 of 11 and allows her to employ 10-sided Hit Dice. Unlike her sisters, Tisiphone may combine her bite and claw attacks with her scourge. She may strike with her scourge, bite, and one talon in a single round, but may not also rake with her rear claws even if all of these attacks hit. Tisiphone's saving throws are made as a 10th level fighter.

Megarea

Known to the Vistani as *the Disputatious,* Megarea possesses the spell casting power of a 10th level wizard. She enters combat having memorized her full complement of spells. She can select any spells from the schools of Abjuration, Alteration, Invocation/Evocation, and Necromancy. Her saving throws are made at the more advantageous number of the fighter or wizard class.

Megarea's preferred spells are *chill touch, color spray, cone of cold, darkness 15' radius, dispel magic, flaming sphere, hold portal, lightning bolt, magic missile, minor globe of invulnerability, passwall, polymorph other, protection from normal missiles, stinking cloud, stoneskin, and web.*

Familiar, Pseudo-

CLIMATE/TERRAIN:	Ravenloft
FREQUENCY:	Very rare
ORGANIZATION:	Solitary
ACTIVITY CYCLE:	Any
DIET:	Special (see below)
INTELLIGENCE:	High (13–14)
TREASURE:	Nil
ALIGNMENT:	Neutral evil
NO. APPEARING:	1
ARMOR CLASS:	Varies
MOVEMENT:	Varies
HIT DICE:	Varies
THAC0:	Varies
NO. OF ATTACKS:	Varies
DAMAGE/ATTACK:	Varies
SPECIAL ATTACKS:	See below
SPECIAL DEFENSES:	+2 or better to hit
MAGIC RESISTANCE:	Nil
SIZE:	T (less than 2′ tall)
MORALE:	Steady (11–12)
XP VALUE:	Varies

A pseudo-familiar is a twisted, evil creature that appears to be a normal wizard's familiar. Called when the *find familiar* spell is cast in the Demiplane of Dread, these sinister beings confer the benefits they would normally bring to their summoners, but reap a deadly harvest in return.

Pseudo-familiars look just like their traditional counterparts (cats, toads, crows, etc.), though they appear to be even more splendid and healthy specimens than usual. Their colors are brighter, they appear robust and healthy, and their eyes gleam with intelligence.

Pseudo-familiars innately understand all human and demihuman tongues and speak telepathically with their chosen wizard and each other.

Combat: Though preferring not to engage in melee combat unless given no alternative, pseudo-familiars can attack and inflict damage as a normal member of their species (cats use claws and bite, crows peck, etc.). Because of the powerful nature of these creatures, they always have one more Hit Die than their mundane cousins (often giving them a better THAC0) and a +2 bonus to their Damage Rolls. In addition, pseudo-familiars are much faster than normal animals, making the AC of such creatures 1 point better than other animals of their type. Pseudo-familiars can only be hit by +2 or better weapons, although magic affects them normally.

The most notable power of the pseudo-familiar is a spell-like ability of *vampiric regeneration* similar to that created by magical rings of that type. This allows them to drain hit points from wounded creatures and transfer them elsewhere. Whenever the familiar or its master takes damage, the creature actuates its power. Each round thereafter, any wounded being with 30 feet of the familiar loses 2 hit points. These points are divided evenly between the familiar and wizard and added to their hit point totals until both are restored to full health. All creatures within range of the familiar, whether friend or foe, are subject to this attack. The creature's eyes glow with a weird purple light while it is using this power.

The pseudo-familiar can also use this power to drain hit points from sleeping characters, but it uses this ability only when there are no wounded ones available. This variation of the *vampiric regeneration* ability is used when the wizard or his familiar is injured, but the rest of his companions are in full health. This attack is much more difficult and drains hit points at a rate of only 2 per hour. Those losing hit points in this manner suffer no obvious wounds, though their sleep is restless and full of nightmares. Upon awakening, victims feel sore and unrested, though they may not realize until later that they have sustained injuries. The creature can cause damage night after night, draining and exhausting the members of a party a little at a time without being discovered.

If the wizard learns of the harm being done to his allies and takes no steps to prevent it, he must make a powers check. The chance of failing this check is 1% per hit point the familiar drained that round. A new check must be made each round.

Habitat/Society: Pseudo-familiars live to control their alleged master and kill his companions. Over the course of his time with the familiar the wizard gradually loses the ability to distinguish between his own desires and goals and those of his familiar. To simulate this, the familiar's so called master must make a saving throw vs. spell every fortnight or fall under the creature's control. A cumulative –1 penalty is applied to this save for every fortnight after the first.

Separating oneself from a pseudo-familiar is not an easy thing. The link between master and servant cannot be broken through use of a *protection from evil, remove curse,* or a similar spell. As a rule, nothing less powerful than an *atonement, dispel evil,* or *banishment* spell will suffice to free the wizard from his burden.

Of course, it is possible to attack and even kill the familiar, but the risks involved for the wizard (see the *find familiar* spell) make this a dangerous proposition at best.

Ecology: Pseudo-familiars sustain themselves on the hit points they absorb from other creatures. While they need no other nourishment, they do sometimes nibble at the foods their normal counterparts enjoy. These creatures never sleep, keeping a watchful vigil over their masters throughout the night.

Familiar, Undead

Climate/Terrain:	Ravenloft
Frequency:	Very rare
Organization:	Solitary
Activity Cycle:	Night
Diet:	Carnivore
Intelligence:	Low (5–7)
Treasure:	Nil
Alignment:	Chaotic Evil
No. Appearing:	1
Armor Class:	7
Movement:	9
Hit Dice:	1+1
THAC0:	19
No. of Attacks:	1
Damage/Attack:	1–4
Special Attacks:	See below
Special Defenses:	See below
Magic Resistance:	See below
Size:	T (2′ or less)
Morale:	Elite (13–14)
XP Value:	1,400

An undead familiar is a sinister being that is created whenever a wizard is directly responsible for the death of his own familiar. By betraying the mystical bonds that link the spellcaster to his companion, the wizard brings into existence a vile creature that seeks only to destroy him.

Undead familiars appear as horridly bloated, rotting versions of their living forms. They may be missing eyes, ears, or other parts, and any wounds that they sustained in death are agape and infected. They move stiffly, as if rigid with death, and the stink of corruption hangs about them. Their eyes gleam with a feral light and evil hangs in an almost palpable aura about them.

The creature's only form of communication is a telepathic cry that constantly invades its former master's mind. So unnerving is this sound that it prevents sleep, disrupts spellcasting, and has driven more than one wizard over the brink of madness.

Combat: Undead familiars avoid combat with any creature other than their former master. If prevented from reaching their preferred target or forced to defend themselves, these foul creatures will employ the attacks that they did in life. In addition to the damage caused by the creature's normal forms of attack, anyone injured by the undead familiar must make a saving throw vs. poison or contract a debilitating disease (as described in the *cure disease* spell). The former master of this terrible creature suffers a –4 penalty on this save.

Once the undead familiar reaches its master, it will attempt to meets his gaze. If this happens, the agony that the creature felt when it died and the shock of its betrayal bombard the wizard's mind through the mystic link they once shared. At this point, the mage must attempt a saving throw vs. spell. A successful save requires the character to make a fear check while failure indicates that the wizard must make a horror check. If the roll not only fails but is a natural "1," the wizard must make a madness check. The power works only against the undead familiar's former master.

Undead familiars cannot be turned by a priest and are immune to the effects of holy water, holy symbols, or other forces that normally harm undead. The power that animates them is the guilt and remorse of the wizard, not the negative material plane or any related region. As such, they are not undead in the traditional sense of the word and have few of the vulnerabilities normally associated with such creatures.

Undead familiars are immune to all *sleep, charm, hold*, and cold-based spells. They cannot be affected by poisons, paralyzation, or disease and are immune to damage inflicted by nonmagical weapons.

Any wound that causes an undead familiar to fall to 0 or fewer hit points seems to kill it. The creature is as relentless as a revenant, however, and even incineration or other means of destroying the body will not rid the wizard of this enemy. Within a fortnight, the creature will return from the mists to seek vengeance for the betrayal it suffered.

If the mage is slain by his undead familiar he will rise again as a ghoul and the familiar will die, finally being freed of its undead existence.

Habitat/Society: Undead familiars exist only to wreak vengeance on their former masters. The bond that tied the pair together has been twisted into a corrupt union that neither can escape—except through death.

Only the death of the wizard will satisfy the creature's hunger for retaliation. If the creature's master manages to escape from Ravenloft, it will lose its obsession with him and begin stalking the nearest wizard. That wizard need not fear the familiar's gaze and can rid himself of the thing simply by killing it. At that point, the familiar will not reappear. Should the creature's former master ever return to the Demiplane of Dread, however, the wronged animal will rise again.

Ecology: Undead familiars are not natural creatures. They consume nothing to sustain themselves and produce no useful products.

Feathered Serpent

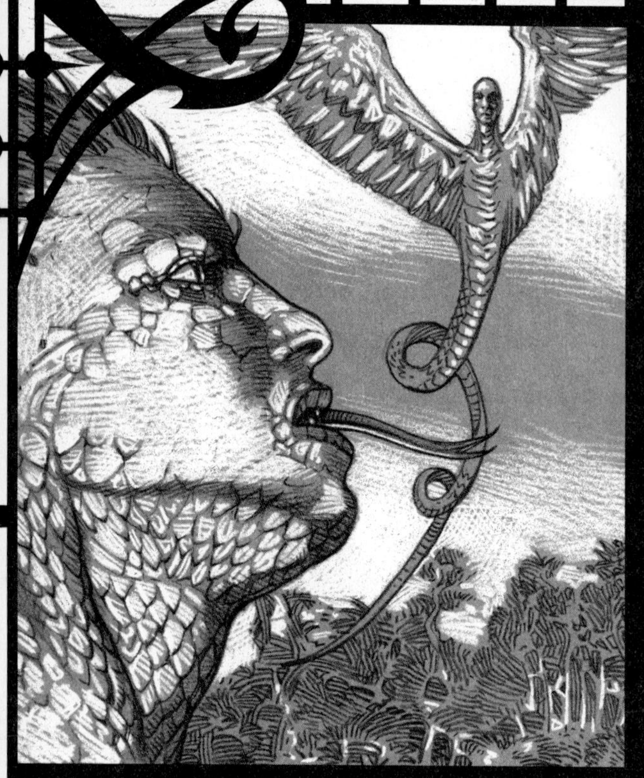

Climate/Terrain:	Tropical lands and subterranean
Frequency:	Rare
Organization:	Solitary
Activity Cycle:	Night
Diet:	Carnivore
Intelligence:	Highly (13–14)
Treasure:	X (E)
Alignment:	Chaotic evil
No. Appearing:	1–3
Armor Class:	7
Movement:	12, Fl 24 (C)
Hit Dice:	2 + 2
THAC0:	19
No. of Attacks:	1
Damage/Attack:	1–3
Special Attacks:	See below
Special Defenses:	Nil
Magic Resistance:	Nil
Size:	H (15′ long)
Morale:	Steady (11–12)
XP Value:	650

Feathered serpents are evil creatures with a snakelike, winged body and a human head. These scaled, feathered predators prefer warmer climates and favor underground lairs. They have been encountered in such disparate locales as Har'Akir and Sri Raji.

Feathered serpents grow to an adult length of 15 feet, with a wingspan that may reach 25 feet. Their otherwise human-looking faces feature bright, compelling, lidless eyes of a luminous blue-green or gold. Their serpentlike bodies are covered with glittering scales that vary in color from azure to emerald green. Their wings and tails are covered with brilliant, graceful plumage similar in color to their scales. Unlike normal snakes, they secrete an oil that makes them slick to the touch but has a pleasant, delicate odor to it.

Their voices are seductive and euphonious. In addition to their own language, they speak the common language of the domain in which they live and can communicate with all manner of serpents.

Combat: Feathered serpents delight in setting clever traps and alarms about their lairs. These are intended to slow those entering the serpent's den and to give warning of their approach, but not to kill or seriously injure the intruder. That is a delight that the creature reserves for itself.

Feathered serpents fight only when they feel they have no chance of capturing or charming opponents to make into slaves. They are not stupid, and will not remain in a losing battle if provided with a way to escape.

Whenever possible, feathered serpents will attempt to use their mesmeric gaze on newly encountered prey. By slowly weaving back and forth while staring into the eyes of their victims these terrible creatures are able to *charm* a potential enemy. The feathered serpent cannot attack or cast spells in any round that it employs this power, but it may attempt to mesmerize as many as three enemies, provided they are fairly close together.

Should combat become necessary, these creatures will generally seek to use their magical abilities to disable dangerous foes before moving in for the kill. They can memorize any two first level spells from the illusion/phantasm school, but favor the *audible glamer, change self,* and *phantasmal force* spells.

When they finally close for combat, feathered serpents attempt to bite their enemies. The needlelike fangs of the creature inflict 1d3 points of damage. In addition, anyone bitten by the snake is injected with a poison that requires the victim to make a saving throw vs. poison or fall asleep for 2d4 rounds. When the effects of the toxin wear off, victims are off-balance and woozy for two rounds, suffering a –2 penalty on their Attack, Damage, and saving throws during that time.

Habitat/Society: Though feathered serpents are solitary creatures, a mated pair will sometimes occupy a large lair. If three are found together, they will be a mated pair and an offspring who has half the normal number of Hit Dice and no special abilities except a poisonous bite.

Though they prefer to dwell underground, they may also be encountered in old ruins or even shallow caves. In some places, they have managed to make their way into the cities of men and assemble a cult of followers who believe them to be divine in nature.

They take great delight in keeping a few *charmed* slaves to build their traps and use as food when times are lean. These slaves will come to the defense of their master if it is threatened. The followers of a feathered serpent are usually normal humans, unskilled in fighting or the use of weapons, but will occasionally include an adventurer or spellcaster.

Feathered serpents may also cooperate with a hebi-no-onna (snake woman), acting as favored servants or guardians for her and receiving choice treasure, food, and a protected lair in return. Though not usually the instigators of the cults that hebi-no-onna build around themselves, they are instrumental in helping gain recruits and dissuading authorities from looking into the cult's activities too closely.

Ecology: The scent glands of a feathered serpent can be used to make a rare, exotic perfume. Those who adorn themselves with this cologne effectively increase their Charisma score by 1 point for 24 hours or until it is washed off with water.

Climate/Terrain:	Moors and swamps of Ravenloft
Frequency:	Very rare
Organization:	Pack
Activity Cycle:	Three nights of the full moon
Diet:	Carnivore
Intelligence:	Animal (1)
Treasure:	Nil
Alignment:	Chaotic good
No. Appearing:	2d4
Armor Class:	4
Movement:	15
Hit Dice:	5
THAC0:	15
No. of Attacks:	1
Damage/Attack:	1d10
Special Attacks:	Baying
Special Defenses:	+2 or better weapon to hit, spell immunity
Magic Resistance:	65%
Size:	L (8′ long)
Morale:	Fearless (19–20)
XP Value:	2,000

Misty moors and steaming peat bogs have always been places where men feared to tread at night. Obviously, such places can be treacherous and deadly. But in quiet whispers, some who live near these macabre wetlands also tell tales of the dreaded fenhounds.

A fenhound appears only in the grim, veiled light of a full moon. It looks much like a large mastiff, being muscular of build and covered in short, coarse brown fur. Although a fenhound's physical form is not unusual, the aura that surrounds it is. Because fenhounds are able to tap into the ambient supernatural power that accompanies the full moon, each is suffused with an eerie, pale yellow light.

Like most breeds of canine, fenhounds cannot speak. Because of their nature as pack hunters, they are able to communicate basic concepts among themselves with barks, yips, and growls.

Combat: Fenhounds are able to sense and flawlessly track those who have been forced to make a powers check while on the moors near their home.

The first sign that victims have of the fenhounds' approach is the sound of their baying. Although this howl has a chilling effect on all who hear it, most people suffer no ill effects from it. However, the person being tracked by the hounds must make a fear check the first time he hears it.

When fenhounds reach their victim, they charge directly into melee combat. Each round, they are able to attack with their powerful jaws for 1d10 points of damage. Although they will do all that they can to reach the object of their hunt, those who try to block their way or protect their chosen victim are quickly attacked as well.

The aura of moonlight that surrounds a fenhound gives it special protection against attacks. This is reflected both in the creature's innate magic resistance and the fact that it cannot be harmed by weapons of less than + 2 magical enchantment. Further, no spell from the priestly Sun sphere can harm or hinder fenhounds. Spells employed by any priest who worships a god of the moon, moors, revenge, or a similar aspect will also not harm the fenhound.

If slain in combat, the body of the fenhound breaks up into a cloud of shimmering vapor that quickly fades away. The person delivering the death blow to the creature becomes marked, however, and will find himself hunted by a pack of fenhounds each time there is a full moon. Only an *atonement* or similar spell can lift this curse from the character. If a character slays all of the hounds stalking him, he is free from their curse until the next full moon, when another pack of hounds will be released from the moors to hunt him anew.

Habitat/Society: Fenhounds are not creatures of the Prime Material plane. Rather, they seem to be some manifestation of the mists of Ravenloft itself. Their curious role as avenging spirits in this land of evil has puzzled many sages and experts on the occult. It may well be that there is some darker purpose to their existence that none have yet guessed.

Fenhounds are not creatures of evil disposition, despite their frightening countenance. Rather, they act against those who have done evil on the moors, swamps, and bogs of Ravenloft. Any person who is forced to make a powers check (success or failure not withstanding) while in a region inhabited by fenhounds will instantly draw their attention. When the next full moon occurs, two or more hounds will appear from the swirling mists on the wetlands to hunt down and destroy the fiends who have earned their wrath. Once the creatures arrive on the Prime Material plane, they will remain until dawn or until they or their victims have been slain.

Ecology: Fenhounds seem to serve a role as guardians of the darkest moors and bogs. Because the mists of Ravenloft both punish and reward those who do evil, it is impossible to guess at their ultimate purpose in creating fenhounds. Whatever else they might do, these beasts serve to torment those evil individuals who have not yet been condemned to the eternal tortures accorded to the lords of Ravenloft's various domains.

Figurine, General Information

Figurines are very small golems that might easily be mistaken for *figurines of wondrous power* by the average adventurer. They are less powerful than larger golems, but each type has unique powers that can make them deadly foes. All known figurines come from the domain of Sri Raji and consequently reflect that land in the sorts of creatures they depict and the materials from which they are made.

Animated by the spirits of the Demiplane of Dread, they are tied to the land as are all other Ravenloft golems. Like their larger kin, they are unable to exist in any realm outside the demiplane of dread. If carried beyond the misty borders of Ravenloft, they lose their powers and become nothing more than common statuary.

Background

The origin of figurines lies with the craftsmen and scholars of Sri Raji. The potters, ivory carvers and gem cutters of Pakat, Muladi, and Tvashsti (the three cities of that domain) have long practiced the arts of carving and sculpting, creating intricate miniature figurines. Depicting tigers, monkeys, insects, and other denizens of Sri Raji's ubiquitous jungle, these small works of art are used as statuettes, decorations, and jewelry. They are generally associated with good luck, strength, wisdom, or some desired happening. Families occasionally commission such decorations as gifts to the various temples of Sri Raji in an effort to show their devotion to the gods.

It is generally believed that the first of these statues were created by a scholar known as Jawahar Zhosh, who taught at the Great University of Tvashsti. Working with local artisans, he created several types of free-standing figurines and attempted to invest them with great powers. He was successful, but in the casting of his spells he called upon magic that was forbidden to the race of man. Within a week, had been slain by the objects to which he had given life.

In time, word of Zhosh's experiments spread to others of his ilk. Attempts to duplicate his efforts followed, leading to the creation of several kinds of figurines. Though their findings were meticulously recorded and given a place among the scrolls of the university, the scholars who brought these small golems to life are deceased, all having been slain by their creations.

Common Characteristics

There are five known varieties of figurines: ceramic, crystal, ivory, obsidian, and porcelain. Each has unique abilities, but all have certain characteristics in common.

The enchantments that imbue figurines with life make them difficult to damage or destroy. As such, they can be struck in combat only by +1 or better weapons.

As nonliving creatures, they cannot be harmed by poisons of any sort. Similarly, they are immune to all types of disease, paralysis, and the like.

Figurines are immune to all manner of mind- or life-affecting magic such as *charm, sleep, hold,* or *finger of death* spells. All figurines are vulnerable to the effects of a *dispel magic.* If the caster of the spell is equal to the level of the figurine's creator, the figurine must make a saving throw vs. death magic or collapse. The creature will appear dead and will not radiate magic if a detection spell is cast upon it. However, the figurine will reanimate after a number of turns equal to the caster's level. Should the caster of the *dispel magic* be of higher level than the figurine's creator, the small golem must make a saving throw vs. death magic or be instantly slain.

Creating Figurines

Each figurine must be created with loving care and special magical spells used to bring it to life. The exact materials and spells required vary for each type and are detailed on the pages that follow.

Though figurines are smaller and less powerful than traditional golems, their creation is no less meticulous and exhausting. The process requires weeks of careful study, diligent preparation, and delicate craftsmanship. Each figurine is not only a magical item, but also a work of art that must be fashioned with the greatest care and attention in order to properly house the animating spirit. Because of the obsessive nature of the work involved, each month of labor requires the creator to make a powers check with a 5% chance of failure.

Those seeking to create figurines must possess the proper secondary skills or nonweapon proficiencies (potter, gem cutter, ivory carver, etc.) to craft the item and some means of spellcasting by which to enchant it. It is possible to employ proxies for either or both of these phases, but such individuals must be carefully watched and directed to prevent mistakes or misunderstandings.

Crafting a figurine takes one month of devoted labor. Once that is complete, the rituals to animate the body require a full month. If this process is interrupted in any way, the entire procedure must be started anew. Spells used in the creation of the figurine may come from any source, including scrolls and devices. The exact spells required for the fashioning of each type of figurine are listed under their individual entries.

Controlling Figurines

Like traditional golems, figurines have a great hatred for all living things and are kept in check only by the will of their creator. Should they escape their creator's domination, figurines will always try to kill their master and become free-willed creatures. The chance of a figurine slipping the bonds of obedience is 10% per month. The death of the creator will instantly free the figurine from control (even if he is later restored to life) as will his escape from Ravenloft.

The wily creature may not immediately indicate that it is now free, lulling its creator into complacence and striking when least expected. Free-willed figurines sometimes allow themselves to be claimed by other people, and willingly serve these new masters for a time, but eventually turn against them as well.

Manuals of Figurines

Detailed instructions for each type of figurine's creation can be found in special tomes known as *Manuals of Figurines.* The most learned sages in Sri Raji claim that but one copy of each manual exists and that these dark tomes have been locked away at the Great University of Tvashsti. Still, stories are told of additional copies of these books that have surfaced in other domains from time to time. Some have even speculated that the original *manuals* were stolen long ages past and that those guarded by the Great University are frauds.

Figurine, Ceramic

CLIMATE/TERRAIN:	Sri Raji
FREQUENCY:	Very rare
ORGANIZATION:	Solitary
ACTIVITY CYCLE:	Any
DIET:	Nil
INTELLIGENCE:	Low (5–7)
TREASURE:	Nil
ALIGNMENT:	Neutral
NO. APPEARING:	1
ARMOR CLASS:	5
MOVEMENT:	12
HIT DICE:	4
THAC0:	17
NO. OF ATTACKS:	1
DAMAGE/ATTACK:	1d4
SPECIAL ATTACKS:	See below
SPECIAL DEFENSES:	See below
MAGIC RESISTANCE:	Nil
SIZE:	T (3″–15″ tall)
MORALE:	Fearless (19–20)
XP VALUE:	975

A ceramic figurine is a brightly painted miniature golem that might easily be mistaken for a *figurine of wondrous power*. Like other magical automatons, they are often employed as guards by their creators.

Though most often depicting an alligator or other lizard, ceramic figurines shaped like turtles, frogs, and snakes are also known. Whatever form they are given, all have a slightly rounded shape and are hollow inside.

They understand their creator's primary language, but are themselves incapable of speech.

Combat: Ceramic figurines follow the orders given to them by their masters, but have a low intelligence that imparts some cunning to them. Thus, they do not usually attack mindlessly as other golems do. Instead, they utilize some basic tactics and strategies to defeat intruders or those they have been commanded to slay. They take advantage of cover and their small size to move in close and strike without warning.

Ceramic figurines are hollow and must be crafted with a small hole in their base so they will not explode when fired inside the kiln. The master of such a creature can fill its interior cavity with acid, poison, oil, or any other liquid and then seal the hole in the base. Such a figurine can spray this liquid at a single target within ten feet. The effects of this attack will vary depending upon the nature of the liquid with which the creature was filled. A figurine can hold enough liquid for two spraying attacks.

If a filled figurine is destroyed by a melee attack, crushing blow, or similar sudden shock, it will shatter. Any liquid within it at this point will splash out, requiring all within 10 feet to make a saving throw vs. breath weapon or be affected by it.

Figurines can attack by biting, clawing, or employing some other attack appropriate to their shape. A successful Attack Roll inflicts 1d4 points of damage. Although they are fearless, ceramic figurines will only make melee attacks if they have been commanded to fight to the death. Otherwise, they withdraw to their master once they have used their special attacks.

Ceramic figurines are immune to all fire, cold, and electrical damage. They are vulnerable to *shatter* or *shout* spells, being forced to make a saving throw vs. spell or be destroyed if either of these is used against them.

Despite their delicate appearance, normal weapons cannot harm these creations. Indeed, any weapon of less than +1 enchantment will rebound from them as it would from the wall of a mighty fortress. They are particularly susceptible to attacks from bashing weapons (provided that such arms have the ability to damage them at all) taking double damage from such weapons.

Habitat/Society: As artificial constructs under the command of their creators, ceramic figurines have no society or particular habitat. They are used to guard valuable items or places. Within the constraints of their orders, they are able to utilize basic tactics.

Ceramic figurines must be molded from clay that has been gathered from the banks of Lake Veda in the domain of Sri Raji. They must then be covered in slip (a clay and water mixture) and baked in a kiln. A colored glaze is then applied and the figurine is returned to the kiln for a second firing. When cooled, a final coat of paint is applied to bring out all the details. Once completed, the figurine is ready to be imbued with life. The spells needed for this are *animate object* and *raise dead*, or *polymorph any object* and *limited wish*.

The creator must have access to a fully functional pottery shop (kiln, pottery wheel, tools, clays, paints, etc.) in order to undertake the creation of a ceramic golem. The cost for outfitting the shop and constructing a ceramic figurine is 7,500 gp. The work takes one and a half months to complete. Additional figurines may be created for only 4,000 gp each. Any liquids to be held inside the figurine must be created or purchased separately.

Ecology: The same mysterious force that imparts a basic cunning and intelligence to the figurines leads them to hate their masters greatly. Free-willed figurines are capable of locating and ingesting the liquids they need to make themselves formidable.

Figurine, Crystal

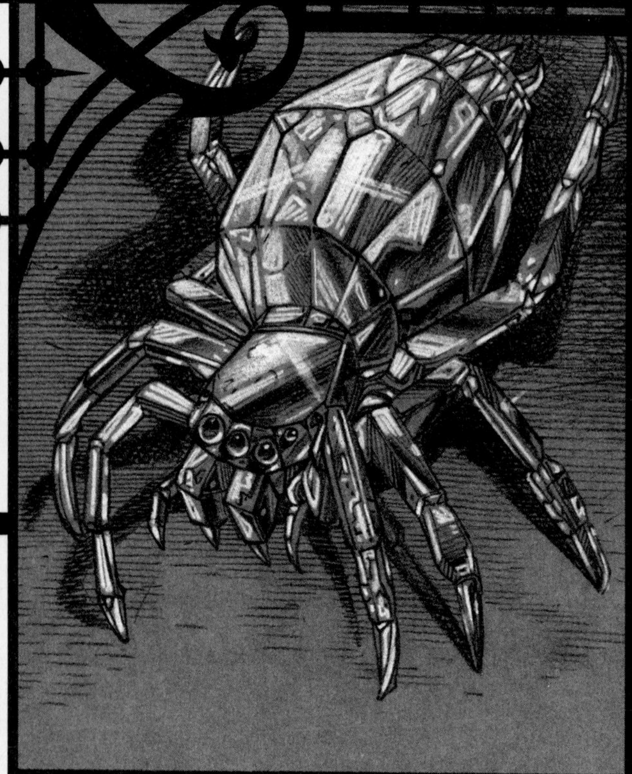

	Crystal	Diamond
CLIMATE/TERRAIN:	Sri Raji	Sri Raji
FREQUENCY:	Very rare	Very rare
ORGANIZATION:	Solitary	Solitary
ACTIVITY CYCLE:	Any	Any
DIET:	Nil	Nil
INTELLIGENCE:	Low (5–7)	Low (5–7)
TREASURE:	Nil	Nil
ALIGNMENT:	Neutral	Neutral
NO. APPEARING:	1	1
ARMOR CLASS:	4	2
MOVEMENT:	9	9
HIT DICE:	6	6
THACO:	15	15
NO. OF ATTACKS:	1	1
DAMAGE/ATTACK:	1d8	1d8
SPECIAL ATTACKS:	See below	See below
SPECIAL DEFENSES:	See below	See below
MAGIC RESISTANCE:	Nil	Nil
SIZE:	T (6″ tall)	T (6″ tall)
MORALE:	Fearless (19–20)	Fearless (19–20)
XP VALUE:	2,000	3,000

Crystal figurines are delicate statuettes created by the finest craftsmen and imbued with life by magical means. They are often employed as guards or assassins by those who manufacture them.

Figurines of this sort are made entirely of clear or colored crystal. Those that are clear are usually made from rock crystal (an especially clear type of quartz) or from diamond. Colored crystal figurines are usually made of emerald, amethyst, or garnet, though rose quartz is sometimes used. Most are shaped like spiders, though crystal ants, scorpions, and other insectoid shapes are not unknown. All crystal figurines are beautiful, though most are highly stylized due to the flat faces and regular angles of the crystals used in their construction.

These creatures do not speak, although they understand the language spoken by their creator. They will generally ignore anyone but their master.

Combat: Like all figurines, these automatons enter combat only at the bidding of their masters. When fighting, they slash with the sharp edges of their many facets to inflict 1d8 points of damage in melee combat.

The magical nature of these creatures makes them difficult to destroy. Not only are they immune to harm from weapons of less than +1 enchantment, but all edged weapons do only half damage to them.

Crystal figurines are impervious to mind- or life-affecting spells as well as electrical attacks. They can be harmed by fire and cold, although such attacks do only half damage to them. A *shatter, shout* or *crystalbrittle* spell will destroy the figurine unless it makes a saving throw vs. spell.

Because of the vibrational properties of crystals, figurines resonate to certain energies, making them highly suited for spellcasting. All such creatures can cast the *chromatic orb, hypnotic pattern*, and *rainbow pattern* spells once per day. In addition, any spell associated with light (*continual light, dancing lights, color spray, prismatic spray*, etc.) that is cast upon the figurine is reflected back upon the caster.

Habitat/Society: Crystal figurines are usually used to guard important or valuable things or places. They are most useful when placed in a spot where they will reflect sunlight or torchlight into the eyes of approaching creatures.

These figurines are often left among jewelry caches, hidden in treasure rooms, or given as presents to someone their creator dislikes. Commanded to remain still until their new owner sleeps, the figurine then attacks. Once the victim is dead, the figurine makes its way back to its creator, often bringing along whatever valuables it might find on the body.

Ecology: Because they are somewhat intelligent, crystal figurines not only utilize basic tactics when fighting, but are capable of understanding and acting upon fairly complex instructions (a few sentences or up to 50 words). If their orders do not cover a specific situation, crystal figurines default to their own thinking capacity and try to improvise.

A crystal figurine must be carved from a single stone by an expert craftsman. In general, the process takes two months to complete and requires an outlay of 10,000 gold pieces. Once the figurine is completed, it must be enchanted with the following spells: *polymorph any object, limited wish, chromatic orb, hypnotic pattern*, and *rainbow pattern.*

Diamond Figurines

It is possible, although quite difficult, to craft these figurines from diamond rather than lesser crystals. Automatons of this type require twice the time and cost to create. A diamond figurine has an Armor Class of 2, takes no damage from edged weapons, and suffers only half damage from all other melee attacks.

Diamond figurines have a 20% chance of breaking any weapons that strike them. This chance is reduced by 5% for each plus of the weapon, while nonmagical weapons shatter automatically on a successful attack roll.

Figurine, Ivory

Climate/Terrain:	Sri Raji
Frequency:	Very rare
Organization:	Solitary
Activity Cycle:	Any
Diet:	Nil
Intelligence:	Non-(0)
Treasure:	Nil
Alignment:	Neutral
No. Appearing:	1
Armor Class:	6
Movement:	9
Hit Dice:	4
THAC0:	17
No. of Attacks:	1 or 2
Damage/Attack:	1d4 or 2d8/2d6
Special Attacks:	See below
Special Defenses:	See below
Magic Resistance:	Nil
Size:	T-L (2″–11′ tall)
Morale:	Fearless (19–20)
XP Value:	975

Ivory figurines, like their counterparts, are small golems. They are often employed as guardians or assigned simple tasks suited to their diminutive size.

Made from the tusks of elephants and similar creatures, these figurines are almost exclusively shaped as pachyderms. A few ivory hippopotami, mastodons, or similar creatures are rumored to have been created, but these may not actually exist. Ivory figurines are covered with scrimshawlike carvings that impart much of the detail of the figurine.

Ivory figurines are not intelligent and cannot speak. They appear to be able to obey rudimentary instruction from their masters.

Combat: When ordered to fight, these figurines attack with their needlelike tusks for 1d4 points of damage. While these are incapable of inflicting anything more than a pinprick to their opponents, they carry a potent enchantment that makes them formidable weapons. Ivory figurines can themselves be hit only by +1 or better weapons.

Three times per day, ivory figurines may use a variant of the *enlarge* spell and grow to a height of 11 feet. The spell lasts for ten rounds but can be cut short with the casting of a *dispel magic* or *reduce* spell. When enlarged, ivory elephants attack with sharp tusks, inflicting 2d8 points of damage. On a natural attack roll of "20" the creature is able to trample its opponent for an additional 2d6 points.

Thrice per day, whether enlarged or at its natural size, an ivory elephant is able to trumpet. This deafens those within 30 feet of the creature for 2d6 rounds and inflicts 2d6 points of damage. A successful saving throw vs. spell negates the deafness and halves the damage inflicted by this attack. Exposed brittle or crystal substances (such as potion bottles and holy water vials) are shattered by this noise unless they make a saving throw vs. crushing blow. All deafened creatures suffer a –1 penalty to their Surprise Rolls, and those that cast spells have a 20% chance to miscast them if they require a verbal component.

Although ivory figurines are immune to cold and electrical attacks, fire and acid do normal damage to them.

Habitat/Society: More like true golems than any other of the figurines, ivory figurines are also more easily controlled. Though they have the normal chance to break free of their masters, they usually wander off seeking other victims rather than turning directly against their creators when this happens. Should the creator attempt to stop them, however, they are as savage as any other free-willed golem.

Ecology: Ivory figurines are carved from elephant tusks and meticulously polished. Once the shape is perfect, intricate scrimshaw patterns are etched into the ivory to make the ears, eyes, mouth, and other decorations. Inks are applied to complete the scrimshaw and the following spells are used to animate the figurine: *polymorph any object* or *animate object, limited wish* or *raise dead, enlarge* or *animal growth*, and *shout*. This takes two months and costs 8,000 gold pieces.

Figurine, Obsidian

CLIMATE/TERRAIN:	Sri Raji
FREQUENCY:	Very rare
ORGANIZATION:	Solitary
ACTIVITY CYCLE:	Any
DIET:	Nil
INTELLIGENCE:	Low (5–7)
TREASURE:	Nil
ALIGNMENT:	Neutral
NO. APPEARING:	1
ARMOR CLASS:	6
MOVEMENT:	9
HIT DICE:	4
THAC0:	17
NO. OF ATTACKS:	1
DAMAGE/ATTACK:	1d8
SPECIAL ATTACKS:	See below
SPECIAL DEFENSES:	See below
MAGIC RESISTANCE:	Nil
SIZE:	T (1″–12″ tall)
MORALE:	Fearless (19–20)
XP VALUE:	650

Obsidian figurines, though they are in many ways the weakest of the five types of figurines, are the most surprising.

Fashioned from volcanic glass, these automatons are usually formed as monkeys, gorillas, and other apes, but human figures have been crafted as well. To the untrained eye, these are the most crudely fashioned figurines. Being highly irregular in shape and laced with sharp edges, they often exhibit only an indistinct resemblance to the animal that they are modeled upon.

Obsidian figurines do not speak, although they are able to understand the commands of their master.

Combat: Obsidian figurines enter combat only when ordered to do so by their master. When they do attack, however, they can be quite dangerous.

Covered by the sharp points and edges that make obsidian valuable for the crafting of weapons, these figurines attack with a frenzy of slashing blows and kicks. In each round, these combine to inflict 1d8 points of damage to the automaton's chosen target. It is not uncommon for the owners of these creatures to coat them in poison before sending them into battle. When this is done, the victim must make a saving throw vs. poison or the damage from the attack is doubled. Enough poison may be applied to allow for three rounds of combat.

In some cases, these creatures are fashioned with as many as 6 needlelike spines jutting out from their bodies. When someone is wounded by a figurine of this type there is a 10% chance per point of damage done (not counting additional damage for poison) that one of the spikes will break off and become lodged in the wound. When this happens, the victim will feel extreme pain and suffer an additional 1 point of damage each round until the spine is removed. If the golem was poisoned, the damage from the spine is doubled unless a saving throw is made. Extracting the spine must be done by someone else and requires one round of dedicated effort on the part of both parties. Once an obsidian golem has lost all of its spines, new ones cannot be attached to it.

While the creature is immune to damage from weapons of less than a +1 enchantment, it is vulnerable to harm by any manner of magical attack. Any weapon used against the figurine releases a shower of minute fragments that fills a 10′ radius. Anyone in that area must make a saving throw vs. breath weapon or suffer 1d2 points of damage. Attacks based upon magical fire, cold, and electricity all cause the obsidian figurine to fracture in this manner.

Habitat/Society: Obsidian figurines have a basic intelligence, but are commanded by their masters and do only as they are told. They do not utilize any other tactics beyond those suggested by their masters, and will attack until slain.

Ecology: Obsidian figurines are the cheapest and easiest of these automatons to make. The creator must craft the form from chips of obsidian which are then fused in a forge or kiln. The spells needed to make an obsidian figurine are *enchant an item, limited wish,* and *mending.* A figurine takes only three weeks to make and costs but 3,000 gold pieces.

Smoothed Figurines

Some obsidian figurines are smoothed and polished after being crafted, making them unusually receptive to magical vibrations. Such creatures are less dangerous in melee combat, doing but 1d4 points of damage each round and bearing no spikes. Smoothed figurines cannot be poisoned.

However, the master of such a figurine may place within it a single spell of any type or level that he knows. This spell will be retained by the automaton until it is cast, at which point the master must infuse it with another. Placing the spell in the figurine requires the same amount of time as memorizing or praying for it.

CLIMATE/TERRAIN:	Sri Raji
FREQUENCY:	Very rare
ORGANIZATION:	Solitary
ACTIVITY CYCLE:	Any
DIET:	Nil
INTELLIGENCE:	Low (5–7)
TREASURE:	Nil
ALIGNMENT:	Neutral
NO. APPEARING:	1
ARMOR CLASS:	1
MOVEMENT:	12
HIT DICE:	6
THAC0:	15
NO. OF ATTACKS:	3
DAMAGE/ATTACK:	2–5/2–5/1–10
SPECIAL ATTACKS:	See below
SPECIAL DEFENSES:	See below
MAGIC RESISTANCE:	Nil
SIZE:	T-L (3″–9′ long)
MORALE:	Fearless (19–20)
XP VALUE:	3,000

Of all the magical figurines fashioned in Sri Raji, those crafted of porcelain are by far the strongest and most fearsome. These are the rarest type of figurine, both because porcelain is more difficult to create and because there are rumors that anyone creating one draws the attention of the Dark Powers.

At one time all porcelain figurines depicted tigers. While the vast majority still do, some now portray rakshasa. Tiger figurines are painted a lifelike deep orange with black stripes and yellow-green eyes. Those made in other shapes are painted in a fashion suited to their form.

Porcelain figurines, whether shaped like tigers or more humanoid creatures, do not speak. They are quite capable of understanding the orders of their masters, however, and obey them without pause.

Combat: While they enter battle only at the behest of their masters, porcelain figurines can be dangerous adversaries. They attack using the small claws and fangs of the creatures they depict. These are not particularly deadly, however, and allow the figurine only a single attack for 1d4 points of damage each round.

When hard pressed or ordered to do so by their masters, porcelain figurines can grow to the size of an adult tiger (roughly 9 feet long). Once enlarged, they may strike twice with their front claws for 1d4+1 points of damage each and bite for 1d10 points of damage.

Porcelain figurines have the excellent senses of their living counterparts as well as several other abilities. For example, their eyesight is so keen that it gives them a natural infravision and enables them to see invisible objects at a range of up to 120 feet.

Three times per day, the figurine may fire a black energy bolt from its eyes that affects its target like an *enervation* spell, though it drains only one level on a successful hit.

These figurines are immune to damage from any weapon that is of less than +2 enchantment. In addition, they are protected by a *glassteel* spell that lowers their Armor Class to 1 and keeps the delicate porcelain from chipping, cracking or breaking during everyday use. Porcelain figurines are immune to magical or mundane fire, but take full damage from cold or electrical attacks.

Habitat/Society: Porcelain figurines are used as sentries for important places and things, but also serve as bodyguards for their creators. Having such a creature so close and in such a trusted position is a two-edged sword, as the figurine may escape the control of its creator and turn on him at any time.

Ecology: Porcelain figurines can only be made of fine white or gray clay of the highest quality. Though they are crafted in much the same manner as ceramic figurines, including the hole in the bottom to prevent their explosion in the kiln. Once the figurine cools, it is coated with a special paint blended from the blood of both a great cat and the master of the miniature golem.

Once formed, the figurine is imbued with life by the casting of a *polymorph any object* or *animate object, limited wish* or *raise dead, enchant an item, infravision, detect invisibility, enlarge, enervation, glassteel,* and *audible glamer* spell. The *permanency* spell must then be used to assure that all the spells continue to work correctly.

To successfully manufacture a porcelain figurine, the creator must have access to a kiln, potter's wheel, paints and other tools. The process takes two months and costs 15,000 gp.

Fleas of Madness

CLIMATE/TERRAIN:	Temperate or tropical lands
FREQUENCY:	Rare
ORGANIZATION:	Infestation
ACTIVITY CYCLE:	Any
DIET:	Blood
INTELLIGENCE:	Non- (0)
TREASURE:	Nil
ALIGNMENT:	Neutral
NO. APPEARING:	Hundreds
ARMOR CLASS:	N/A
MOVEMENT:	3
HIT DICE:	N/A
THAC0:	See below
NO. OF ATTACKS:	See below
DAMAGE/ATTACK:	Special
SPECIAL ATTACKS:	Madness
SPECIAL DEFENSES:	Nil
MAGIC RESISTANCE:	Nil
SIZE:	T
MORALE:	Nil
XP VALUE:	270 per infestation

While the normal flea is a parasitic pest that has plagued mankind since the dawn of time, its Ravenloft cousin is a terrible curse. By comparison, the mundane flea is a blessing.

Fleas of madness resemble any other flea: tiny (smaller than a grain of rice), black, and difficult to get rid of once an infestation has occurred. Like normal fleas, they feed on blood and usually reside within the fur or hair of mammals. They transfer themselves from one creature to the next by leaping to any new host who touches the fur or hair of the original. They also lurk in carpets and bedding, where they can go without food for several days while waiting for a new host to infest.

As one might expect, these minute creatures have no ability to communicate.

Combat: The bite of a flea of madness is almost insignificant. The victim may feel a slight sting and afterward develop a small red welt, but otherwise takes no real damage. The danger lies not in the bite, but in the magical disease these fleas carry.

For each hour (or portion thereof) spent in an infested area (or in the company of an infested creature), there is a 75% chance of suffering 1d4 flea bites. Each bite has a 25% chance of immediately causing the victim to experience effects similar to either the 2nd level wizard spell *Tasha's uncontrollable hideous laughter* or the 8th level wizard spell *Otto's irresistible dance.*

In addition, the victim must make a saving throw vs. poison for each bite suffered. Failure of any saving throw means the victim slips into madness over a period of 1d4 days.

If the victim is an animal (or is only semi-intelligent), the madness takes the form of simple delusions. The animal believes itself to be some other creature with which it is already familiar. Alternatively, an animal may believe itself to be human and may attempt to walk about on its hind legs and perform many of the activities humans do.

If the victim is a human, hallucinations result. A victim might see a setting different from the one that actually exists (for example, a jungle as opposed to a stone corridor), might see fellow humans as monsters, or might see creatures or items that do not actually exist. Erratic, inexplicable behavior results.

Note: Once madness has set in, the victim no longer needs to make additional saving throws vs. poison, as no intensification of the madness takes place. The victim is, however, still susceptible to the effects of *Tasha's uncontrollable hideous laughter* and *Otto's irresistible dance* with subsequent flea bites.

The madness caused by the fleas can be cured by magical means. Effective wizard spells include *limited wish* and *wish*; effective priest spells include *cure disease, heal, heroes' feast,* and *restoration.* The psionic science psychic surgery can also be used to cure madness.

Once the victim is cured, however, there is a good chance that the madness will recur with further flea bites. The only way to ensure safety is to deal with the infestation itself. Wizards might act as exterminators, using such spells as *stinking cloud, cloudkill,* or *deathfog* to fumigate a building. Priests can use the spells *anti-vermin barrier* or *repel insects* to cleanse an individual. Psionicists can offer similar protection with an inertial barrier devotion. The spell-like effects of the flea bites (magical laughter and dancing) can be eliminated with a *dispel magic* spell.

Habitat/Society: Fleas of madness are insects that are unique to the Demiplane of Dread. They appear in scattered locations throughout the Ravenloft world, infesting one area for a summer, then dying out in the winter months and reappearing somewhere else the next summer. On occasion, they are carried indoors during winter by household pets or vermin. When this happens, individual households or towns might be afflicted with the madness the fleas carry, while neighbors are not.

Ecology: There is much speculation as to how fleas of madness originated. Those who study science say these are ordinary fleas that carry a disease and believe there might be a natural plant or chemical substance that can counteract the madness the fleas induce. Others point to the fact that two of the effects produced by the fleas resemble wizard spells, and believe the fleas of madness have a magical origin. They speculate that the fleas may be the result of a wizard whose curse tainted a *summon swarm* spell. Still other sages speculate that the fleas might be the work of an evil priest who combined a *summon insects* or an *insect plague* spell with the madness-inducing spell *mindshatter.*

Climate/Terrain:	Any (border ethereal)
Frequency:	Very rare
Organization:	Solitary
Activity Cycle:	Night (usually)
Diet:	Nil
Intelligence:	Varies
Treasure:	Nil
Alignment:	Varies
No. Appearing:	1
Armor Class:	10
Movement:	Fl 12 (A)
Hit Dice:	Nil
THAC0:	Nil
No. of Attacks:	Nil
Damage/Attack:	Nil
Special Attacks:	Panic
Special Defenses:	Invulnerable
Magic Resistance:	Special
Size:	M (6′ tall)
Morale:	Fearless (19–20)
XP Value:	0

A geist is the undead spirit of a person. It resembles a ghost or haunt, but is relatively harmless. It is a transparent image of the person at the moment of death. Since death can be violent, geists may have broken necks or gaping, fatal wounds. Others, who died more peacefully or perhaps as a result of poison, may show no outward signs of trauma. Geists always appear to be clothed in the garments they wore at the time of death.

These spirits leave no trace of themselves on the real world. They have no odor, and cannot manipulate physical objects. Even the sight and sound of a geist is elusive; like a hallucination, it is only seen and heard in a person's mind. Characters who are protected from mental attacks cannot perceive a geist. At times a geist may wish to be witnessed by some people in a group but not others. The geist can choose who will sense it and who will not.

Geists can speak, and choose who will hear them. Language is not a barrier; a geist speaks the universal language of the mind.

Combat: A geist cannot engage in combat; its most powerful weapon is speech. An Armor Class of 10 has been provided above because characters may attempt to strike it. Any "hit" passes right through the geist's body. The spirit may pretend to attack a character, but its attacks pass through the victim's body harmlessly.

The sight of a geist is highly alarming. Usually, viewers assume that they are seeing a ghost or haunt. Characters who see a geist must make a successful Fear Check or flee in panic. If the geist is particularly gruesome, a Horror Check may be in order.

A geist can give the impression it is teleporting. It decides to not be visible, moves to a new spot, and becomes visible again. It can move through any physical object unimpeded. Magical wardings do keep a geist out, however.

Spells or magical items cannot divine information about a geist, such as its alignment, truthfulness, etc. A *true seeing* spell or equivalent magic allows a character to perceive a blurry, white image of the geist even when it chooses to be invisible. *Dismissal, banishment, wish, abjure,* and *holy word* spells (or equivalent magic) will send the geist to its final resting place. Otherwise, it is immune to all magic and all spells.

Habitat/Society: A geist can exist in any climate. It usually haunts the location of its death, and its territory is limited to a single building or small area. In rare cases, a geist may be able to roam farther.

As solitary undead creatures, geists have no society of their own. A geist may be willing to talk to living beings, however. Its personality and alignment at the time of death determine its attitude and reactions. Some geists are helpful, while others spread lies and confusion.

Ecology: A geist is created when a person dies traumatically. Usually there is some deed left undone or some penance to be paid. The spirit of the person refuses to leave the plane (or demiplane) on which he died, becoming a geist instead.

Greater Geist

These spirits can cast illusions that include sound. However, the illusions always have a transparent quality to them and are never believed to be real. The greater geist can make itself appear as solid flesh, though it is not. It can alter the appearance of its clothing and the condition of its body. For example, it might choose to remove its head and carry it around. It cannot change its appearance to resemble another person. Most often, however, a greater geist looks as it did at the time of death.

Ghost, Animal

	Bear	Boar, Wild	Horse, Wild	Lion, Mtn.	Stag	Wolf
CLIMATE/TERRAIN:	Temperate land	Temperate land	Any non-mountainous	Warm or temperate	Temperate land	Non-tropical land
FREQUENCY:	Very rare	Very rare	Very rare	Very rare	Very rare	Very rare
ORGANIZATION:	Solitary	Solitary	Solitary	Solitary	Solitary	Solitary/Pack
ACTIVITY CYCLE:	Night	Night	Night	Night	Night	Night
DIET:	Nil	Nil	Nil	Nil	Nil	Nil
INTELLIGENCE:	Semi- (2–4)	Semi- (2–4)	Animal (1)	Semi- (2–4)	Animal (1)	Low (5–7)
TREASURE:	R	R	R	R	R	R
ALIGNMENT:	Lawful evil	Lawful evil	Lawful evil	Lawful evil	Lawful evil	Lawful evil
NO. APPEARING:	1	1	1	1	1	1
ARMOR CLASS:	0 or 8	0 or 8	0 or 8	0 or 8	0 or 8	0 or 8
MOVEMENT:	12	15	24	12	24	18
HIT DICE:	5+5	3+3	2+2	3+1	3	3
THAC0:	15	17	19	17	17	17
NO. OF ATTACKS:	3	1	1	3	1 or 2	1
DAMAGE/ATTACK:	1d3/1d3/1d6	3d4	1d3	1d3/1d3/1d6	1d3/1d3 or 2d4	1d4+1
SPECIAL ATTACKS:	Age	Age	Age	Age	Age	Age
SPECIAL DEFENSES:	Ethereal	Ethereal	Ethereal	Ethereal	Ethereal	Ethereal
MAGIC RESISTANCE:	Nil	Nil	Nil	Nil	Nil	Nil
SIZE:	L (9′ tall)	M (5′ long)	L (8′–9′ long)	M (4′–5′ long)	L (8′ tall)	S (3′–4′)
MORALE:	Fearless (19–20)	Fearless (19–20)	Fearless (19–20)	Fearless (19–20)	Fearless (19–20)	Fearless (19–20
XP VALUE:	2,000	1,400	975	1,400	1,400	1,400

Animal ghosts are the spirits of woodland creatures that died under some unusual circumstance. In the case of pets, they may have been killed while attempting to serve their masters. For wild beasts, it may be that they died while in a panic or other emotionally charged state. Whatever the cause of their unlife, they are doomed to roam the place of their death, haunting those who killed them or seeking to complete an unfinished task. They instinctively hate all life and have an undying hunger that can only be satisfied by drawing the essence from those still living.

Ghost animals retain the basic forms they had while living, but may show gaping wounds, look emaciated, glow with an eerie luminescence, or appear faint and transparent.

They still bark, growl, hiss, or make whatever other sounds they did in life, although these now have a haunting, spectral quality to them.

Combat: Like other ghosts, these undead animals are incorporeal. Though usually encountered only by those in a like state, the residue of their being is visible to non-ethereal creatures and is so frightening that those viewing it must immediately make a fear check. Succumbing to this fear causes the victim to temporarily lose one point of Strength, in addition to the other effects of the failed check. Priests of 5th level or paladins of 8th level are immune to this effect and all other characters of at least 7th level receive a +2 bonus to their fear checks.

Those who do not retreat promptly upon encountering the ghost are likely to be attacked by it. After spending one round to assume a semicorporeal form, the animal attacks as it would have while alive. In this state, however, its claws, fangs, or other natural weapons will not harm the living. The ethereal touch of such an animal causes those hit by it to age 5–20 (5d4) years.

While semicorporeal, a ghost animal has an Armor Class of 0 and can be struck only by silver or magical weapons. Spells cast upon the creature will affect it normally. Semicorporeal ghost animals can be turned by priests as if they were spectres and may be harmed by holy water, which does 2d4 points of damage per vial.

When in its ethereal state, the ghost animal can only be combated by another in the Ethereal plane. If this is the case, it has an Armor Class of 8. They can be attacked by spells, but only if the caster is also ethereal.

Any living thing killed by a ghost animal is drained of its life essence and is dead beyond the power of normal magic to revive. No force other than a *wish* can breathe life into someone slain in this manner.

Habitat/Society: In most cases, ghost animals are confined to a small area. Usually, this is place where they died, though they may haunt their former lair, or that of the person that killed them. Occasionally, the ghost animal's range extends to the territory the creature once roamed or claimed.

Most animal ghosts have specific reasons for their hauntings. They are prone to seek revenge on those who ended their lives or were cruel to them. They are very dangerous, as they often do not distinguish between the specific person who slew them and an innocent traveler passing through the area.

Ecology: The fear that animal ghosts engender has nothing to do with their appearance or the fact that they are dead. The fear they cause and their ability to age a victim through touch are manifestations of their supernatural power. Bravery is not enough to protect someone from their powers.

Any treasure found with a ghost animal is usually that of former victims, for the creature has no interest in such things itself.

CLIMATE/TERRAIN:	Lamordia
FREQUENCY:	Very rare
ORGANIZATION:	Solitary
ACTIVITY CYCLE:	Any
DIET:	Nil
INTELLIGENCE:	Average (8–10)
TREASURE:	Nil
ALIGNMENT:	Chaotic evil
NO. APPEARING:	1
ARMOR CLASS:	6
MOVEMENT:	12
HIT DICE:	9 (40 hp)
THAC0:	11
NO. OF ATTACKS:	2 (fists)
DAMAGE/ATTACK:	2d8 / 2d8
SPECIAL ATTACKS:	Strangulation
SPECIAL DEFENSES:	See below
MAGIC RESISTANCE:	Special
SIZE:	L (8′ tall)
MORALE:	Fearless (19–20)
XP VALUE:	5,000

While flesh golems of any sort are frightful in the extreme, those crafted amid the mists of Ravenloft are even more horrible than their kin from other realms.

Stitched together from the collected body parts of various corpses, flesh golems have a horrific appearance. Since they are composed of the body parts of many different people, they can have a variety of appearances. All are gruesome and ghastly.

Combat: Ravenloft flesh golems attack by battering an enemy with their powerful fists. Each fist can strike once in a combat round, inflicting 2d8 points of damage.

If the golem hits with both fists in the same round, it can begin strangling its victim on the next round. This is an optional attack, not required of the creature. Strangulation does 3d8 points of damage each round automatically. Because of the golem's physical might, the victim is unable to escape unless he has a Strength of 19 or greater. It is possible for two people to break the grip (one on each arm) so long as they each have at least a 17 Strength.

The Ravenloft flesh golems are immune to cold and electricity in any form. Cold or electrical attacks do half damage at most and none if the golem makes its saving throw. Electricity does not regenerate hit points for these creatures as it does for traditional flesh golems.

Spells may do damage to a flesh golem, but all other types of spell effects are ignored. This only applies to spells cast directly upon the golem, including area effect spells. It does not include the side effects of spells, such as a *wall of stone* falling on it. The golem does not eliminate the wall with its touch, and is still required to deal with it. However, spells like *charm person, sleep,* and *teleport others* will fail on golems. The golem does not see through illusions, unless directly cast on it, as in the case of a *phantasmal killer,* nor can it automatically see invisible creatures.

Although flesh golems are immune to normal weapons and physical attacks, they can be harmed by magical weapons with a +1 enchantment or better and attacks from monsters with 4+1 or more Hit Dice. Lesser attacks will not penetrate their skin.

Fire does normal damage to golems, as does acid. Indeed, only fire or acid can permanently destroy the body of a flesh golem. Anything less and it can be reanimated at a later date (see below).

In its own way, the flesh of the golem is alive. It is vulnerable to poison, level draining, gases, and other things that affect the average human. It has a high resistance to such attacks, however, and receives a +4 bonus to all saving throws it must make. The exception to this rule is that flesh golems are completely immune to disease.

The flesh golems of Ravenloft have unique regenerative powers. While a normal human heals 1 hit point for every day of full rest, the flesh golem recovers 1 point an hour whether or not it is resting.

If the golem is brought below 0 hit points, it no longer heals. However, the creature is not slain by this trauma. Rather, the body is incapacitated and the mind dormant. If the golem's wounds are stitched up and other physical damage repaired, a powerful electrical charge (such as a lightning bolt) can restore the creature to life.

The flesh golem has one inherent weakness: its fear of fire. It must remain at least 10 feet from small flames (torches, candles, etc.) and at least 25 feet from larger flames (bonfires, housefires, etc.). In the case of a small flame, a golem may attempt to move past the fire or knock it from its holder, but only if a successful Fear Check is made. The Fear Check for flesh golems is normally an 8 but they have a –4 penalty when faced with fire.

Habitat/Society: Made to serve the selfish purposes of their mad scientist-creators, flesh golems long to be accepted as people. The inevitable rejection they suffer causes them to develop a hatred of living creatures.

Normal flesh golems are mindless automatons; Ravenloft flesh golems are not. The spirit that kindles life in the flesh of the golems is keenly aware of its existence. The spirit belongs to the brain used to make the golem. This spirit is usually damaged by the process of animation and is much more primitive and bestial than the original.

Ecology: Flesh golems are not natural creatures, and contribute nothing to the ecology of the world. Indeed, by denying the scavengers of the world their corpses, they might even be detrimental to it.

Golem, Mist

CLIMATE/TERRAIN:	Ravenloft
FREQUENCY:	Very rare
ORGANIZATION:	Solitary
ACTIVITY CYCLE:	Any
DIET:	Nil
INTELLIGENCE:	Low (5–7)
TREASURE:	Nil
ALIGNMENT:	Chaotic evil
NO. APPEARING:	1
ARMOR CLASS:	–2
MOVEMENT:	9
HIT DICE:	18 (90 hp)
THAC0:	3
NO. OF ATTACKS:	2
DAMAGE/ATTACK:	3d6/3d6
SPECIAL ATTACKS:	See below
SPECIAL DEFENSES:	See below
MAGIC RESISTANCE:	25%
SIZE:	L (12′ tall)
MORALE:	Fearless (19–20)
XP VALUE:	14,000

Mist golems are creatures of fate, brought into being accidentally by misguided wizards and priests who do not fully understand what they are doing. No one sets out to build a mist golem, but in a fool's rush to complete the building of some other automaton, tragic circumstance often takes a hand, and even the most dedicated of labors goes astray.

Mist golems look very much like swirling wisps of vapor and billowing clouds of steam mystically constrained in the shape of a 12-foot-tall man or woman. They often resemble the man or woman responsible for creating them. When moving through areas of fog, they are all but invisible, although they may be plainly seen whenever they wish to be.

Mist golems do not speak, but can create a mournful howl that can be heard as far away as a mile.

Combat: When in an area or mist or fog, these creatures often surprise their enemies. Anyone attacked by a mist golem in such a place suffers a –2 penalty on his surprise roll.

As mentioned above, mist golems are able to attack with their mournful howling. Indeed, the hearing of this sound is often the first warning that a group of adventurers will have that they are in the presence of such a creature. So dreadful is this keening that all those within 50 feet of the creature must make a fear check upon hearing it.

The mist golem may strike once per round with each of its two fists, doing 3d6 points of damage on any successful hit. So powerful are these blows that they function as battering rams when the creature employs them against structures (consult the demolition rules in the *DUNGEON MASTER Guide*).

On any natural Attack Roll of 20, the target of the golem's attack is infused with the creature's ethereal essence. If the damage generated by this attack is sufficient to kill the target, his body instantly dissolves away into mist and seemingly dissipates into nothing. In truth, the character has been transformed in a wandering mist horror (as described in the first *MONSTROUS COMPENDIUM: RAVENLOFT Appendix*). No attempt to restore life to the character will succeed unless his new form is sought out and captured somehow.

If the damage generated in the attack does not kill the target, a lesser transformation takes place. For the next ten rounds, the person infused with the golem's power becomes an ethereal being of mist and fog. Looking like a faintly projected image, the victim is unable to take any action. Wounds inflicted upon the golem while one or more transformed creatures exist do not affect the automaton. Instead, the infused being suffers them, a fact obvious to all who can see the incorporeal character. Attacks directed at the ethereal character will not harm him unless a +2 or better weapon is used. A character who dies while infused with the power of the mist golem becomes a mist horror as detailed above.

Whenever it wishes to do so, a mist golem may envelop itself in a shroud of vapor that fills an area some 15 feet about the creature. The cloud is magical in nature and can have one of ten different magical effects. Each effect can be manifested only once per day, so that the cloud could be created only ten times in any given day, each time with a different mystical property. If the golem is surprised, it instinctively releases this cloud, with the DM rolling 1d10 to see which effect it has. No matter which of the cloud's effects is chosen, characters caught in the mist are entitled to any saving throws and the like that they would normally receive. However, a –4 penalty is applied to all such checks because of the golem's great power.

1. *Cloudkill*
2. *Irritation*
3. *Blindness*
4. *Hold Person*
5. *Tasha's Uncontrollable Hideous Laughter*
6. *Otto's Irresistible Dance*
7. *Stinking Cloud*
8. *Silence, 15′ Radius*
9. *Vampiric Touch*
10. *Slow*

Regardless of past exposure to this cloud, a character must make a new check each and every time he is exposed to these magical vapors.

Because of the vaporous nature of the mist golem's body it is seldom hampered by physical objects. While it cannot fly per se, it can drift through even the smallest of apertures. Traps that are triggered by things like trip wires or pressure plates fail to go off when the virtually weightless mist drifts over them.

Like most of the automatons forged in the fires of Ravenloft, the mist golem cannot be harmed by any weapon of less than +2 enchantment. All other physical attacks directed at the creature pass through it without harm, although they do cause a slight rippling in the swirls of fog that make up its body.

Magic is all but useless against these creatures. They are immune to all manner of mind- or life-affecting spells and attempts to disrupt them with spells like *gust of wind* will have no effect upon them. On a similar note, magical and natural forces in and around the creature, like fire, cold, and so forth, do not harm it in any way. The casting of a *dispel magic,* which is so deadly to all other magical automata, has no effect upon a mist golem.

Magical attacks employed directly against the golem, like a *lightning bolt* or *magic missile* spell, do not harm the automaton. Indeed, if the creature has recently been injured it will employ the power of these magics to regenerate lost hit points at a rate of 1 for every 2 points of damage that the attack would normally have done to it. Thus, a 14-point *fireball* would supply the golem with enough energy to heal 7 points of damage.

When it is hard pressed by an enemy, a mist golem can escape into the vaporous fabric of Ravenloft. In order to do so, the creature must take no other action for one round. During this time, all attacks against the golem are made with a +2 bonus. On the next round, the creature appears to ripple away into nothingness, leaving no indication that it had ever been present save for a dense bank of fog that thins out gradually over the course of the next hour.

Habitat/Society: Mist golems are not social creatures. At best, only a handful of them have ever been created, and most of these wander to endless expanses of Ravenloft's vaporous clouds, avoiding all contact with the living. For the most part, they are encountered only when someone foolish seeks them out or attempts to control them. On rare occasions, however, they wander into a domain or one of the demiplane's islands, leaving a trail of destruction behind them until they are again consumed by the mists and vanish.

Like the Vistani, mist golems are able to navigate the mists of Ravenloft without effort. Whenever a golem uses its ability to escape into the mists, it can reappear anywhere else in Ravenloft after walking only a short distance. No matter how far the creature wishes to travel, its journey is always one of 99 steps. As soon as it takes the last of these steps, it materializes again in the real world. If the creature has no destination in mind, it need not leave the mists. If it wished to, the golem could wander forever among the swirling clouds of mist that make up this ethereal domain of the mist horrors.

The creation of any mist golem, accidental though it might be, also results in the manifestation of an unusual focus. No two of these objects are alike, yet all function in the same way. At the time of the monster's animation, when the physical body that was to have housed it fades away, some nearby object acts as a lens through which the animating power of the mists is concentrated, focused, and transferred upon the creature.

While it is impossible to say what object will be given this mantle of mystical energy, there are a few things that all known foci have had in common. First, a focus will always be within 50 feet of both the golem and its creator at the time of the transformation. Second, it will always be of great value (generally not less than 10,000 gold pieces). Third, foci are never very large, weighing at most 5 pounds and generally seldom more than half that. Lastly, the item must be bathed in direct moonlight at the time of the transmutation. As one might gather from the last point, mist golems are always created in the dead of a cloudless night.

From the moment of its creation, this focus is the bane of the golem's existence. Whoever holds the focus in his hand can command the golem to do for him no fewer than five tasks. So long as the golem's master keeps the focus on his person (either in hand, worn as an amulet, or so forth), the golem can do him no harm and must obey his instructions to the letter. As is often the case, of course, the intent of the orders or their ramifications may be perverted dangerously. As a rule, the first order is carried out exactly as its master wishes, with each additional one being more and more twisted. With the completion of the fifth task, the focus is consumed by the mists, vanishing to reappear somewhere else in Ravenloft. For its part, the golem becomes obsessed with the destruction of its former master.

Ecology: Unlike other golems, these mysterious creatures are not intentionally created. The first of them (and presumably all others since then) was manifested when an ancient sage attempted to animate a more traditional golem by tapping directly into the mists of Ravenloft. Aware that the land was held together by some mysterious power, but unable to fathom its true nature, the golem's architect fathered a creature more powerful and deadly than anything he could have imagined.

Invariably, the mist golem hungers for destruction and death. First it longs to see the one who sought to control it torn apart and then it begins an endless rampage in which any who encounter the ethereal creature become fair game. From time to time, it must obey a master who holds the focus that empowers it, but these occasions are fleeting and always end with the death of its would-be sovereign.

Golem, Snow

Climate/Terrain:	Arctic lands and mountain tops
Frequency:	Very rare
Organization:	Solitary
Activity Cycle:	Any
Diet:	Nil
Intelligence:	Semi- (2–4)
Treasure:	Nil
Alignment:	Neutral
No. Appearing:	1
Armor Class:	1
Movement:	9
Hit Dice:	12
THAC0:	9
No. of Attacks:	2
Damage/Attack:	2–24
Special Attacks:	See below
Special Defenses:	See below
Magic Resistance:	Nil
Size:	L (11′ tall)
Morale:	Fearless (19–20)
XP Value:	7,000

First discovered on the arctic island of Todstein (as described in the adventure *Ship of Horror*), snow golems are similar to greater golems. Like others of their ilk, they are usually employed to guard an important item or entryway.

A snow golem can be sculpted in any appearance, but is usually portrayed as a humanoid figure wearing armor and a helmet. It usually carries no weapons and does not use a shield. Their helmets are usually sculpted into bizarre, frightening shapes such as snarling animals or horrid, leering faces. Because they have been hardened beyond the consistency of snow, they resemble white marble statues. Indeed, they are often mistaken for such things or for snow-covered topiary figures.

Snow golems cannot speak, although the wind seems always to blow mournfully when they move, creating a haunting sound that can chill the heart as surely as the cold climate does the flesh.

Combat: Snow golems share the characteristics common to all Ravenloft golems, being damaged only by +2 or better weapons, immune to all manner of mind- or life-affecting spells (such as *charm, sleep, hold*, or *finger of death*), and taking no damage from poison or similar substances. They are likewise immune to all water- or cold-based attacks, and regain 1 hit point for every die of damage that such attacks would have caused.

If hit with an electrical attack while touching another creature, the attack is conducted through the body of the snow golem and does full damage to this being. If attacked in this way when not in contact with someone else, the golem seems unaffected. In actuality, it stores the charge, doing as much damage as it would have sustained to whomever it next comes into contact with.

Snow golems are able to breathe a *cone of cold* once every five rounds. This functions as if the spell of that name were being cast by a 10th level wizard.

In melee, they have two main modes of attack. The first (and favored) is to strike with their two massive fists for 2d12 points of damage each. In some instances, however, they will forego such attacks and attempt to grapple with their enemies. Such attacks are resolved using the normal rules for wrestling in the *Dungeon Master Guide*. Snow golems have a Strength score of 19 for the purposes of unarmed combat.

Due to the extreme cold of their bodies, nonmagical weapons made of metal shatter when used against a snow golem. Even magical arms are not immune to this effect, having a 35% chance of being destroyed with each successful blow. This chance is reduced by 5% for every plus of the weapon above +2 (i.e. a +3 weapon has only a 30% chance of shattering).

Attacks employing magical fire harms them, but also release a cloud of scalding steam in a 20′ radius. Anyone caught in this vapor must make a saving throw vs. breath weapon or be burned for half the damage sustained by the creature. A successful saving throw negates all damage.

Habitat/Society: Snow golems are automatons capable of following a few simple commands. They are under the complete control of their master unless they manage to break his domination. Normally, they have no society, although there are rumors that free willed snow golems are sometimes found in one another's company.

Ecology: A wizard of 15th or greater level can create a snow golem. The body is sculpted of snow, taking four weeks and costing 45,000 gold pieces for materials and components. Obviously, this lengthy process must be undertaken in a naturally cold or refrigerated area. Once the body is completed, it is animated with the casting of *wish, polymorph any object, cone of cold*, and *permanency* spells.

Golem, Wax

CLIMATE/TERRAIN:	Ravenloft
FREQUENCY:	Very rare
ORGANIZATION:	Solitary
ACTIVITY CYCLE:	Any
DIET:	Nil
INTELLIGENCE:	Average (8–10)
TREASURE:	Nil
ALIGNMENT:	Neutral
NO. APPEARING:	1–25
ARMOR CLASS:	4
MOVEMENT:	12
HIT DICE:	8
THAC0:	13
NO. OF ATTACKS:	1
DAMAGE/ATTACK:	2d6
SPECIAL ATTACKS:	See below
SPECIAL DEFENSES:	See below
MAGIC RESISTANCE:	Nil
SIZE:	M (5′–6′ tall)
MORALE:	Fearless (19–20)
XP VALUE:	5,000

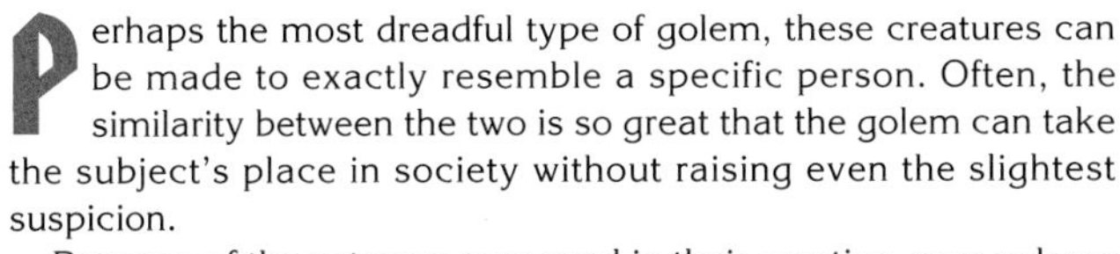

Perhaps the most dreadful type of golem, these creatures can be made to exactly resemble a specific person. Often, the similarity between the two is so great that the golem can take the subject's place in society without raising even the slightest suspicion.

Because of the extreme care used in their creation, wax golems are easily mistaken for the person they have been crafted to resemble. Only an indepth examination of the creature will reveal that it is not what it appears to be.

Wax golems are able to absorb the memories of those they resemble and can speak the languages known by their living counterpart.

Combat: Wax golems are not generally used in combat situations. While other automata might be primarily intended as watchmen or sentries, these creatures serve as spies or agents to infiltrate and supplant local rulers or other important people.

When forced into combat, a golem will tend to employ the weapons that its counterpart was proficient in. The great strength of the creature gives it a +4 bonus on all Damage Rolls. If these are not available, it will attack with its fists, delivering a volley of powerful blows that do 2d6 points of damage.

The primary ability of the wax golem is its memory drain. From the moment that it is animated, the creature is instantly aware of the location of its model. Its first task is always to seek out that person and destroy him. Each successful blow landed by the golem on its living twin forces the victim to make a saving throw vs. death magic. If the roll is failed, the attack does no physical damage. Instead, the golem steals one experience level from the victim, acquiring for itself all the memories and abilities associated with it. Each additional blow repeats this process until the target is utterly drained of its memory and vitality, leaving only a comatose shell of a body behind. A person who escapes from the creature before losing the whole of his personality to it will have vast gaps in his memory and must make a madness check each week until the golem is destroyed.

Care must be taken that the body does not die once a golem has absorbed its mind. If this happens, the force animating the simulacrum is freed and the golem softens and melts, leaving behind only a pool of wax.

The golem uses the stolen memories and powers to assume the victim's place. Any valuables (including magical items) which the victim had are taken by the golem to aid it in its masquerade.

Wax golems have the powers and weaknesses common to all Ravenloft golems. They are immune to electrical and cold-based attacks. Magical fire melts their features, making them run and revealing them at once for what they are.

Habitat/Society: Unlike most golems, these creatures cooperate willingly with their creator and with any other wax golems in their plans to usurp authority or take the place of living beings.

A number of wax golems, working in concert, may be used to infiltrate a village, town, or stronghold, replacing those within while remaining undiscovered. They use their new positions to change laws, commit robberies, assume positions of power, and act as advance troops to prepare places for other wax golems.

Ecology: Wax golems are created from fine-quality wax that must be blended with mimic ichor, obliviax dust, and doppleganger blood. *Polymorph any object, limited wish, strength*, and *permanency* spells are then used to animate the golem. Wax golems are tremendously expensive to create, costing fully 75,000 gold pieces each in supplies and equipment.

Gremishka

CLIMATE/TERRAIN:	Ravenloft
FREQUENCY:	Rare
ORGANIZATION:	Swarm
ACTIVITY CYCLE:	Night
DIET:	Omnivore
INTELLIGENCE:	High (13–14)
TREASURE:	Z
ALIGNMENT:	Chaotic evil
NO. APPEARING:	3–18 (3d6)
ARMOR CLASS:	4
MOVEMENT:	12
HIT DICE:	½ (1–4 hit points)
THAC0:	20
NO. OF ATTACKS:	1
DAMAGE/ATTACK:	1–3
SPECIAL ATTACKS:	Swarm
SPECIAL DEFENSES:	+4 on saving throws
MAGIC RESISTANCE:	Nil
SIZE:	T (2′ tall)
MORALE:	Unsteady (5–7)
XP VALUE:	35

Like their close cousins, the gremlins, these diminutive humanoids are parasites and nuisances. They live under buildings and steal from the inhabitants.

From a distance, a gremishka might be mistaken for a small dog or a large cat. It is furry, with pointed ears and a protruding muzzle. The fur can be of any color or pattern. The mouth is overly large for the face, as are the yellow eyes, which have vertical pupils like those of a cat. Unlike a gremlin, the gremishka has no wings. These creatures can manipulate any tool with their dexterous fingers. A gremishka rarely carries a weapon around for more than an hour before dropping it or hiding it, however. They wear no armor or clothing, although they understand the uses of both.

Gremiska speak the languages of normal gremlins as well as their own. It is not uncommon for one of these beasts to know a half-dozen or more human tongues as well.

Combat: Gremishka do not engage in hand-to-hand combat unless they are trapped or cornered. They are extremely fast and nimble, able to slip between legs or around their opponents. This speed gives them their unusually high Armor Class and a +4 bonus to saving throws caused by attacks with an area effect. They gain a +2 bonus on attack rolls against any opponent over 4′ tall, because such foes make nice, big targets.

As a group, gremishka employ a tactic of swarming. They climb onto an opponent en masse, biting and tearing at him for 1d3 points of damage each. They must make a successful attack roll to get a good grip, but each round after that, damage is automatic. Half the gremishka in the swarm will gnaw through straps, open clasps, or filch anything that is not tied down.

Anyone who attacks a swarming gremishka may harm the character beneath the creatures. If the attacker inflicts more damage than is needed to kill the gremishka, the character beneath the swarm takes the extra damage.

The gremishka's low morale may cause them to retreat if any great show of force is made. Anything the creatures manage to filch will be taken back to their lair.

Habitat/Society: Gremishka are not fond of sunlight, but it does not harm them. They live in basements and under buildings, usually large homes. If possible, they choose a lair that gives them easy access to many parts of the building.

Gremishka keep the spoils of their raids in their lairs. Treasure is always a random collection of stolen trinkets, some with real value. They love to take things, although their taste in treasure is dubious at best.

Gremishka seem to derive extreme pleasure from the rage and frustration of larger humanoids. They enjoy playing vicious, destructive pranks on their hosts. They recognize no leaders among their own kind. They may cooperate to cause mischief, however, and follow the cue and instructions of the gremishka that suggested a prank. Some of their traps get very elaborate, owing to their high intelligence. They hide in the walls and under floorboards to watch and listen for potential victims. When a victim discovers the prank or activates their trap, he often hears the gremishka's high, chittering laughter.

Ecology: Gremishka eat anything. They trap small creatures such as rats, cats, or dogs. They have been known to form a temporary attachment to children who are their size and live near their lairs. Gremishka are hunted by just about anything that can find and catch them, including large snakes, dogs, giant spiders, kobolds, and many more—especially humans.

	Annis	Green	Sea
Climate/Terrain:	Any land	Any land or river	Any water
Frequency:	Very rare	Very rare	Very rare
Organization:	Covey	Covey	Covey
Activity Cycle:	Night	Night	Night
Diet:	Nil	Nil	Nil
Intelligence:	High (13–14)	High (13–14)	Very (11–12)
Treasure:	(D)	(X,F)	(C,Y)
Alignment:	Chaotic evil	Neutral evil	Chaotic evil
No. Appearing:	1–3	1–3	1–3
Armor Class:	0	–2	2
Movement:	15, Sw 12	15, Sw 12	15, Sw 15
Hit Dice:	8	9	6
THAC0:	13	11	15
No. of Attacks:	1	1	1
Damage/Attack:	1d8+6	1d8+6	1d8+6
Special Attacks:	See below	See below	See below
Special Defenses:	See below	See below	See below
Magic Resistance:	20%	35%	50%
Size:	L (8′ tall)	M (6′ tall)	M (6′ tall)
Morale:	Champion (15–16)	Fanatic (17–18)	Champion (15–16)
XP Value:	7,000	7,000	5,000

A spectral hag is the undead spirit of a hag who died during an evil ceremony. Returned to a mockery of the life she once knew, the hag is doomed to inhabit desolate places and seeks only to slaughter all she encounters. Though she retains many of her dread powers and is gifted with those of a spectre as well, she is a miserable creature who hates all life and light.

Spectral hags are translucent reflections of their living forms. All have scraggly hair, withered faces, blackened teeth, and flesh covered with moles and warts. They wear the tattered and filthy garb of peasant women.

As a rule, spectral hags speak common and one or two other languages.

Combat: Spectral hags have a Strength score of 18/00, adding +3 to their Attack Rolls and +6 to their Damage Rolls. Their chilling touch does 1d8 points of damage and drains two life energy levels from the victim of the attack. Any being totally drained of life energy by one of these foul hags becomes a full-strength spectre under the control of the crone. In general, any encounter with one of these creatures will also include 3d6 spectres who represent the past enemies of the shrew.

Spectral hags can only be hit by +1 or better weapons and are immune to all *sleep, charm, hold*, and cold-based spells. Similarly, poisons, disease, and paralyzation cannot harm them.

Being undead, these creatures are subject to the turning ability of priests and paladins. Holy water inflicts 2d4 points of damage per vial splashed upon them and a *raise dead* spell destroys the hag immediately if a saving throw vs. spell is failed and the creature's natural magic resistance is overcome. Daylight makes them powerless by weakening their ties to the Negative Material plane, although it does not actually harm them.

Habitat/Society: Although they are usually solitary creatures, there is a chance that any spectral hag who was a member of a covey in life will retain contact with her foul sisters. Indeed, if all were killed while engaged in an evil ceremony, the dark trio might all have attained undead stature and present an even more deadly force for adventurers to deal with. If one member of a covey was killed and later slew her sisters, she is the master and the other two are under her control.

Ecology: Though partially insubstantial, spectral hags still crave humanoid flesh. The fact that they can neither taste nor consume this vile delicacy causes them no end of suffering.

Annis

The spectral annis is certainly the most terrible of these creatures. In addition to all the powers she had when living, this undead horror has acquired the power to conduct a dark ceremony on the night of the new moon which transforms any single female captive into a living annis under her command. Being utterly evil, these hags use this power to cause as much suffering to the living as they can.

Green Hag

Like annis, green hags who become undead acquire the ability to preform a sinister ceremony by which they create more of their living sisters. In the case of these foul crones, the victim is a young elf woman and the ceremony must be held by the light of the full moon.

Sea Hag

As with the other dark sisters, spectral sea hags are able to transform the innocent into wretches like themselves. When a sea hag wishes to employ this power, she seeks out a halfling, gnome, or dwarf woman. When the moon slips into an eclipse, the sea hag holds her foul ritual and the helpless captive becomes like her, condemned to an existence of horror and misery.

Head Hunter

Climate/Terrain:	Ravenloft
Frequency:	Rare
Organization:	Solitary
Activity Cycle:	Any
Diet:	Carnivore
Intelligence:	Average (8–10)
Treasure:	Nil
Alignment:	Neutral evil
No. Appearing:	1–3
Armor Class:	3
Movement:	6, Wb 12
Hit Dice:	5 + 5
THAC0:	15
No. of Attacks:	1
Damage/Attack:	2–8 (2d4)
Special Attacks:	Poison
Special Defenses:	Nil
Magic Resistance:	20%
Size:	T (1′ diameter)
Morale:	Very steady (13–14)
XP Value:	1,400

A head hunter is a horrid, spiderlike creature believed to have been created by the mysterious drow or some related, but even more sinister, race.

Head hunters look like long-legged spiders with human heads in place of bodies. First seen in the dread realm of Arak, they have recently been spotted in Arkandale, Borca, Darkon, and Dementlieu.

These frightful creatures can understand and speak drow, elvish, and several human tongues. It is almost certain that they have a language of their own, but if this is true it has never been heard by man.

Combat: Most encounters with a head hunter begin not with a sighting of the beast itself, but when some hapless soul wanders into its giant web. Spun in the same manner that a true spider would employ, the head hunter's web is fashioned from tremendously strong, sharp filaments. Those walking or running into the nearly invisible web have a 75% chance of lopping off one of their limbs. If such a loss is indicated, the DM should roll 1d10 to determine the exact nature of the injury. On a roll of 1–9, the victim has lost an arm or leg (determined randomly). Such a loss also inflict damages equal to one-quarter the character's base hit points, potentially killing a wounded character. If the roll was a 10, the character has been beheaded and is instantly killed. As one might expect, the head hunter can move freely in its web without any chance of injury.

Once the head hunter's web has done its work, the creature may resort to melee combat if the odds appear to be in its favor. They begin such combat by spitting type-N poison (contact, 1 minute, death/25) at one target up to 15 feet away. A head hunter can spit in this fashion three times per day.

If forced into direct physical combat, head hunters attack by biting for 2d4 points of damage. Those bitten by the head hunter are injected with its poison whenever the creature rolls doubles on its damage dice.

Head hunters are immune to all poisons and can easily walk on the webs of all other spiders. They are particularly susceptible to fire, taking one extra point per die of damage. They have poor eyesight past about 20′ but are especially sensitive to vibrations, which allow them to track moving or speaking targets.

Habitat/Society: Head hunters hate all humans and demihumans, but particularly despise elves. Whenever possible, they will use their stolen bodies (see **Ecology**) to bring misery and suffering to the ranks of the fair folk.

Ecology: The most terrible aspect of the head hunter is not its combat ability, however. Once battle is done, the creature will gather up any corpses beheaded by encounters with its web and begin to transform them into vessels that can serve its dark schemes. Climbing atop the neck of the still-warm body, the head hunter slips its slender legs deep into the corpse and takes control of the body. Like the master of some organic machine, the head hunter can now cause the body to move about as if it were still alive. An animated corpse fights and makes saving throws as a 0 level human.

Over the course of the next week to ten days, the head hunter will feed upon the internal organs of the body. At the end of that time, it will abandon its host, leaving behind an empty shell not unlike the discarded skin of a growing snake. During that time, however, the head hunter will attempt to infiltrate human society and sow discord by passing itself off as a normal human.

In cases where more than one beheaded corpse is available to the creature, the head hunter will envelop those it does not intend to use in a cocoon of webbing. This quickly hardens, perfectly preserving the body within for up to 12 months. At any time during this period, the head hunter can recover and animate the corpse.

It is not uncommon for a head hunter to set up its lair within a human or demihuman city. As a rule, such places will have at least one secret chamber that houses several preserved bodies that will act as future vessels for the creature.

Hebi-No-Onna

Climate/Terrain:	Rokushima Táiyoo and Sri Raji
Frequency:	Very rare
Organization:	Solitary
Activity Cycle:	Any
Diet:	Omnivore
Intelligence:	Genius (17–18)
Treasure:	U (A)
Alignment:	Lawful evil
No. Appearing:	1
Armor Class:	0
Movement:	12, Sw 12
Hit Dice:	14
THAC0:	7
No. of Attacks:	3
Damage/Attack:	1–6/1–6/1 point
Special Attacks:	See below
Special Defenses:	See below
Magic Resistance:	Nil
Size:	M (4′–5′)
Morale:	Fanatic (17–18)
XP Value:	10,000

Hebi-no-onna, also known as *snake women,* are powerful spellcasters who can control snakes of all sorts. They often dupe normal men and women into forming cults dedicated to themselves in order to further their selfish and evil aims.

Hebi-no-onna have the bodies of exceptionally beautiful women with writhing serpents instead of arms. They have the skin tones, dark hair, elegant eyes, and delicate bone structure characteristic of oriental regions. Hebi-no-onna most often wear finely made kimonos, so that they may easily hide their arms within the voluminous sleeves. They adorn themselves with jewelry, especially that which features valuable gemstones.

They speak the common languages of several eastern realms and all reptilian tongues.

Combat: Hebi-no-onna prefer to cast spells and use their hypnotic gaze on opponents before engaging in close combat.

Hebi-no-onna have the magical ability of 14th level Enchanters, including their modified saving throws and bonus spells. They do not need material components, though they must be able to speak and gesture freely. Their most frequently used and favorite spells include *charm person, friends, ray of enfeeblement, hold person, suggestion, charm monster, confusion, minor globe of invulnerability, chaos, domination, feeblemind, hold monster, geas, globe of invulnerability,* and *teleport without error.* In combat situations, they prefer to englobe themselves in protective spells and then paralyze or control their foes. In this way, they hope to acquire prisoners who can later be turned into servants or slaves.

In addition to their magical abilities, hebi-no-onna have a hypnotic gaze that they use to great advantage. This functions like the first level wizard spell *hypnotism* except that even those who are wary or hostile receive no bonus to their saving throws. When the snake woman directs this attack at someone, her eyes change to the yellow, slit-pupiled orbs of a snake. The hebi-no-onna cannot engage in melee or cast spells in the same round that she uses this ability. Those who are aware of this power have a 50% chance of avoiding the creature's gaze, while others will find it impossible to elude.

The bite of a snake woman causes 1 point of damage and injects a terrible poison into the target's body. Known by the Vistani as *daigatu* (nightmare wine), this mysterious toxin causes anyone bitten by the creature to attempt a saving throw vs. poison or begin to suffer vivid and horrifying hallucinations for 1d10+2 rounds. Characters caught in the grip of these nightmares are unable to fight, defend themselves, or take any other action. Instead, they howl in terror and thrash about as their deepest fears torment them. After three bites, the hebi-no-onna is unable to use her poison for 24 hours, though her fangs still cause their normal damage.

Both of the snake woman's arms can strike in a single round of combat. These arms may appear to be any of several varieties of poisonous snakes. In order to determine the exact properties of the hebi-no-onna's arms, the DM should roll 1d8 on the following table four times. These indicating the type of snake, the damage done by its bite, the type of poison that it injects with its bite, and the lethality of the venom. The "Poison Strength" column refers to **Table 51: Poison Strength** in the *Dungeon Master Guide* and the "Poison Intensity" column is a modifier to the victim's saving throw vs. poison.

1d8 Roll	Snake Type	Bite Damage	Poison Strength	Poison Intensity
1	Asp	1d2	A	Diluted (+4)
2	Cobra	1d3	B	Weak (+2)
3	Mamba	1d3+1	C	Mild (+1)
4	Urutu	1d4	D	Average (+0)
5	Adder	1d4+1	E	Average (+0)
6	Pit Viper	1d6	F	Potent (–1)
7	Coral	1d6+1	O	Strong (–2)
8	Krait	1d8	P	Concentrated (–4)

Hebi-no-onna are immune to all venoms and poisons. In addition, they are immune to the gaze attacks of any reptilian creature (including other snake women) and to the ESP powers of dark nagas.

Snake women are able to control all sorts of normal and giant snakes without using any spells to do so. So long as such creatures can hear the spoken commands of these sinister women, they will obey them. Because of this, there will always be 5–40 (5d8) snakes in a hebi-no-onna's lair, many of them poisonous. These obey her without question, even dying in her defense should she command them to do so.

The hebi-no-onna takes great care never to place herself where anyone not under her control can easily reach her. Foes must make their way through her guards while she casts spells or uses her hypnotic gaze from inside her *globe of invulnerability*. If she believes she is in real danger, she always attempts to use her *teleport without error* spell to save herself. Unless she has sustained heavy damage, however, she is usually too proud to flee.

Habitat/Society: Hebi-no-onna may live in vast underground cavern and tunnel complexes, old ruins, abandoned temples, or walled private residences. They revel in creating secret cults around themselves. These snake-worshiping cults dedicate themselves to doing evil in the hebi-no-onna's name, deferring to her as if she were a goddess. The cultists commit robberies to provide money for their temple, steal beautiful clothing or jewelry to adorn the hebi-no-onna, kidnap innocents for use in sacrifices, and desecrate shrines and temples to good deities. Those who discover signs of the cult's existence or their activities are forced to join or be killed.

Most of the hebi-no-onna's spells are used to dominate and control her most powerful servitors. She uses many different kinds of dominated and controlled creatures as guards and they will always be deployed to her best advantage. There will usually be 2d10 human and demihuman slaves in her lair. These are completely under her domination and fight until they are slain or the snake woman is killed.

In addition to their magically dominated guards, hebi-no-onna surround themselves with human or demihuman cultists. These are fanatically loyal people who have come to believe that the snake woman is some manner of deity. In many cases they have been brainwashed and do not recognize the nature of the creature they serve. Some of the followers, however, will simply be evil men and women who wish to serve the terrible hebi-no-onna. Cultists are usually 0 level humans or demihumans, though some may be higher level adventurers.

Hebi-no-onna occasionally associate with spirit nagas or dark nagas and keep feathered serpents as favored servants. Whenever they cooperate with nagas there is usually a power struggle. Eventually one or the other will be forced to leave or be killed by the other. Until this time they usually cooperate, using their skills to control whole villages. Both the nagas and the feathered serpents delight in constructing traps and when several traps are found in a hebi-no-onna's lair it is indicative of the presence of one or the other type of creature.

All hebi-no-onna are quite vain and acquisitive. They love artwork, jewelry, gemstones, and insist on the finest materials and most beautiful patterns in the kimonos they wear. Many of their controlled minions are used as personal body servants who help them dress, wash, arrange their hair in intricate designs, and apply their make-up and perfumes.

Though their lairs may be in ruins or caverns, snake-women refuse to accept anything but the best furnishings and most costly, comfortable decor in their private rooms. There are always several mirrors in a hebi-no-onna's lair as a tribute to her vanity.

They are particularly fond of faceted gems such as rubies, diamonds, sapphires, and emeralds, though fine jade and colored pearls also interest them. They prefer gold and platinum settings for jewelry, but occasionally take a liking to a particularly beautiful or finely worked piece made of ivory or coral. Hebi-no-onna have no interest in money for its own sake; what treasure they acquire must be beautiful. All other riches, whether trade goods, coins, or aesthetically displeasing treasures are used to further the aims of the cult.

Hebi-no-onna seek to manipulate others into doing their will and providing them with beautiful items. They gain great satisfaction from forcing others to do their bidding and from being admired and worshiped. They are totally selfish and do not truly care for anyone other than themselves. Their lives are dedicated to surrounding themselves with beautiful luxuries and fulfilling all their desires. They believe that they have the right to rule because they are stronger and more intelligent than any other creature. They cannot be forced to serve anyone else. If they cannot escape certain capture, they will die rather than being brought under another's dominance.

Ecology: There are no male hebi-no-onna. In order to produce offspring, the snake-woman must mate with a human, elven, or half-elven partner. When the hebi-no-onna chooses a prospective mate, she tries to select someone who is intelligent, strong-willed, healthy, and handsome in order to provide these advantages for her child. Such a prospect is often resistant to her charms, forcing the snake woman to capture him and then break his spirit. It may require several weeks of *conditioning* before her chosen mate can be convinced to cooperate.

Once his work is done, the mate is sacrificed in a grand ritual attended by all the cult members. Because of the stringent requirements for a prospective mate, hebi-no-onna often devise plans to manipulate adventurers into discovering their cults and maneuver them into ill-planned attacks that are foiled by unforeseen traps. The most promising male adventurer is then chosen as the hebi-no-onna's mate, while the others are conditioned to be guards or slaves.

The offspring of the union is always a hebi-no-onna. These are as helpless as human children until they reach maturity (at about age 12), though their snake arms cause 1–4 points damage and may cause those bitten by them to experience severe nausea (save at +3 to avoid). At that time, they develop their powers and are strongly encouraged to move on and find another lair far from their mother's territory. On rare occasions, a daughter hebi-no-onna is allowed to stay and take over her mother's place. Whenever this occurs, however, it is because the mother is in failing health.

The spellbooks of hebi-no-onna contain variations of normal spells that allow their casting without the use of material components. If a spellcaster devotes one month per level of spell to learning these spells, he may then cast them without material components.

Hearth Fiend

CLIMATE/TERRAIN:	Open fires (Ravenloft only)
FREQUENCY:	Very rare
ORGANIZATION:	Solitary
ACTIVITY CYCLE:	Any
DIET:	Special
INTELLIGENCE:	Low (5–7)
TREASURE:	Nil
ALIGNMENT:	Chaotic evil
NO. APPEARING:	1
ARMOR CLASS:	0
MOVEMENT:	See below
HIT DICE:	Varies
THAC0:	Varies
NO. OF ATTACKS:	1
DAMAGE/ATTACK:	Varies
SPECIAL ATTACKS:	Firebolt & *Charm*
SPECIAL DEFENSES:	Hit only by magical weapons
MAGIC RESISTANCE:	Nil
SIZE:	Varies
MORALE:	Elite (13–14)
XP VALUE:	Varies

Since the dawn of time, humankind has looked upon fire as a mixed blessing. It drives away the night and holds back the cold. Wild animals will not approach it, and much of civilization depends upon it. Still, there are times when the flames that have nurtured mankind from the Stone Age into an era of steel and magic turn upon him. Fires escape the confines of lanterns, and houses are burned to the ground. Someone reaching into a warm hearth stumbles and scorches his hand on the dancing flames within it. Often, this is just chance. Sometimes, however, a more sinister force is at work.

The hearth fiend is an evil creature from the elemental plane of fire. Similar in many ways to the water weird, it is brought into Ravenloft as an accidental side effect of certain magical spells. As soon as they arrive in the Demiplane of Dread, hearth fiends begin to do evil. Hearth fiends have been encountered on other planes of existence, usually unwittingly carried by adventurers escaping from Ravenloft.

A hearth fiend is found only in a source of open fire: the guttering flame of a candle, the stout radiance of a torch, the warming blaze of a campfire, and so on. Here, it is visible occasionally (5% chance if closely examined) as a malevolent face that flickers menacingly in the fire. If the creature wishes to, it can make its features obvious to all who look upon it, otherwise it can be seen only with a *detect magic, detect invisibility,* or similar spell.

Hearth fiends communicate with others of their kind through the flickering of their flames and the pops and crackles they emit. When they wish to, which is seldom, they can speak to those near them in the common tongue of men. In such cases, their voices are sharp and crackling with hissing, whispery overtones. There is a 75% chance that those who hear the voice of the hearth fiend will not recognize it as speech unless they are aware of the creature's presence.

Combat: Hearth fiends attack by releasing powerful bolts of flame from their bodies. One bolt can be fired per combat round, and the amount of damage it inflicts is based upon the size of the fire that hosts the creature (see **Ecology**). These firebolts have a range of 5 feet per Hit Die of the creature. A normal attack roll is made by the fiery monster when it employs this assault. Anyone struck by the flames must make a saving throw vs. breath weapon. Success indicates that only half damage is taken from the attack. Failure indicates that the creature takes full damage and that some or all possessions must make saving throws vs. magical fire or be destroyed. Items stored within other items need not save unless the item holding them is destroyed.

Those wishing to harm the hearth fiend by direct assault must employ magical weapons. Any nonmagical item employed against the creature inflicts no damage and must save vs. magical fire or be destroyed.

Magical attacks based on lightning, electricity, heat, or flames inflict no damage upon the creature. Spells that rely upon cold or ice to inflict injury cause half damage to the hearth fiend. Those spells that create water in large quantities can be used to smother the hearth fiend, inflicting ld4 points of damage per gallon of magically created water thrown upon the creature. Nonmagical water, including holy water, has no effect on the hearth fiend and may actually be burned and consumed by the creature just like any other material object that it comes into contact with.

Spells like *resist fire* and *flame walk* can be used to protect oneself from the ravages of a hearth fiend, although the creature is assumed to be composed magical fire. Spells that drive creatures back to their native planes or limit their actions (*dismiss fire elemental* or *protection from evil,* for example) affect the hearth fiend normally.

Those who hear the whisperings of the fire and recognize that it is speaking to them can be *charmed* by the creature, and it is in this way that the creature begins to spread its evil. Those who are aware that the fire is magical or know of its true nature are immune to the enchanting effects of the whispers. Thus, as soon as adventurers learn that a given flame is actually controlled by a hearth fiend, they become immune to its charm ability. The hearth fiend can *charm* only one individual at a time, so this power is limited.

Habitat/Society: Hearth fiends are solitary creatures that delight in causing mischief and evil. Once the monster takes up residence in a given fire, that flame cannot be extinguished by normal means. It continues to burn so long as there is fuel available. Because the magical fires of this creature can consume stone and water as easily as wood or coal, it almost always has something to consume. Hearth fiends have a taste for living flesh as a fuel source, however, and enjoy nothing more than the consumption of thrashing, screaming victims caught in their fiery embrace.

Thrice per day, the hearth fiend can release 2–12 (2d6) ember eyes. These appear as innocent embers, still smoldering from the heat of the fire, that drift out into the air. The eyes remain hot and glowing for 1d6 rounds, during which time they drift about at the speed of a walking man. The hearth fiend is able to see and hear all that comes to pass near the eyes, so it uses them to gather information about its surroundings. Ember eyes can be smothered by anything that would quench normal fire (a cup of water, etc.) or anything that robs them of their enchantment (like a *dispel magic* spell).

In addition to their use as sensory organs, the ember eyes can ignite anything they are directed to land upon. The object in question must make a saving throw vs. normal fires or begin to burn. If they land on a person, that individual must make a saving throw vs. breath weapon or suffer one point of damage.

Once the embers have ignited a fire, the hearth fiend can instantly transfer itself to these new flames. This takes but one round, during which time attacks on either the new or old location can affect the creature. As a rule, a hearth fiend will be reluctant to jump from a larger fire to a smaller one, for this diminishes its power. This is, however, the only way that a hearth fiend can move about on the Prime Material plane, so it is often forced to leap into smaller fires to escape destruction at the hands of adventurers.

As soon as a hearth fiend enters a new flame, it is fully healed of damage it might have suffered, and its hit points are rerolled based on its new size. Further, the old fire is no longer considered to be magical and can be extinguished normally, while the new fire now becomes enchanted.

Typically, the hearth fiend will wait for several days after entering a new fire before taking any actions that might reveal its presence to those around it. When it begins its evil doings, it typically does so by whispering to those who are not likely to guess at its origins: a young child, a bar maid, or a dim-witted bully.

It begins to promise things to this person in exchange for his help in spreading its evil. At first, the promises are innocent and even helpful ("I will keep your inn warm and brightly lit . . .") and the demands minimal (". . . if only you will bring me some tasty yew to feed upon.").

As time goes on, and the creature begins to acquire the trust and friendship of the fire's tender, the promises become more insidious and the demands greater. It might promise never to burn the evening meal, or even the family children, in exchange for a small animal being tossed into it once per month. Further, because the fire can see many things with its ember eyes that the tender cannot, it will begin to offer disturbing news. The intent of its efforts is to goad the person it speaks to into helping the hearth fire do more evil deeds.

For example, it might reveal to a housewife whose fireplace it inhabits that her husband has been having an affair with the serving girl. Of course, the fire will be only too happy to burn the girl's face, scaring her for life, the next time she comes near it. Because of the cruel nature of the fire, there may not have been any actual romance between the master of the house and his servant, but the wife may never learn that.

Eventually, the hearth fiend will demand great sacrifices from its host; perhaps intelligent beings lured near to it so that it can lash out at them with its firebolts or the transportation of its ember eyes to places where they will ignite and allow the creature potential refuge. Often, it will cloak these requests in terms that will make them pleasing to the person it has charmed.

For example, it might ask to have one of its embers transported to the hearth of a neighbor who has offended its tender. Once there, it vows to destroy the house, driving the inhabitants out and forcing them to seek a new home elsewhere. In actuality, of course, the creature will see to it that the neighbors are unable to escape the flames that engulf their home so that it may delight in the taste of their seared flesh.

Ecology: Whenever a wizard or priest employs a fire-based spell in Ravenloft, there is a 1% chance per level of the spell that it will cause a hearth fiend to appear. The creature will instantly be drawn into the nearest source of nonmagical fire, which it will enter. The power of the creature is based wholly upon the size of the fire that it inhabits, as indicated on the following chart:

Fire	HD	THAC0	Firebolt	XP
Candle or lamp	1	19	1d4	120
Torch or cooking fire	3	17	2d4	270
Campfire or fireplace	5	15	3d4	650
Large hearth	7	13	4d4	1,400
Bonfire	9	11	5d4	3,000
Burning house	11	9	6d4	5,000
Burning mansion	13	7	7d4	7,000
Burning fort	15	5	8d4	9,000
Forest fire	17	3	9d4	11,000

On their native plane, hearth fiends are lesser creatures. They drift about, always at the mercy of even the most minor inhabitants of the elemental plane of fire. The only thing that makes them unique and potent in any way is their ability to sense the use of magic that draws upon the elemental fire of their home dimension. Whenever a hearth fiend senses such a spell, it will latch on to the enchantment and leave behind the elemental plane of fire.

Once on the Prime Material plane, a hearth fiend is more powerful. Its fiery nature makes it dangerous and its intelligence makes it cunning enough to survive. Thus, hearth fiends are greatly reluctant to return to their plane of origin. If confronted with the possibility of banishment from the Prime Material plane, they will be more than willing to bargain and haggle for a chance to remain. Of course, they will lie and deceive those they must deal with in any way possible, planning all the while to destroy them at the earliest opportunity.

Just as the hearth fiend is drawn into the Prime Material plane by magic, so, too, can it be used to foster magic. It is known that Azalin of Darkon once harnessed the power of several of these creatures in a forge that is said to have burned hotter than any known before. Of course, in order to fuel the forge he was forced to cast living people, usually criminals from his dungeons and foolhardy adventurers, into it. However, this effort was rewarded with a device that proved unusually suited to the creation of magical items. There are those who say that each and every one of his dreaded Kargat vampires is armed with a weapon forged in the flames of this evil device. The means by which Azalin built this forge and contained the elemental creatures are unknown, but it is certain that the darkest of dark magics was involved.

Hound, Phantom

Climate/Terrain:	Ravenloft
Frequency:	Very rare
Organization:	Solitary or pack
Activity Cycle:	Any
Diet:	Nil
Intelligence:	Semi- (2–4)
Treasure:	P (X,Y)
Alignment:	Neutral
No. Appearing:	1–6
Armor Class:	6
Movement:	18
Hit Dice:	2+2
THAC0:	19
No. of Attacks:	1
Damage/Attack:	2–8 (2d4)
Special Attacks:	fear check & poison
Special Defenses:	+1 or better weapon to hit
Magic Resistance:	Nil
Size:	M (5′–6′ long)
Morale:	Steady (11–12)
XP Value:	175

A phantom hound is a dog so devoted to its former master that it returns after its death to guard that master's property or final resting place.

First noted in Sanguinia, a phantom hound is always some very large dog such as a mastiff, wolfhound, or Great Dane. Due to the corrupting influences of the Demiplane of Dread, the faithful canine is transformed into a terrifying, coal black creature with spectral eyes that glow a deep green. The beast's snout dribbles phosphorescent foam and the lips are pulled back into a snarl, revealing enormous, sharp, elongated teeth.

Although they cannot speak, these creatures understand all that is said to them in the language of their former master. It is quite common for them to fill the night air with a mournful howl.

Combat: Phantom hounds pose no threat to those who do not trespass on the lands they guard. Those who unwisely drawn near these sinister creatures, however, will be attacked without mercy.

When it senses someone drawing near to its territory, the phantom hound announces its presence with a blood-chilling, wavering howl that can be heard across great distances. So dreadful is the sound of this cry that all who hear it must make a fear check.

The hound attacks with its powerful jaws, doing 2d4 points of damage with each successful bite. Anyone bitten by the beast must make a saving throw vs. poison with a +2 bonus or lose a point of Strength from the toxic foam that drools from the hound's mouth. A victim's Strength returns at the rate of 1 point per hour.

Although they look quite solid, phantom hounds are intangible creatures. As such, they can only be harmed by magical weapons of at least +1 enchantment. Lesser weapons simply flash through the body of the creature without harm.

Phantom hounds are immune to all manner of mind- or life-affecting magic but can be turned as if they were ghosts. Holy water that is splashed upon them caused 1d6+2 points of damage per vial.

Habitat/Society: Phantom hounds have no society per se, existing only to continue their devotion to their masters even beyond death.

Should interlopers take anything from a site guarded by a phantom hound, the hound will leave its territory to pursue them. The only way to escape such a hound is to kill it or return the stolen item. Offering such an item to the hound to preserve one's life has a 50% chance of causing the hound to take the item and return to its protected area.

Though usually solitary creatures, packs of phantom hounds may be encountered where a master kept a number of dogs. Whenever a pack is encountered, there will be 1d6 normal phantom hounds and one pack leader with 3+2 Hit Dice and an Armor Class of 5. The leader's cry causes those hearing it to suffer a –2 penalty on their Fear Checks.

Ecology: Phantom hounds will often go through the same routines in death that they did in life. It would not be uncommon for adventurers exploring an estate haunted by a phantom hound to see the beast digging in a flower garden, chasing phantom rabbits, rolling in decayed matter, or trotting along watchfully at the edge of the property.

Hound, Skeletal

Climate/Terrain:	Ravenloft
Frequency:	Very rare
Organization:	Solitary or pack
Activity Cycle:	Any
Diet:	Nil
Intelligence:	Non- (0)
Treasure:	Nil
Alignment:	Neutral
No. Appearing:	2–20 (2d10)
Armor Class:	8
Movement:	6
Hit Dice:	1–1
THAC0:	20
No. of Attacks:	1
Damage/Attack:	1–4
Special Attacks:	Nil
Special Defenses:	See below
Magic Resistance:	See below
Size:	S–M (3′–5′)
Morale:	Fearless (19–20)
XP Value:	65

Skeletal hounds are the magically animated skeletons of dogs created as guardians by evil wizards or priests.

Originally created by Spelaka of Mordent, a reclusive necromancer, the creatures appear to have no ligaments, muscles, or joinings that would hold their bones together and allow movement. They lack internal organs, flesh, and eyes. They are given the semblance of life and held together by the magic of an *animate dead* spell.

They have no vocal cords, but have somehow retained their ability to bark and growl.

Combat: Skeletal hounds fight only at the behest of their creator. They move somewhat stiffly and slowly and do not fight as well as normal dogs.

Skeletal hounds attack with a bite which causes 1–4 points damage. Very small dogs used as skeletal hounds inflict only 1–2 points damage.

Skeletal hounds that were hunting or war dogs while living retain some memory of their former training. Such animals work as a pack, concentrating their attacks so that several hounds attack a single target simultaneously. War dogs try to move into strategically sound positions before attacking. Other than this instinctual strategy, skeletal hounds have no minds at all.

They are immune to all *sleep, charm*, and *hold* spells. Because the hounds are assembled from bones, cold-based attacks have no effect on them. Likewise, they are not affected by poisons or any sort of paralyzation. Skeletal hounds, like their humanoid counterparts, are also immune to *fear* spells and never need to check morale, as they are usually commanded to fight until destroyed.

Since they have no internal organs or soft tissues, edged and piercing weapons (like swords, daggers, and spears) inflict only half damage when used against skeletal hounds. Blunt weapons, such as maces, staves, and clubs, which have larger heads and are designed to break and crush bones cause normal damage.

Fire also causes normal damage to skeletal hounds, and holy water inflicts 2–8 points of damage per vial striking the creatures. When skeletal hounds are destroyed, they fall to pieces.

Habitat/Society: Skeletal hounds have no social life, nor do they engage in any activities beyond those assigned to them. They are found wherever there are wizards or priests of sufficient power to create them. They may be used as singular guards, assigned to watch a specific doorway, hall or room and commanded to bark when intruders enter the area. Piles of their bones may be scattered throughout treasure rooms or temple anterooms and commanded to flow together, animate and attack strangers. Packs of skeletal hounds may be loosed inside walled estates and told to roam and guard against trespassers.

Some priests who worship deities of death or dying create armies of skeletal hounds to serve alongside humanoid skeletons when they are needed for war or defense of the temple. Priests of good alignment, though they have less reservations about animating dogs than humanoids, may still find it repugnant to disturb any creature's eternal rest. Druids might be particularly disturbed by this violation of the natural order.

Skeletal hounds are capable of understanding and implementing simple commands. These may be as simple as the commands given to normal dogs (sit, stay, roll over, play dead) or as complex as those accorded guard dogs (watch and bark, guard and attack, etc.). Anything more complex leads to confusion and inaction or to wild attacks against anything that moves. Skeletal hounds take orders only from their creator or a person designated as their master of hounds during the casting of the *animate dead* spell.

Ecology: Unless their remains are destroyed or widely scattered, skeletal hounds may be recreated by another *animate dead* spell.

CLIMATE/TERRAIN:	Ravenloft
FREQUENCY:	Very rare
ORGANIZATION:	Unique
ACTIVITY CYCLE:	Night
DIET:	Carnivore
INTELLIGENCE:	Very (11–12)
TREASURE:	O
ALIGNMENT:	Chaotic evil
NO. APPEARING:	1
ARMOR CLASS:	0
MOVEMENT:	6, Fl 18 (B)
HIT DICE:	3 (20 hit points)
THAC0:	17
NO. OF ATTACKS:	1
DAMAGE/ATTACK:	1–2
SPECIAL ATTACKS:	Disease
SPECIAL DEFENSES:	See below
MAGIC RESISTANCE:	100%
SIZE:	T (1′ tall)
MORALE:	Fearless (19–20)
XP VALUE:	5,000

The wishing imp is an imp that has assumed the form of a small statuette. It grants wishes to its owner, though these are always twisted and perverted to evil in some way. When alone with its master, the imp may move around and even fly, but usually remains completely still, with a lifeless appearance on its face when around others.

The wishing imp looks like a small, deep black, bat-winged figurine with a slender, barbed tail. It has pointed ears, granitelike skin and a set of small horns. Strangely, its face is quite attractive, looking like that of an innocent child, with appealing deep brown eyes and a sweet smile.

The wishing imp communicates telepathically, but will seldom speak to anyone except their owner. Language does not appear to be a barrier to conversation with this sinister creature.

Combat: Luckily, the wishing imp is not usually met in combat. When called upon to fight, this deadly creature uses the barb on its tail against its foes. Though this stinger does only 1–2 points of damage, those struck by it must save vs. death magic or contract a disease that is fatal in 2d4 days unless cured through magical healing.

The wishing imp is completely resistant to all types of magic and cannot be hit by any weapons, mundane or magical, unless they are made of stone. Flint or obsidian arrowheads, throwing stones, sling stones, stone-tipped clubs, even swords pried from the hands of statues will all harm the imp, doing a maximum of 1d4 points of damage with each successful hit. When the imp takes enough damage to kill it, it falls and shatters, only to reform within 24 hours and return to its owner.

The only way to rid oneself of the wishing imp is to sell it or give it away. In either case, the new owner of the imp cannot be deceived about the powers of the creature. He must be told that the item he is receiving will grant him wishes, but that these will come only at a dire cost. Of course, many are those who feel that they can escape the dreadful power of the imp. They long to see their wishes granted and are certain that no ill-effects will befall them. Indeed, it is the avarice of man that seems to delight and somehow sustain this mysterious imp.

For some unknown reason, the wishing imp is anchored to the misty domains of Ravenloft. If its owner somehow escapes from the Demiplane of Dread, the creature will be left behind. Since it still belongs to that person, however, it will do whatever it can to draw its master back into Ravenloft.

The wishing imp can only be slain by a stone weapon that has been specially blessed by a priest for just that purpose. The person landing the blow that destroys the wishing imp will earn himself the creature's dying spell, a foul enchantment that is the equivalent of a lethal curse. The exact nature of this wizardry will be tailored to the individual upon whom it is cast.

Habitat/Society: Though it might seem a great benefit when first acquired it, the wishing imp is soon exposed as a truly horrific creature. The imp is able to grant its owner one *wish* each day, subject to the normal limitations of that spell as described in the *Player's Handbook*, but these are always perverted in some fashion. Usually, the spell causes the loss of something very dear (whether an item or a person) to the one wishing even as it grants the actual *wish*. Furthermore, it tries to fulfill the *wish* in such a way that it creates a need for its owner to request more wishes, most often in an attempt to undo something an earlier *wish* caused.

The only way to rid oneself of the wishing imp without incurring more trouble is to escape from Ravenloft, sell it to someone, or give it to someone who willingly takes possession of it.

Ecology: The wishing imp is a magical creature of unknown origin. Since it first appeared in Ravenloft some centuries ago, however, the fiend has caused nothing but heartache and misery. Passed from owner to owner, it has been in every domain or island at one time or another.

For some reason, it seems impossible for the wishing imp to leave the Demiplane of Dread. Countless theories have been put forth to explain this, but none has been substantiated to date.

Ivy, Crawling

CLIMATE/TERRAIN:	Temperate lands
FREQUENCY:	Very rare
ORGANIZATION:	Colony
ACTIVITY CYCLE:	Any
DIET:	Blood / body fluids
INTELLIGENCE:	Semi- (2–4)
TREASURE:	Nil
ALIGNMENT:	Neutral
NO. APPEARING:	3–10 (1d8+2)
ARMOR CLASS:	6
MOVEMENT:	6
HIT DICE:	7 or 8
THAC0:	13
NO. OF ATTACKS:	2
DAMAGE/ATTACK:	1–6
SPECIAL ATTACKS:	*Entangle* and blood drain
SPECIAL DEFENSES:	Spell immunities
MAGIC RESISTANCE:	Nil
SIZE:	G (4′ per Hit Die)
MORALE:	11
XP VALUE:	7 HD: 1,400 8 HD: 2,000

Crawling ivy is a semi-intelligent plant that was developed through magical experimentation. It is usually found on the walls of old houses, encircling large trees or as ground cover. This many-branched vine moves to trap and feed upon those who stray too close to it. It can move to bring a victim within range, grasping with its rootlets and crawling along a wall or the ground.

Looking much like normal ivy, crawling ivy is a dark, glossy green. The leaves are triangular and veined. In autumn, crawling ivy erupts with clumps of yellow flowers which produce bitter, black berries. The woody stem of the plant is supported in its climb by masses of small rootlets on its underside that cling to crevices and irregularities. Crawling ivy can be distinguished from normal ivy by its veining, which is not green, but a pale magenta. Close examination of the leaves reveals tiny pores or openings throughout the surface.

Crawling ivy appears to have no ability to communicate with other creatures. Proper use of magic might make it possible to speak with the plant, but what it might reveal is uncertain.

Combat: Anyone coming into contact with or standing within 3 feet of crawling ivy may be attacked by it. The plant prefers to let its victims get as close as possible before striking. If someone is actually climbing the wall where crawling ivy has established itself (or walking through a bed of it, when it is used as ground cover), the ivy gains a +4 bonus on its attack rolls. Because it looks so ordinary, those who do not know of its properties are given a –3 penalty to their surprise rolls when the plant attacks.

Crawling ivy begins its attacks by trying to *entangle* a victim (as per the 1st level priest spell). Those subjected to this attack must save vs. spell or be caught.

Once the victim is rendered immobile, the ivy makes two attacks per round with its leafy vines. The leaves fasten upon the captive while the vine itself moves to strangle the victim, doing 1–6 points of damage per successful hit.

Should the victim not be *entangled*, he may fight back or try to move out of range of the ivy. If caught, however, the captive is powerless to help himself.

Those who are held fast must be rescued by a third party or must make a successful bend bars roll to get an arm free. When the victim has lost half his hit points, or at the end of the fourth round that he fails to break free from a strangling vine, the ivy has rendered him unconscious.

At that point, the vines simply hold the captive, while the leaves take over. These open their pores and begin exerting a powerful suction on any exposed skin they can reach, pulling the victim's blood up through the lesions thus created. This inflicts 1d6 points of damage per round, and only ceases when the victim is a dried husk with no body fluids left.

Crawling ivy is vulnerable to spells that affect plants. It is immune to mind affecting or illusion spells, and takes only half-damage from fire or cold-based attacks.

Habitat/Society: Crawling ivy feeds on blood and body fluids. It has no need for sunlight or water. A very sophisticated valve and pump system within the veins of the leaves allows the suctioning of blood and pumps fluids throughout the plant. Crawling ivy must receive sustenance equal to one victim for each Hit Die it has per week or begin to brown and die.

Often used as a guardian by those who value their privacy, the ivy is intelligent enough to serve a master in return for food. Though several colonies may reside side-by-side, they do not compete for space or food.

Ecology: The berries produced by crawling ivy may be planted in blood-soaked earth to begin a new colony. The flowers are used in making *healing potions*, and in an emergency may be pressed to a wound to stop bleeding and reduce pain.

Jack Frost

Climate/Terrain:	Arctic lands & mountain tops
Frequency:	Rare
Organization:	Flurry
Activity Cycle:	Any
Diet:	Body heat
Intelligence:	Low (5–7)
Treasure:	B
Alignment:	Neutral evil
No. Appearing:	3–30 (3d10)
Armor Class:	0 or 5
Movement:	12, Fl 18 (C)
Hit Dice:	5
THAC0:	15
No. of Attacks:	1
Damage/Attack:	2d4 or 1d6
Special Attacks:	See below
Special Defenses:	See below
Magic Resistance:	Nil
Size:	S (3′–4′ tall)
Morale:	Elite (15–16)
XP Value:	3,000

A jack frost is a malicious ice spirit that lives on mountain tops or in arctic terrain. It delights in tormenting helpless creatures and subsists on the body heat that it drains from its victims. Jack frosts travel in groups called flurries. Though they are referred to by a masculine name, individual jack frosts may appear to be either male or female.

Jack Frosts have several forms and can change from one to another at will. They may appear as a flurry of beautiful and intricately patterned snowflakes, a vaporous white cloud, or as small, pale blue humanoids with silver eyes and white or silvery icicle-like hair. Even in the heaviest snow or coldest region, they wear only gauzy white clothing and go barefoot. Those who might be identified as males wear tunics and trousers, while those regarded as females prefer gowns.

They all have mischievous, beguiling smiles, and speak only their own language.

Combat: In their snowflake forms, jack frosts are so beautiful that anyone viewing them falling from the sky and tumbling about must save vs. spell or be hypnotized by their loveliness (as per the *hypnotic pattern* spell). Once they have gotten close to their victims through this ruse, these ice spirits change form into a cloud of freezing vapor ten feet in diameter. It is not uncommon for several frosts to combine and create a larger cloud. In this form they are able to sweep across their victims, causing 5d6 points of cold damage. A save vs. breath weapon is allowed for half damage.

After the initial attack, they change into humanoid form and reach out to individual targets to touch them with chilling grasps or to nip them with freezing, numbing bites. A jack frost's touch sends a searing, freezing shock through its victim's body, causing 2d4 points of cold damage and draining some of his body heat.

A bite from the creature causes 1d6 points of damage, also from loss of body heat, but renders the part bitten numb as well. Favored targets for a jack frost's bite are the lips, nose, ears, fingertips and (if they can somehow reach them) the toes. They always attack these parts in preference to any other, and suffer no penalties to their attack rolls when they do so.

A jack frost's nip causes frostbite. If the injured region is not properly tended to within the hour through gentle warming, *healing potions*, or the like, there is a 75% chance that the part will have to be amputated as gangrene will set in.

While in either snowflake or cloud form, they are AC 0 and can only be hit by +2 or better weapons. In humanoid form they are AC 5 and can be hit by any weapons. While in nonhumanoid form, they are immune to all spells except *gust of wind* or *weather summoning* and *control* spells (which cause them to flee). In humanoid form, they are susceptible to all spells except those that rely on cold to inflict damage.

Habitat/Society: Jack frosts wander the arctic landscape seeking nourishment in the form of body heat and amusement in the torment of mortals. They possess several powers that endanger travelers in the regions they inhabit.

They have no true society as such, existing to play elaborate games. Their thought processes are completely alien to mortals, being composed of strange yearnings and sly, incomprehensible ploys to "win" the latest game, whatever it may be.

Ecology: Jack frosts have no true sexes and reproduce by warming to the point of melting and reforming as two creatures. They often take treasure gained from former victims and strew it about to attract other prey to their current wandering grounds. Other than this, however, they have no use for such trinkets.

Jolly Roger

Climate/Terrain:	Sea of Sorrows
Frequency:	Rare
Organization:	Solitary
Activity Cycle:	Night
Diet:	Nil
Intelligence:	Average (8–10)
Treasure:	R
Alignment:	Chaotic evil
No. Appearing:	1
Armor Class:	4
Movement:	9, Sw 12
Hit Dice:	6+2
THAC0:	15
No. of Attacks:	1
Damage/Attack:	1–6
Special Attacks:	See below
Special Defenses:	Spell immunity, +2 or better weapon to hit
Magic Resistance:	Nil
Size:	M (6′ tall)
Morale:	Fearless (19–20)
XP Value:	2,000

A jolly roger is the undead spirit of a pirate or buccaneer who died at sea. These foul creatures were usually captains or officers while living, and retain their taste for command after death. They are often found as captains of vessels crewed by sea zombies.

Jolly rogers look quite similar to the zombies they command, resembling human corpses that are bloated, discolored, and dripping with water and bits of sea weed. They generally wear the remains of once-garish pirate garb (pants, vests, cutlasses, eye patches, scarves, etc.), and may be peg-legged or have a hook for a hand. Though they may carry weapons, they do not use them in combat. Invariably, jolly rogers have terrible, frozen grins on their faces that make them look both gruesomely affable and chillingly insane. They are ever so slightly transparent, causing some people to mistake them for ghosts. Their eyes are bright pin points of crimson within otherwise empty sockets; they smell of fish and brine.

The jolly rogers' only communication with the living is a rasping chuckle that escapes from between their grinning teeth, an unnerving phenomenon that gives rise to their name. They communicate with their crew via telepathy and do not communicate with the living at all.

Combat: Those viewing a jolly roger's grin and hearing its crazed, nerve-grating chuckle must make a saving throw vs. spell or be affected as if by a *Tasha's uncontrollable hideous laughter* spell that lasts for 1d4 rounds. The creature prefers to attack those who fall prey to its spell, leaving others to its zombie crewmen.

Advancing on its victim, a jolly roger attempts to touch him or her. A successful touch requires the victim to save vs. death magic or be slain. A +3 bonus is allowed on this roll. If the save is not made, the victim dies of laughter within 1d4 rounds unless a *dispel magic, remove curse,* or similar spell is cast on him before that time. Those making their saves receive 1d6 points of damage. Those who fail their saving throw but are magically saved from death will suffer 1d6 points of damage per round between the touch and the casting of the spell that saved them.

Those slain by a jolly roger's touch will rise as sea zombies in 24 hours unless their bodies are blessed and then committed to the deep in a traditional burial at sea. *Raise dead, resurrection*, or *wish* will also counter this if used carefully and promptly. Newly created sea zombies are under the control of the jolly roger.

Jolly rogers are immune to *sleep, charm*, and all illusion or mind-affecting spells. They take half damage from fire or fire-based spells and are unaffected by water or cold-based spells. If *raise dead* or *resurrection* is cast on them, jolly rogers must save vs. spell with a –2 penalty or be utterly destroyed. If a jolly roger is successfully turned, (as a vampire), any sea zombies under its command are turned as well, though the zombies are usually immune to such. Jolly rogers can only be hit by +2 or better weapons.

Habitat/Society: Like those they command, jolly rogers are driven by hatred for the living. Though they do not need to eat, they rend and chew the flesh of those they slay, probably to cause fear. Their smiles never waver as they chew.

Jolly rogers are only rarely discovered alone. They are usually found aboard broken and decaying ghost ships. These spectral craft are raised from the bottom of the sea and set sailing (though they are not at all seaworthy) by a strange power of the jolly roger. Anyone living who attempts to board the jolly roger's ship must save vs. death magic or be transformed into a sea zombie. If they make this roll, they may explore the ship freely. However, each turn they have a 30% chance of falling through rotting planks or otherwise injuring themselves.

Jolly rogers may lead their crewmen on raids against ships at anchor or into towns along the sea coast when the fog rolls in.

Ecology: Jolly rogers are evil, undead creatures native to the demiplane of Ravenloft. For some reason, they are tied to that region and are never encountered elsewhere. If one were to somehow escape from the misty confines of Ravenloft, it seems likely that the spirit would simply cease to be.

CLIMATE/TERRAIN:	Rokushima Táiyoo
FREQUENCY:	Very rare
ORGANIZATION:	Solitary
ACTIVITY CYCLE:	Any
DIET:	Life energy
INTELLIGENCE:	Exceptional (15–16)
TREASURE:	Z
ALIGNMENT:	Lawful evil
NO. APPEARING:	1
ARMOR CLASS:	0
MOVEMENT:	12, Fl 18 (C)
HIT DICE:	10
THAC0:	11
NO. OF ATTACKS:	1
DAMAGE/ATTACK:	1d10
SPECIAL ATTACKS:	Energy drain & spell use
SPECIAL DEFENSES:	Reanimation
MAGIC RESISTANCE:	20%
SIZE:	M (6' tall)
MORALE:	Fanatic (17–18)
XP VALUE:	9,000

A kizoku is an oriental creature that assumes the form of an irresistibly handsome man. He courts beautiful women, leading them to betray and murder their lovers or husbands. This foul deed done, the fiend claims the woman's spirit and devours her life force.

Kizoku look like extremely muscular and handsome oriental men. Their hair is thick and luxurious, their demeanor noble, and their taste in clothing and personal adornment is impeccable. They always seem rich, confident, and trustworthy. Most kizoku appear to be powerful samurai or other warriors, though a few prefer to disguise themselves as wizards or priests. The only clue that might give away the identity of the kizoku is a small, inky black mole shaped like a crescent moon that is always located somewhere visible on his body (usually the face or hands).

When a kizoku consumes a woman's essence, he gains the ability to speak any languages she knew. Because of this, most of these creatures have a plethora of tongues at their disposal.

Combat: Although kizoku carry the traditional weapons of a samurai (or an ornate dagger or staff if they appear to be some other class), they prefer not to use these weapons in combat, avoiding melee combat all together if possible. If attacked themselves, they will attempt to flee before resorting to direct violence.

Whenever they must fight, they utilize spells designed to facilitate their escape from the situation or to *hold, charm,* or *confuse* their adversaries. They can cast the following spells each once per day at will: *audible glamer, change self, charm person, friends, hold portal, hypnotism, alter self, darkness 15' radius, forget, improved phantasmal force, hold person, slow, wraithform, confusion,* and *dimension door.*

Kizoku possess natural *infravision* to 90' and have the ability to *fly* and become *invisible* at will.

For purposes of lifting and throwing, opening doors, and bending bars, kizoku possess 18/00 Strength. Unlike vampires, however, they do not receive the normal attack and damage bonuses associated with their exceptional strength.

They are slain beyond hope of reanimation only by piercing them through the heart with a wooden stake made from the wood of a weeping willow tree. Any other attack that drives the creature to 0 hit points does not truly kill the kizoku. Even if its body is destroyed, the creature will reform and rise again after 24 hours.

Habitat/Society: Kizoku are solitary monsters. They do not associate with one another or have normal families. Their homes are made at the heart of man's cities, where they can find an endless supply of victims to corrupt and feed upon.

Once he has chosen a victim, the kizoku secretly visits her whenever possible, bringing her gifts, encouraging her in whatever talents she possesses, and lavishing compliments on her. The kizoku may also bring a woman he is trying to seduce to his home to show her all his fine treasures, promising to make them hers if she will forswear her husband or betrothed and become his.

Time is meaningless to a kizoku once he has chosen a victim. Even if he is driven off by her protectors, the creature will return later to continue his corruption of the innocent maiden.

Through his manipulations of her emotions and desires, the kizoku causes a sort of euphoria in his chosen victim. Whenever she is with him, she feels almost intoxicated with love, vibrant energy, and attractiveness. Conversely, whenever he is away, she feels depressed, unsatisfied with everything in her life, and drab.

Though he does not force his mistress to take any steps to rid herself of her husband or lover, he whispers suggestions to that effect in her ear whenever she seems weakest in her resistance to his pleas for her love. Only by killing her lover or husband can she be truly his, the fiend argues.

Once she agrees to the betrayal and kills her lover, the kizoku claims his new "bride" and takes her to his lair. As their lips meet for a passionate kiss, he claims her spirit and draws her life force out of her body.

Ecology: Scholars are undecided as to whether the kizoku is akin to the vampire. Though it may be slain only by a stake through the heart, the kizoku is not itself an undead creature. It lives, breathes, and is warm to the touch. Nevertheless, it feeds off the life energy of living creatures much as a vampire drains energy or blood.

Lashweed

Climate/Terrain:	Ravenloft
Frequency:	Rare
Organization:	Patch
Activity Cycle:	Night
Diet:	Blood
Intelligence:	Semi- (2–4)
Treasure:	Nil (I)
Alignment:	Neutral
No. Appearing:	2–20 (2d10)
Armor Class:	7
Movement:	9
Hit Dice:	4
THAC0:	17
No. of Attacks:	4
Damage/Attack:	1d4 (×4)
Special Attacks:	Spit poison & entangle
Special Defenses:	Spell immunity
Magic Resistance:	20%
Size:	M (5′ tall)
Morale:	Fearless (19–20)
XP Value:	270

Lashweeds spew a terrible poison into the eyes of their prey, then move in for the kill with slashing tendrils. Even those victims fortunate enough to retain their sight will have a difficult time escaping the fell plants as lashweeds can slither through the thickest vegetation as if it weren't there, easily overtaking their prey as it tumbles through the clutching brush.

Lashweeds are large plants composed of a collection of veiny stems coiled about a central stalk. The stalk is a disgusting black color with porous skin from which seeps the digested blood of the lashweed's victims. The leaves are a dark green hue with serrated edges stained a deep crimson. The plant's "feet" are a veiny mass of wiggling fibers that allow it to catch their stunned prey.

These terrible plants emit a drumlike pounding when hunting. It is highly likely that this is part of an echo location system similar to that employed by bats or dolphins. There are those who say that this unnerving pounding is also a means of communication, but none have survived long enough in the company of these plants to say whether that is true or not.

Combat: Lashweeds can sense the vibrations that animals and men make when they walk upon the earth. Any creature of small or larger size will be noticed when it comes within 20′ of a patch. When this happens, the plant slowly begins to shamble toward the prey until it is within striking range.

Because they blend into any thick vegetation, lashweed plants impose a –2 penalty on their victim's surprise rolls in such environments. Alert characters can usually hear rustling in the foliage around them, negating this penalty.

Just before it strikes, the plant quickly emits its deep pounding sound several times to establish the exact position of its target.

Lashweeds always begin their attacks by spitting a poison at their opponents. Immediately after it has located its target, the plant releases a cloud of black spray that forms a cone 10 feet long and 6 feet wide at its base. Anyone within this cone must make a saving throw vs. poison or be blinded for 1d4 days. While blinded the character attacks and saves at –4. Each plant may spit only once in any three-hour period.

Once it has blinded its enemies, the plant moves in for the kill. Each lashweed has four special tendrils that strike like barbed whips. A successful hit by one of these limbs tears into the target's flesh, causing 1–4 points of damage. All four of the limbs may attack a single target or each may strike independently of the others. When the plant attacks, all other lashweeds in the patch are attracted to the melee and overcome by a desire for the victim's blood.

Should their prey attempt to flee, lashweeds are quick to pursue. No matter how dense the foliage they are moving through, lashweed plants are not slowed in any way. This is identical to the special ability that Druid characters receive at 3rd level. This, when combined with the weed's ability to cast an *entangle* spell thrice per day, makes it almost impossible to escape from the slashing tendrils of these dreadful plants.

Habitat/Society: Lashweeds live in patches of 2–20 individual plants. The patch spreads itself out over a wide area, usually forming a rough circle with 20 or 30 feet between each weed.

Ecology: Vistani claim that lashweed was created when a band of druids fought together against a powerful necromancer. The defeated druids were staked out in the fields to die. The men chanted in unison throughout the long day, cursing the necromancer for their fate. The Dark Powers sensed their anguish and somehow transformed them into a patch of living plants to seek revenge.

CLIMATE/TERRAIN:	Ravenloft wetlands
FREQUENCY:	Uncommon
ORGANIZATION:	Solitary
ACTIVITY CYCLE:	Any
DIET:	Magical energy
INTELLIGENCE:	Non- (0)
TREASURE:	Nil
ALIGNMENT:	Neutral
NO. APPEARING:	5–30 (5d6)
ARMOR CLASS:	10
MOVEMENT:	0, Sw 3
HIT DICE:	1 hit point
THAC0:	20
NO. OF ATTACKS:	Nil
DAMAGE/ATTACK:	Nil
SPECIAL ATTACKS:	Magic drain & energy burst
SPECIAL DEFENSES:	Magic resistance
MAGIC RESISTANCE:	99%
SIZE:	T (1″ long)
MORALE:	Steady (11–12)
XP VALUE:	15

In the wet grasses of some realms lurk strange leeches capable of draining a wizard's magical essence. They are a bane to any magic-wielding creature or those who depend on spellcasting in combat. When feeding, they disrupt incantations, drain spells from the minds of wizards or priests, and are even capable of rendering magical objects useless and mundane.

Magical leeches look no different from normal ones, save that they occasionally emit tiny sparks of purplish energy from their grotesquely bloated bodies.

As one might expect, these creatures have no language and do not communicate with other creatures in any way.

Combat: Magical leeches do not need to make physical contact with their victims to feed—simply being within 1 yard allows them to draw forth the tendrils of sorcery that feed them. This makes magical leeches difficult to detect, for there is often nothing for the victim to feel.

The very presence of a leech makes it harder for spellcasters to activate their powers. Whenever one or more of these creatures is within one yard of them, a spell user must make a successful Ability Check on Intelligence or Wisdom (as appropriate) to cast a spell. If the check is failed, the spell simply peters out and does not take effect.

Magical leeches may also drain memorized spells from the minds of wizards or priests. The chance that a spell will be drained each round is 10% plus 1% per leech within 1 yard. Magical leeches drain a caster's highest-level spells first, with the exact enchantment lost being randomly determined. The absence of the spell is noticed only when the wizard or priest attempts to cast it.

Magical leeches can also feed on the energy of a magical object, although they prefer the taste of energy drained from the humanoid mind instead. Every round that leeches are present, there is a 5% chance, plus 1% per leech, that one power, function, or plus of a magical object is destroyed. The exact effect of the leech's feeding is determined randomly.

Removing a magical leech is a painful task. When touched, magical leeches release a fraction of the energy stored in their bodies as an electrical discharge that causes 1–2 points of damage. For every spell, ability, or other essence the leech has consumed within the last 8 hours, the burst causes an additional 1 point of damage.

Habitat/Society: Magical leeches live in swamps or even tall wet grasses. They never leave their habitat under their own power. Anyone who walks through an infested area is likely to pick up 1d6 of the creatures, though there are usually 5–30 actually present at a particular site.

Ecology: After draining its host of magical energies, the leech drops off as soon as its host enters a swamp or similar wetland in which it can spawn. The magical energies ingested by the leech allow the filthy creature to give birth to 1–6 new leeches in 3d4 days.

Leech, Psionic

CLIMATE/TERRAIN:	Ravenloft wetlands
FREQUENCY:	Uncommon
ORGANIZATION:	Solitary
ACTIVITY CYCLE:	Any
DIET:	Psionic energy
INTELLIGENCE:	Non- (0)
TREASURE:	Nil
ALIGNMENT:	Neutral
NO. APPEARING:	5–30 (5d6)
ARMOR CLASS:	10
MOVEMENT:	0, Sw 3
HIT DICE:	1 hit point
THAC0:	20
NO. OF ATTACKS:	Nil
DAMAGE/ATTACK:	Nil
SPECIAL ATTACKS:	Psionic Drain
SPECIAL DEFENSES:	Nil
MAGIC RESISTANCE:	Nil
SIZE:	T (1′)
MORALE:	Steady (12)
XP VALUE:	15

These disgusting leeches lurk in ponds, swamps, or other wet areas, waiting to drain the mental energies of any psionicists unlucky enough to wander into their midst.

Physically they look little different from their magical or natural cousins, save for a distinctive bluish tinge to their rubbery black hide and the faint aura of crimson light that can be seen to surround them in darkness.

Psionic leeches do not have ability to communicate with other creatures.

Combat: Psionic leeches drain mental energy in much the same way that magical leeches drain the mystical powers of wizards and priests. Because psionic energy is much less common than magical energy in the realm of Ravenloft, psionic leeches have become very efficient parasites. Every leech can drain 1 Psionic Strength Point per turn from any creature within 1 yard.

Detecting a psionic leech is difficult as their slow absorption of energy isn't likely to alert most victims. The percentage chance that a character will notice the drain is equal to the number of psionic points stolen by the parasites. The victim should be allowed to attempt this check once per turn.

Once alerted, the host will still have to find the creatures if the drain is to be halted. This can be difficult as the foul creatures crawl into the wrinkles of clothing, downturned cuffs, boots, or even the joints of armor. Finding each leech requires an Intelligence check and takes 1 round.

Removing the creatures from their chosen hiding place is even more difficult than finding them. When touched, psionic leeches release their energy in the form of a psychic blast that causes 1 point of damage for every PSP stolen by the leech in the last 8 hours. Mental defenses such as *tower of iron will* or *mindblank* can reduce the draining effects of the leech or the damage caused by its psychic blast by half.

Psionic leeches are able to sense the mind of a psionicist even when he has expended all of his PSPs. This does not deter the creatures from attempting to feed upon that mind. When this happens, the target must make a madness check each round. Only one check is required, no matter how many leeches are attempting to feed upon his depleted mind.

Habitat/Society: Psionic leeches have no communal structure, but are generally found in groups of 5–30 (5d6) members. They prefer wetlands like swamps and marshes, but can also be found in open ponds, wet grasses, or slow-moving streams. Anyone passing through one of their nests will pick up 1d6 of the parasites.

Psionic leeches have tiny hooks along the edges of their flat bodies that catch on clothing or fur. This allows them to cling to their host tenaciously, dropping off only when the psionic powers of the victim have been exhausted or a better source of food comes along.

Ecology: Psionic leeches bloat with stolen energy until they become too large and fall from their host. At this point they slowly crawl to the nearest wetland and give birth to 1–6 more leeches in 3d4 days.

Climate/Terrain:	Athas or Ravenloft
Frequency:	Very Rare
Organization:	Solitary
Activity Cycle:	Any
Diet:	Nil
Intelligence:	Supra-Genius (19–20)
Treasure:	R,X (E)
Alignment:	Chaotic evil
No. Appearing:	1
Armor Class:	0
Movement:	6
Hit Dice:	11+
THAC0:	9
No. of Attacks:	1
Damage/Attack:	By weapon or 1d10
Special Attacks:	See below
Special Defenses:	+1 or better weapons to hit
Magic Resistance:	Nil
Size:	M (6′)
Morale:	Fanatic (17)
XP Value:	8,000

Psionics Summary:

Level	Dis/Sci/Dev	Attack/Defense	Score	PSPs
10	4/5/15	all/all	15	120

Telepathy - Sciences: domination, ejection, mindlink. **Devotions:** aversion, awe, contact, conceal thoughts, ESP, life detection, send thoughts.
Psychokinesis - Sciences: telekinesis. **Devotions:** control body, control wind, levitation, soften.
Psychoportive - Sciences: teleport. **Devotions:** dimension door, dimension walk, time / space anchor.

Though there is nothing more loathsome than the foul undead, the defiler lich raises even this putrid circle of fiends to new levels of destruction and malevolence. Some that tread across the blasted domains of these creatures have heard them called by another name: *kaisharga.*

Defiler liches look like gaunt and skeletal wights or mummies. Tiny green points of light float in the blackness of their empty eye sockets and their bony fingers can quickly flay the flesh from the bones of an unarmored man.

All liches are arrogant creatures, so most dress in the clothes of local nobility or elaborate garb reminiscent of the profession they held before their transition to unlife. Even the fanciest of garments does little to hide their true appearance, however. Defiler liches emanate an aura of atrophy that slowly rots their clothes and anything around them. Cloaks begin to tatter, sleeves fray, and fruit at the same table as the defiler will quickly turn brown and spoiled.

Combat: Like other liches, defilers rarely engage in melee combat with their foes. If forced, however, the lich is more than able to stand up to all but the strongest opponents. The effective Strength, Dexterity, and Constitution scores of a *kaisharga* rise to 20 at the moment it assumes its undead state. In addition, any psionic powers that the defiler might have had in life are greatly magnified.

Simply approaching a defiler lich is enough to test the mettle of most opponents. Any creature of less than 5 Hit Dice (or 5th level) who sees the defiler must make a saving throw vs. spell or flee in terror for 5–20 (5d4) rounds.

The touch of a defiler lich is slightly different from that of its cousins. Those touched by the thing feel their magical essence drawn from the very marrow of their bones. Nonspellcasters suffer 1–10 points of damage from this attack. spellcasters (wizards and priests) are much more sensitive and lose 2–20 hit points per touch.

Liches can only be hit by weapons of at least +1 enchantment, magical spells, or by monsters with at least 4+1 Hit Dice or magical powers of their own. The magical nature of the lich and its undead state make it utterly immune to *charm, sleep, enfeeblement, polymorph, cold, electricity, insanity,* or *death* spells. Priests of at least 8th level can attempt to turn a lich, as can paladins of no less than 10th level.

Of course, the most powerful ability of the defiler lich is its vast repertoire of spells. Defilers have the same spell casting ability as a living wizard of equivalent Hit Dice. They often have spells never before seen by other eyes, however, as well as a plethora of magical weapons, devices, and potions. Liches have usually had centuries to create the magical artifacts that surround them, so their effects and abilities are often well suited to the creature's environment, lair, and temperament.

What truly sets the defiler lich apart from its cousins is the strange effect its spellcasting, and indeed its very presence, has on the environment around it. Defilers draw their energy from the living things of the world. It is a quicker and dirtier process that makes casting easier, but at the expense of the land and beings in the area. This process literally turns plant life to ash. Its effect on the living is less traumatic, though extremely painful.

The radius of this effect depends upon two things: the abundance of vegetation in the area, and the level of the spell cast.

Defiler Magical Destruction Table

Terrain Type	Spell Level								
	1	2	3	4	5	6	7	8	9
Stony Barrens	10	14	17	20	22	24	26	28	30
Mountains, rocky	10	14	17	20	22	24	26	28	30
Seashore, beach	10	14	17	20	22	24	26	28	30
Seashore, grassy	3	4	4	5	5	5	5	6	6
Forest	1	1	2	2	2	2	2	3	3
City	10	14	17	20	22	24	26	28	30
Village	3	4	4	5	5	5	5	6	6

The number shown is the radius, in yards, around the defiler where all vegetation is turned to ash. The effect is instantaneous with the casting of the spell.

If a defiler casts more than one spell from the same location, the radius of destroyed vegetation expands around it. Consult the Defiler Magical Destruction Table for the highest level spell cast from that location, then add one yard for every other spell cast. Spells equal to the highest level spell are treated as additional spells.

Though usually only plants are destroyed within this radius, living creatures suffer great pain. Any being in the radius of a defiler lich's magic suffers an immediate initiative modifier penalty equal to the level of the defiler spell cast. No matter how high the resulting initiative roll, though, the pain can never keep a character from performing an action during a round. The initiative penalty only postpones when the action occurs.

Animate plants in the area of effect, such as undead treants or lashweeds, suffer greatly from defiler spells. Only their high level of innate magical energy keeps them from being destroyed outright. Any plant rated with Hit Dice takes 1d4 points of damage for every level of the spell that affects it. Thus, a patch of lashweed in the destruction radius of a fifth level spell would take 5d4 points of damage each.

Any plant-based spell components within the area of effect are ruined.

Habitat/Society: In life, defiler liches were spellcasters of great power who learned to garner their magical energies from the very land around them. Trees, grasses, and the very essence of all living things provide fuel for their infernal spells.

No one seems to know where the first defiler lich came from. With the many gates and portals existing in the demiplane, it is most likely that the foul things came from some other place far removed from Ravenloft. Rumors abound that the world of their origin was blasted into desert by their ilk, but thus far no proof has been offered of this theory.

What is evident is that the rich forests of the Ravenloft realms provide a virtually unlimited power source for their small numbers. Of course, this very same advantage can often be the first clue that such a creature has entered an area. If once lush forests suddenly turn to lifeless gray ash, few will doubt that there is a defiler in the land.

Due to the very nature of a defiler's magic, its lair is normally devoid of vegetation. Underground lairs may lie beneath blasted heaths, ruined keeps have none of the typical ivy growing up the side, and any haven is likely to lie in the midst of a gray and dusty plain. Defilers will often use illusions to cover their abodes, but an astute adventurer will notice the dusty film that covers his gear and collects in his throat and eyes.

The ash created by defiler magic is black and gray, completely devoid of life or life-giving elements. Nothing will grow in an area of ash for one year. The ash itself is very light and usually blows away, leaving behind a lifeless, circular scar on the ground. Even with the ash gone, though, the defiler's magic has leeched all life-giving nutrients from the soil, so that a defiled area may take many years to recover, if it ever does.

There are rumors that many of the defiler liches chased from places like Barovia or Falkonovia have migrated to the more familiar environment of Bluetspur. Some even say that several of these fiends have stricken unholy alliances with the illithids that live there. If this is true, it is likely that the defilers will use their allies to push their way back into lands with more flora to power their ruinous magical arts.

Ecology: Defilers have the same basic goals that other liches have; the eventual ascension to demilich status and even transcendence to other planes and forms of existence. In the meantime however, these undead fiends have thousands of years in which to wait impatiently for some condition or circumstance. During this period their evil plots often grow far beyond the comprehension of mere mortals.

Defiler liches gain their status in the same way that other liches do. This includes the construction of a phylactery and its enchantment. Adventurers seeking to battle such a creature would do well to locate the fiend's phylactery and focus their efforts on it.

Demi-Defilers

Defiler demiliches gain the same benefits and invulnerabilities as others of that ilk. The major difference between the two is the nature of the demilich's *curse* ability. All demiliches can pronounce a single *curse* on anyone who disturbs them. This can be incredibly powerful, such as always being hit by one's enemies, never making a saving throw, or never being able to wield magical items.

In addition to this however, the curse of the defiler dooms one to an aura of entropy that kills all plant life in a radius equal to the character's level, in feet. The effect isn't as sudden or dramatic as that of the defiler's own spellcasting, but it can be devastating nonetheless. Within one minute, all flowers, leaves, or other light vegetation turns brown and begins to wilt. Within one turn, light vegetation is withered and dead. Trees and other larger plants develop dark blotches of disease-ridden bark or stems. In one half hour, light vegetation crumbles to dust. Trees and the like rot and may collapse, turning to ash one hour later. Animated plant-based lifeforms take 1d4 points of damage per round spent within the cursed character's aura of entropy. Spell components and similar organic things must make a saving throw vs. disintegration or crumble into dust.

Optional Rule: Druids and rangers are very sensitive to the land and cannot tolerate the presence of such a blasphemous creature in their midst. Should either of these character types enter the blasted realm of a defiler lich or demilich, they should stop at nothing to find the source of the contagion and eliminate it. Those that turn their back on the situation will forever feel haunted, and their deities may disfavor them. The Dungeon Master should deny the druid or the ranger the use of some ability formerly granted to them by their patron. A druid might lose a granted power or a ranger may lose his ability to becalm wild beasts.

If the druid or the ranger takes part in defeating the *kaisharga*, the DM should award them an extra 10% of the creature's experience point value including minions and henchmen.

	Drow	Drider
CLIMATE/TERRAIN:	Subterranean	Subterranean
FREQUENCY:	Very rare	Very rare
ORGANIZATION:	Solitary	Solitary
ACTIVITY CYCLE:	Night	Night
DIET:	Nil	Nil
INTELLIGENCE:	Supra-genius (19–20)	Genius (17–18)
TREASURE:	U (G)	Z (G)
ALIGNMENT:	Chaotic evil	Chaotic evil
NO. APPEARING:	1	1
ARMOR CLASS:	0	–1
MOVEMENT:	12	12
HIT DICE:	11	11
THAC0:	9	9
NO. OF ATTACKS:	1	1
DAMAGE/ATTACK:	1d10	1d4
SPECIAL ATTACKS:	See below	See below
SPECIAL DEFENSES:	See below	See below
MAGIC RESISTANCE:	Varies	Varies
SIZE:	M (6′ tall)	L (9′ tall)
MORALE:	Elite (13–14)	Elite (13–14)
XP VALUE:	9,000	9,000

Drow liches are perhaps the most terrible of these undead horrors. They are found in three varieties (wizard, priest, and drider), each with its own unique and ghastly powers.

Wizards and priests look much like other liches. They have a tall, skeletal form with dark skin stretched tight over their long bones. Their skin is, of course, a pale black, here and there spotted gray with decay and age. Mages tend to wear dark red robes with loose folds and numerous pockets in which to secret their spell components. Priestly liches often wear garb emblazoned with the image of their patron, the spider goddess Lolth.

Driders are much stranger creatures, and much more rare as well. In drow society, individuals who fail to please Lolth are either slain or transformed into driders by priestesses of the spider goddess. Driders have the upper torso of a drow (almost always male) and the lower half of a giant spider. The vast majority of driders are driven into battle by their kin and live short, violent lives. A very few have escaped to continue their studies, and perhaps even to seek revenge on those who twisted their bodies into their present state. Of these, a few have eventually pursued their black arts into the realm of lichdom. Drider liches are now macabre combinations of mummified torsos attached to the deteriorating carapaces of skeletal legs and abdomen.

All manner of drow liches speak the numerous languages they knew in life. In addition, they have a natural ability to converse freely with any manner of arachnid.

Combat: All drow and drider liches have the standard abilities of other liches, including an aura of magical power that surrounds the beast. Any creature of fewer than 5 Hit Dice (or 5th level) which sees it must save vs. spell or flee in terror for 5–20 (5d4) rounds.

Their touch is icy cold and delivers 1d10 points of damage to anyone who feels their evil caress. The victim must also make a saving throw vs. paralysis or become unable to move or act until a *dispel magic* or similar spell is cast upon them.

Liches can only be hit by weapons of at least +1 enchantment, by magical spells, or by monsters with 4+1 or more Hit Dice. The magical nature of the lich and its undead state make it utterly immune to *charm, sleep, enfeeblement, polymorph, cold, electricity, insanity,* or *death* spells. Priests of at least 8th level can attempt to turn a drow lich, as can paladins of no less than 10th level.

Drow liches are able to use spells as they did in life, but each type has special abilities or powers that can affect this. All retain the natural drow ability to cast *dancing lights, detect magic, faerie fire, darkness, levitate,* and *know alignment* once per day.

One of the natural abilities they retain in unlife is their phenomenal resistance to magic. Drow liches have 50% magic resistance plus 2% per Hit Die.

Drow Wizard Liches

Drow wizards who transform themselves into liches are smoldering powder kegs of sorcerous energy threatening to destroy anything in the area. Though their thoughts may be cold and calculating, their fiery tempers often win out over logic.

These dark creatures hoard and covet magical items. Besides those found in the thing's treasure cache, every such lich will have a magical weapon such as a *staff of power, wand of fireballs,* or some other suitably powerful device. In addition, the creature will have some form of magical defense such as *bracers of defense.*

Mage liches have often imbued their raiment with other properties as well, such as the ability to render the wearer *invisible* three times per day. By combining such magical clothing with rings and other magical objects, the drow lich can unleash a terrible barrage of sorcery upon those who disturb them.

Mage liches frequently maintain nests of hairy spiders about their lair. These creatures swarm over anything that walks through their territory, often including the lich (though they can do this walking corpse no harm).

Drow Priestess Liches

Devout followers of the drow spider-goddess, Lolth, are sometimes rewarded with immortality through the transformation into lichdom. Although highly sought after by the followers of that sinister deity, it is a mixed blessing at best. Drow liches of this type are always female.

Though they are not magic hoarders like wizard liches, they still maintain a deadly arsenal of staves, weapons, and protective devices.

The real power of the priestess lich lies in her command of the undead and the magical abilities granted to her by Lolth. Lolth grants her priestess liches the ability to control and *transform* spiders. With this power the lich can transform up to twenty normal spiders into a like number of large spiders, transform ten normal spiders into a single huge spider, or transform twenty normal spiders into one gargantuan spider. This power may be used three times per day. The duration of the transformation is a number of hours equal to the priestess' Hit Dice, usually 11+.

Priestly liches can control undead in the manner described under "Evil priests and the Undead," in the *Dungeon Master Guide.*

Drider Liches

Driders are the forlorn of Lolth. Years ago these pathetic wretches failed the cruel tests of their spider goddess and were sentenced to a lifetime of suffering in the miserable half-form of spider and drow. A few of these creature's fates were tragic enough to attract the attentions of the Demiplane of Dread, and there the pitiful driders found a home. A very few of these continued in their magical research and eventually mastered the magics that made them liches.

Perhaps the strangest aspect of the driders, both in their normal state and as a lich, is that priests who become driders maintain their spell casting ability. Why the spider-goddess continues to bestow failed worshipers with her power is anyone's guess. Perhaps the goddess enjoys the strife and grief that her forsaken create among their own race. Whatever the case, the powers of Ravenloft seize upon this miserable condition with rapacious enthusiasm. For the minuscule number of driders that are capable of continuing their magical research to the point of lichdom, there seem to be a relatively large number of them within the Demiplane of Dread. Perhaps the powers that be find their tragic existence appealing in some sinister way.

Drider liches can be either mages or priests, but gain none of the advantages described above for either. Instead, the mists of Ravenloft have granted these bizarre creatures other abilities instead.

Most liches can control any undead with half or less of their own Hit Dice. Drider liches have similar control, but cannot command humanoid undead through innate abilities (they may control them through spells or magical items, however). The undead minions of the drider lich are made up of insectoid skeletons, generally the animated carapaces of giant spiders and other creatures that lived near the drider's lair.

Another of the drider lich's powers is the innate ability to cast a strong and sticky web from its thorax three times per day. This functions exactly as the second level wizard's *web* spell.

Drider liches are also able to communicate with and control all spiders within a number of yards equal to its Hit Dice. Most maintain nests of hairy spiders throughout their lairs to deal with intruders.

Habitat/Society: There are very few drow in the realms of Ravenloft. It is the unfortunate luck of the people that live in the demiplane that, of the few that are present, a relatively high number of them have discovered the secrets of lichdom. It is highly possible that the dark nature of the race encourages the quest and hastens the process, but the powers of Ravenloft seem also to welcome them with open arms.

Drow liches, both wizard and priests, tend to live near large villages or cities where they can easily find victims for their terrible experiments. They often interact with the surrounding populace much more than once-human liches, perhaps because their devious and arrogant nature enjoys fooling those around them.

Driders are much more solitary, mostly because their appearance is harder to disguise, but also because they often resent society and blame others for their miserable condition. Their lairs are always underground and filled with thousands of hairy spiders waiting hungrily for intruders.

Ecology: Both drow and drider liches are created in the same manner as their human cousins, including the creation and enchantment of a phylactery. Like all liches, these foul creatures are offensive to all natural things and will cause all animals within 100 yards to become jittery and nervous.

Drow Demiliches

Wizard and priest drow may become demiliches in the usual manner. They gain the new abilities of demiliches and retain the additional powers of their type. Drider liches have never been known to make the ascension to demilich. Whether this is because no one has yet discovered such a creature and lived to tell about it or because Lolth enjoys allowing the things to quest for the unattainable is unknown.

CLIMATE/TERRAIN:	Ravenloft
FREQUENCY:	Very rare
ORGANIZATION:	Solitary
ACTIVITY CYCLE:	Night
DIET:	Nil
INTELLIGENCE:	Supra-Genius (19–20)
TREASURE:	W (C)
ALIGNMENT:	Chaotic evil
NO. APPEARING:	1
ARMOR CLASS:	0
MOVEMENT:	6
HIT DICE:	11
THAC0:	9
NO. OF ATTACKS:	1
DAMAGE/ATTACK:	By weapon or 1d10
SPECIAL ATTACKS:	See below
SPECIAL DEFENSES:	+1 or better weapon to hit
MAGIC RESISTANCE:	Nil
SIZE:	M (6′ tall)
MORALE:	Fanatic (17–18)
XP VALUE:	25,000

Elemental liches are diabolical wizards who studied and mastered the use of Ravenloft's strange elements before or during their undeath. Now the fiends continue their practices near the boneyards of the realms, conjuring massive monsters of bone, blood, fire, and mist to sow terror in the hearts of the innocent.

Elemental liches take on the likeness of their profession. Their skin is gray and ashen like that of the dead, their white hair blows in gentle wisps like the mists, their robes whip and snap in the wind like fire, and their rotting skin constantly seeps heavy drops of thick, crimson blood.

As one might expect, these creatures retain any linguistic abilities they might have had in life. In addition, however, they are also able to converse freely with any creature from the elemental planes.

Combat: Few liches like to engage in hand-to-hand combat with their foes, but elemental liches are a rare exception. Their usual tactic is to surround themselves with elementals of all types and undead minions, then wade into the fray to deliver their deadly *touch of the grave, pyre, blood,* or *mist.* A lich may use each of these attack forms once per day, per target. After this it attacks as a normal lich, doing 1d10 points of damage but without the ability to paralyze its victims.

The *touch of the grave* is the lich's most deadly attack. On a successful hit, the victim must make a saving throw vs. death magic. If successful, he takes 1d10 points of damage but may continue to fight normally. If the save is failed, the victim is wracked with pain as the very bones in his body crack and attempt to rend their way out of their screaming shell. Unless a *heal* spell is administered within one round, the adventurer dies. If a *heal* spell is cast in time, the victim must make a System Shock roll or die anyway from the trauma of having his body sundered and repaired so quickly.

The *touch of the pyre* is another deadly attack form of the elemental lich. On a successful hit, the victim suffers a smoldering wound that does 1d10 points of damage. In addition, his clothing or armor must make a saving throw vs. magical fire or burst into flame. This magical flame burns the wearer for 1d10 points of damage each round and can be extinguished only by a *dispel magic, control flame,* or other magical methods, but not by immersion in water or other normal means. Luckily, this fire does not spread and will vanish once it has reduced the burning object to ash (in 1d4 rounds).

The *touch of blood* is a foul and evil power that the lich uses to drain the very life essence from a character. If the creature successfully hits its target, the victim takes 1d10 points of damage and must make a saving throw vs. paralyzation. If the roll fails, blood begins to ooze from the victim's every pore. The bleeding causes 1d4 points of damage per round until *dispelled* or magically healed. If a character loses 12 or more hit points to bleeding damage (not counting the normal 1d10 points caused by the lich's touch), he loses one level of experience. This reduces Hit Dice, class bonuses, spell abilities and so forth exactly as does the touch of a wight.

Elemental liches use the previous three attack forms when directly confronting their opponents. The *touch of mist* is often used in more subtle and diabolical situations. This touch causes no damage, but those who are hit and fail a saving throw vs. spell are infused with evil. This changes the victim's alignment to chaotic evil and puts him in the direct service of the lich. The lich can communicate with his pawn telepathically over a number of miles equal to his Hit Dice. In order to regain their original alignment and break the lich's control, infused characters must receive a *remove curse* spell cast by an individual of their true alignment.

Besides its various magical touches, a lich may conjure a single Ravenloft elemental of each of the four types per day. These are always of the grave, pyre, blood, or mist varieties with 8 Hit Dice.

Elemental lich's cannot control undead as most others of the kind do.

Like other liches, the elemental variety has an aura of power about it that causes creatures of 5 Hit Dice or less to make a saving throw vs. spell or flee in terror for 5–20 (5d4) rounds.

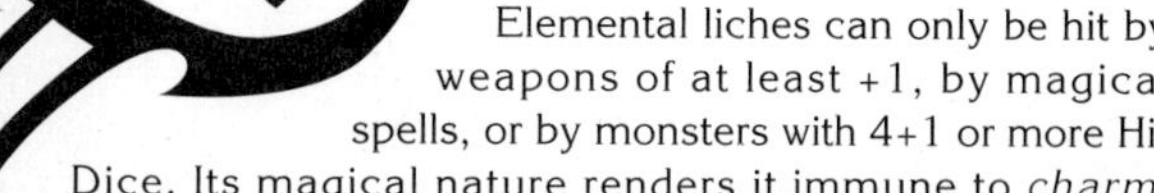

Elemental liches can only be hit by weapons of at least +1, by magical spells, or by monsters with 4+1 or more Hit Dice. Its magical nature renders it immune to *charm, sleep, enfeeblement, polymorph, cold, electricity, insanity,* or *death* spells. Elemental liches are not immune to the attacks of Ravenloft elementals, but those creatures will not attack an elemental lich unless controlled by a character of higher level than the lich, or unless they were conjured by a rival elemental lich.

Like any other lich, elementals have spellcasting ability appropriate to their Hit Dice. They almost always carry as many *conjure elemental* spells as possible. The things love to surround themselves with their creations in combat to lessen the risk to themselves and give them the freedom to use their multiple *touch* attacks.

Priests of at least 8th level can attempt to turn an elemental lich, as can paladins of no less than 10th level.

Elemental liches who have their physical form destroyed will retreat into a phylactery in the same manner as other liches. This is similar to a *magic jar* spell. To truly annihilate the lich, its phylactery must be destroyed as well as the creature's physical form.

Habitat/Society: Elemental liches seem to seek the same dark power that others of their undead kind do. The main difference seems to be the path they use to get there. Where most liches control hordes of undead minions, elementalists control the very spirits of the elements themselves.

The *touch of mist* power of the lich makes it easy for the creature to control large segments of a local population. Usually this is a town, hamlet, or some other place where the folk aren't likely to recognize the work of a lich and seek help in having it destroyed. The lich uses its magically controlled minions to sow discontent and death, but not in so overt a manner as to attract any do-gooders that happen to wander by.

Ecology: Elemental liches commune daily with the demiplane's elemental powers. Whether they are servants, peers, or masters isn't known, but there are certain conditions that the creatures must fulfill to maintain their powers. An elemental lich's phylactery must first be buried in a nearby grave. Then a great fire of burning bones is ignited on that spot. Blood is then poured over the ashes and allowed to soak into the ground. If the elemental powers decide to grant the lich its powers, the mists of the demiplane will roll in and obscure the site from prying eyes.

This means that finding an elemental lich's phylactery is both easier and harder for those who would slay the vile thing. Knowledgeable adventurers will know that their prey's phylactery will be in the ground near a misty area, such as an old graveyard, burial mound, or even an isolated clearing in a deep dark forest. The mists maintained by the elemental powers are infused with the power to cause *confusion* in anyone who cannot make a saving throw vs. spell. Every turn spent in the mists requires a successful save. Those who fail are confused for 1d10 turns as per the 4th level wizard spell.

If the earth is penetrated directly above the phylactery, the elemental powers will telepathically warn the lich of the danger. The creature usually arrives 1d10 rounds later prepared to slay any living thing in the immediate vicinity.

Demi-Elemental Liches

Elemental liches can become demiliches, but benefit from a few minor changes due to their close ties with the elemental planes of Ravenloft.

The teeth of the elementalist demilich are made of 1d4+4 gems that cast a *trap the soul* spell. If the saving throw to resist that spell is failed, the target's life force is trapped within the gem. Unlike other liches, however, the body of the victim immediately transforms into a 16 Hit Die elemental of a random type (1-grave, 2-pyre, 3-blood, 4-mist) under the demilich's control. The body of the victim is completely consumed by the process, so only a *wish* spell can bring them back to life. The elemental remains under the demilich's control for a number of months equal to the summoner's Hit Dice. For obvious reasons, the lairs of the elemental demiliches are filled with the burnt and broken bones of those who sought to slay them.

CLIMATE/TERRAIN:	Ravenloft or Athas
FREQUENCY:	Very rare
ORGANIZATION:	Solitary
ACTIVITY CYCLE:	Night
DIET:	Psionic energy
INTELLIGENCE:	Supra-genius (19–20)
TREASURE:	A
ALIGNMENT:	Any evil
NO. APPEARING:	1
ARMOR CLASS:	0
MOVEMENT:	6
HIT DICE:	9+18
THAC0:	11
NO. OF ATTACKS:	1
DAMAGE/ATTACK:	1d8+2
SPECIAL ATTACKS:	Psionics, mind strike, & psionic draining
SPECIAL DEFENSES:	Psionics, spell immunity, & +1 or better weapon to hit
MAGIC RESISTANCE:	Nil
SIZE:	M (6′ tall)
MORALE:	Fanatic (17–18)
XP VALUE:	16,000

PSIONICS SUMMARY:

Level	Dis/Sci/Dev	Att/Def	Score	PSPs
20	6/10/25	all/all	18	82

Clairsentience—Sciences: aura sight, object reading; **Devotions:** spirit sense.
Psychokinesis-Devotions: animate shadow.
Psychometabolism—Sciences: death field, life draining, shadow-form; **Devotions:** aging, cause decay, displacement, ectoplasmic form.
Psychoportation—Sciences: teleport; **Devotions:** astral projection, dimensional door, dream travel.
Telepathy—Sciences: domination, mindwipe, psychic crush, tower of iron will; **Devotions:** contact, ego whip ESP, id insinuation, inflict pain, intellect fortress, mental barrier, mind bar, mind blank, mind thrust, psionic blast, thought shield.
Metapsionics—Sciences: empower; **Devotions:** psionic sense, psychic drain, receptacle, wrench.

Note: These are the powers common to psionic liches, but it is not unusual for some to have different abilities.

There are few who dare to argue that the power of a master psionicist is any less than that of an archmage. Proof of this can be found in the fact that the most powerful psionicists are actually able to extend their lives beyond the spans granted them by nature, just as powerful wizards are known to do.

Psionic liches look much like their magical counterparts. Their flesh has mummified, pulling it tight over their bones and giving them a gaunt, skeletal appearance. Their eye sockets are empty and burn with crimson pinpoints of light. Often, a psionic lich will be found in the clothes it favored in life. Because this can be anything from the grand robes of nobility to the plate armor of a mighty knight, it is impossible to spot these creatures by their garb. (Metallic armor, if worn, will lower the lich's psionic power score, as per *The Complete Psionics Handbook;* small shields will not do so.)

Psionic liches retain the abilities that they learned in life: languages, proficiencies, thieving skills, etc. Further, a psionic lich who was human may actually have been a dual-class character in life, and thus be able to employ psionic powers plus magical or clerical spells. Creatures with such abilities are rare, thankfully, but are truly terrible opponents.

Combat: Psionic liches seldom engage their foes personally, as they surround themselves with legions of minions. Hence, many adventurers never learn the true nature of their enemy. When forced to take part in direct combat, however, psionic liches are among the most deadly opponents that any band of heroes is ever likely to face.

The emanations of power that shroud a psionic lich are detectable even by those without psychic abilities. Those who come within 50 yards of such creatures will be affected by this aura, requiring them to save vs. spell or become mind struck. Such characters make all attack and damage rolls at a –2 penalty and must double the casting time of any spells (which allows saving throws for victims at a +2 bonus). The effects of this aura can be countered by any spell or psionic power that would diminish or remove fear or inspire bravery.

If the lich is able to deliver a touch attack in combat, the malignant aura of psionic power that encircles it rips at the opponent's life force, causing 1d8+2 points of damage. In addition, psionic characters will find their PSPs drawn away. Each physical blow will strip the victim of a number of PSPs equal to twice the number of points of damage the blow inflicted. This loss is not permanent, and the PSPs can be regained through normal means.

Just as normal liches have spent decades or even centuries in the research of new and unique magical powers, so too do the undead masters of the mind have powers undreamed of by mortal men. It is not at all uncommon for adventurers who come across these dreaded creatures to be confronted with psionic powers that have never been documented elsewhere. These new powers will conform to the general standards established in *The Complete Psionics Handbook* for function, damage, area of effect, range, etc., but may differ greatly from standard powers in terms of their effects. Insight into the creation of new psionic powers can be gleaned from the section on spell research in the *DMG*. Further Information can be gained from the *Forbidden Lore* boxed set or the RAVENLOFT campaign setting.

Further, liches are able to employ magical items just as they did in life and may have quite a formidable collection of enchanted trinkets to use against adventurers.

It is important to note that psionic liches differ from the traditional ranks of the undead. Because the force sustaining them is mental and not mystical, they are far more resistant to spells, spell-like powers, or psionic sciences and devotions involving charm, fear, or the like. Dungeon Masters should treat them as having the equivalent of a 25 Wisdom for purpose of determining what spells they are resistant to (see the *Player's Handbook*, Table 5). Spells like *sleep* or *finger of death*, which base their effects upon a biological function in the target, also do not affect psionic liches; again, psionic powers similar to these spells are also ineffective (e.g., *life detection*).

Psionic liches can be turned by priests, paladins, and similar characters, but since they are not magical in nature, they are more resistant to this power than are other undead. Thus, they are turned as "special" creatures.

Psionic liches are immune to harm from normal weapons but can be struck by weapons of +1 or better enchantment. Lesser weapons can not pierce the aura of power that hangs about the lich.

Spells or other powers based upon cold have no effect upon them. Other spells inflict normal damage on the lich. Psionic liches can be attacked in normal psionic combat, except as noted before.

In order to protect itself from destruction, a psionic lich employs a special form of phylactery (see "Ecology") that houses its life force. Although a lich may be defeated in combat, it cannot be truly destroyed unless its phylactery can be found and obliterated. As most liches will take great care to protect these vital objects from the prying hands of heroes, this can be quite a challenge.

Habitat/Society: Psionic liches are powerful espers who have left behind the physical demands of life in pursuit of ultimate mental powers. They have little interest in the affairs of the living, except as they relate to the lich's search for psychic mastery and knowledge. Those who encounter the lich usually do so when the creature feels that it must leave its self-imposed isolation for a time.

Psionic liches often hide themselves away in some place that feels safe to them. Since most of them can sense the auras and emanations of the world around them quite keenly, their judgment is usually sound. For the most part, however, these creatures will reside in places associated with death or learning. If the two can be combined in some way, all the better. For example, an ideal lair for a psionic lich might be the great library of a castle that was buried in a volcanic eruption long ago. Not only does the location bear the taste of death about it, for everyone in the castle was slain by the disaster, but it also has a solid foundation of knowledge for the lich to pursue research into the secrets of the mind.

When it comes out into the world, a psionic lich generally assembles a great network of minions. Curiously, these followers are seldom undead themselves. More often than not, they are young espers who seek to learn from an obvious master. What they often do not understand is that their leader has little interest in them apart from their role in his immediate plans. Once the master's goal has been accomplished, be it the retrieval of some ancient tome on psionic powers or the testing of a new psionic defense mode, the followers will be cast aside without thought. Those who do not simply leave when the lich demands it will probably find themselves mercilessly slain.

The first psionic lich encountered in Ravenloft was reported on the fringes of Bluetspur, the dread domain of the mind flayers, in the land of Kartakass. There is some evidence that the creature was challenged and destroyed by Harkon Lukas, the master of that domain. Many scholars agree, however, that it seems probable that the lich escaped and survives to this day. Additional sightings of these horrible creatures leads one to believe that at least three more psionic liches have come into existence at various points in Ravenloft.

Ecology: Being undead, psionic liches have no place in the natural world as we know it. Although the power that transformed them is natural (not supernatural, as it is with other liches), the extent to which psionic liches have pursued their goals is not natural. By twisting the powers of their minds to extend their existence beyond the bounds of mortal life, psionic liches become exiles. Cast out from the land of the living, these creatures sometimes lament the foolishness that led them down the dark path of the undead.

By far the most important aspect of the existence of the psionic lich is the creation of its phylactery. To understand this mystical device, it is important to understand the process by which a psionicist becomes a lich. Before a psionicist can cross over into the darkness that is undeath, he must attain at least 18th level. In addition, he must be possessed of a great array of powers that can be bent and focused in ways new to the character.

The first step in the creation of a phylactery is the crafting of the physical object that will become the creature's spiritual resting place. Phylacteries come in all shapes, from rings to crowns, and from swords to idols. They are made from only the finest materials and must be fashioned by master craftsmen. Generally, a phylactery is fashioned in a shape that reflects the personality of the psionicist. The cost of creating a phylactery is 5,000 gp per level of the character. Thus, a 20th level psionicist must spend 100,000 gp on his artifact.

Once the phylactery is fashioned, it must be readied to receive the psionicist's life force. This is generally done by means of the metapsionic empower ability, with some subtle changes in the way the psionicist uses the power that alters its outcome. In order to complete the phylactery, the psionicist must empower it with each and every psionic ability that he possesses.

Although an object cannot normally be empowered with psychic abilities in more than one discipline, the unusual nature of the phylactery allows this rule to be broken. However, before "opening" a new discipline within the object, the would-be lich must transfer all of his powers from the first discipline into it. For example, if a character has telepathic and metapsionic abilities, he must complete the empowering of all of his telepathic powers before he begins to infuse the object with his metapsionic ones. Once a discipline is closed it cannot be reopened.

During the creation of the phylactery, the psionicist is very vulnerable to attack. Each time that he gives his phylactery a new power, he loses it himself. Thus, the process strips away the powers of the psionicist as it continues. Obviously, the last power that is transferred into the phylactery is the empower ability. The effort of placing this ability within the phylactery drains the last essences of the psionicist's life from him and completes his transformation into a psionic lich. At the moment that the transformation takes place the character must make a system shock survival roll. Failure indicates that his willpower was not strong enough to survive the trauma of becoming undead; his spirit breaks up and dissipates, making him forever dead. Only the powers of a deity are strong enough to revive a character who has died in this way; even a *wish* will not suffice.

Living Tatoo

	Dark Man	Living Spear	Panther	Raven	Winged Snake
CLIMATE/TERRAIN:	Nightmare Lands	Nightmare Lands	Nightmare Lands	Nightmare Lands	Nightmare Lands
FREQUENCY:	Very rare	Rare	Rare	Rare	Very Rare
ORGANIZATION:	Bonded	Bonded	Bonded	Bonded	Bonded
ACTIVITY CYCLE:	Any	Any	Any	Any	Any
DIET:					
INTELLIGENCE:	Low (5–7)	Animal (1)	Semi- (2–4)	Very (11–12)	Average (8–10)
TREASURE:	Nil	Nil	Nil	Nil	Feathers
ALIGNMENT:	Chaotic neutral	Neutral	Neutral	Neutral good	Neutral
NO. APPEARING:	1	1–2	1	1	1
ARMOR CLASS:	7	1	6	6	5
MOVEMENT:	12	Nil	15	1, Fl 36 (B)	12, Fl 18 (B)
HIT DICE:	3+3	2+2	3+2	2+2	4+4
THAC0:	17	19	17	19	17
NO. OF ATTACKS:	1	1	3	1	1
DAMAGE/ATTACK:	2–5	2–7 (1D6+1)	1–3/1–3/1–8	3–6 (1D4+2)	1–4
SPECIAL ATTACKS:	Strength drain	Poison	Surprise, rear claw rake	*Detect lie*	Poison, spark shower
SPECIAL DEFENSES:	+1 or better Spell immunity	+1 or better Spell immunity	+1 or better Surprised on 1	+1 or better Resist illusions	+1 or better Resist electricity
MAGIC RESISTANCE:	Nil	Nil	Nil	Nil	Nil
SIZE:	M (6′)	M (4′–5′)	M (5′–6′)	S (3′)	M (4′–5′)
MORALE:	Steady (11–12)	Steady (11–12)	Steady (11–12)	Elite (13–14)	Elite (13–14)
XP VALUE:	420	420	270	420	975

One of the most worthy and stalwart companions found in the Land of the Mists, a living tattoo is actually a spirit convinced to leave the swirling chaos of the Nightmare Lands for a more stable existence in the mystically prepared shelter of a magical tattoo. Only the Abber nomads have mastered the process by which these spirits are lured and captured.

Living tattoos come in many varieties, but the powers of the creature and the role that it is to play in its owner's life are always reflected in the shape of the tattoo. For example, a hunter who desires a tattoo that will help him track prey might have one fashioned in the image of a wolf or keen-sighted eagle.

Even while separated, both the bearer and the tattoo are instantly aware of each other's thoughts and feelings and can act almost as one in battle. If either bearer or tattoo is wounded, the other feels the pain as well. The tattoo is able to communicate in whatever way a natural creature of its type would and also has mastery of the languages that its bearer speaks.

Combat: A living tattoo will always work with its bearer, aiding the character to the best of its ability and even fighting to the death if necessary. Because the tattoo is a free-willed creature, it is responsive to the wishes and commands of its master, but not under any magical obligation to obey them.

A living tattoo can separate from its bearer at will, becoming a distinct, three-dimensional physical being. A living tattoo can only use its abilities when in full physical form.

The exact nature of a living tattoo's combat abilities vary with the design of the creature. Exact details on some of the more common types are provided at the conclusion of this entry.

No matter what form they take, living tattoos can only be hit by magical weapons of +1 or better enchantment.

Once bonded to a living tattoo, the character's life force is fundamentally tied to the spirit's. If the tattoo dies the character must make a system shock check or perish as well from the terrible psychic shock of his spirit-companion's death.

When a living tattoo loses hit points a character can will the creature one of his own. This process, however, is irreversible. Once the character gives up a hit point it is lost to him forever. Such a sacrifice immediately raises the living tattoo to full hit points. Note that this process does not grant the living tattoo an additional permanent hit point.

Habitat/Society: The living tattoo is utterly bonded to its bearer. It cares nothing for other people or beings except to note how such individuals and beings affect its partner.

Only the shamans of the Abber nomads know the secret of calling and bonding living tattoos. No Abber nomad has ever told the secret of this process to an outsider, although these shamans can occasionally be persuaded to bond one of the spirit beings to an outsider. Normally, the outsider must perform some service for the Abber nomads in order to earn such an honor.

The form a living tattoo can take is limited only by the creative and artistic skills of the shaman who designs it. The role the living tattoo is meant to play in the life of its bearer often determines the design. A hunting companion may not make a good guardian, while a guardian may not serve well as an advisor.

The Abber nomads view the bearing of a living tattoo as both an honor and a responsibility.

Once the design has been determined the shaman carefully cuts into the skin of his subject with an ink filled thorn or sharpened bone. The process is painful and laborious and the larger tattoos can take up to twelve hours to create. Once the design is complete the subject joins the shaman on the shifting plains of the Nightmare Lands. There the two call to the spirits, importuning one to take up residence in the tattoo. During such prayers the character promises to value the spirit's life as he does his own.

The character's entreaty will be answered within one day or not at all. The character must make either an Ability Check on either his Wisdom or a Strength, whichever is higher. If this is successful a spirit answers the character's summons and takes up residence in the tattoo. Failure indicates no spirit has answered the call; although the character will always have the tattoo, it will never house a spirit.

There is a 5% chance that an evil spirit will enter the tattoo. This spirit has all the abilities of a normal living tattoo, however it will betray its bearer at the first opportunity. Such tattoos are not truly bonded to their bearers and are merely freed upon the bearer's demise. The DM should make a separate, secret roll to determine if the spirit entering the tattoo is of this type.

Ecology: A living tattoo can spend up to one month detached from its bearer. The tattoo will fade away and die if it remains away any longer, as the spirit-being requires contact with its bearer's spiritual essence in order to survive. This contact is the only food a living tattoo requires.

Whenever a living tattoo is away from its bearer the only sign of the tattoo's presence is a slight tracing of scars that form the outline of the tattoo. Should the bearer survive the death of a tattoo, the entire area of the tattoo blackens and burns, leaving an angry red scar in its place.

Dark Man

The dark man is almost identical in powers, appearance and abilities to a shadow. It is not evil, however, reflecting only the outward aspects of a true shadow and not its spiritual depravity.

The physical tattoo of a dark man is designed by pricking a series of gray and black dyes into the subject's skin. The tattoo covers the bearer's entire back, from the crown of his head to the backs of his heels. Many bearers of this tattoo keep the back of their head shaved out of respect for their companion spirit.

Except in bright light, the dark man is 70% undetectable due to its shadowy appearance. The dark man most often attacks from behind, attempting to grab its opponent and drain his strength. Every time the dark man scores a successful hit it does 1d4+1 points of damage and drains 1 point of strength. The dark man is immune to *sleep, charm,* and *hold* spells.

Living Spear

The physical tattoo of a living spear is normally drawn across either the bearer's back or chest. It is possible for a character to bear two living spears, although this is a rare honor accorded to only the noblest of warriors or huntsmen.

Although living spears can be thrown in battle, they prefer to remain in the hands of their bearer. Living spears enjoy battle greatly. A living spear does 1d6+1 points of damage per hit. In addition, three times per day the spear can excrete a small amount of poison. Anyone hit by a poisoned spear must make a saving throw vs. poison. Anyone failing this roll suffers a –2 penalty on all attack rolls and saving throws for the next 2d6 rounds as his body is wracked with pain. Living spears are immune to all mind-affecting spells.

Panther

This tattoo is normally drawn across the bearer's back, with the front paws of the panther draped across the bearer's shoulders and its tail trailing around the bearer's waist. The panther is most often considered a hunting spirit.

In battle, the panther attacks as a normal giant cat, using its claws and sharp teeth, doing 1d3, 1d3, and 1d8 points of damage respectively. If both its forepaws hit the panther can rake with its two rear claws doing another 1d4 points of damage each. Panthers are alert creatures who can only be surprised on a 1.

More than other tattoos, panthers prefer to remain physically separate from their bearer. This is due to their desire to guard their bearer. Panthers trust no other living being save their bearer.

Raven

The raven tattoo is always drawn across the bearer's chest, with one wing swooping across the lower part of his face. This positioning represents the wisdom of head and heart the raven brings the bearer. The raven can *detect lie* at will and is ever-vigilant in protecting its bearers from the falsehoods of others.

The raven is a knowledge-spirit, yet it will fight to protect itself and its bearer. The raven attacks with its sharp beak doing 1d4+2 points of damage.

The raven-spirit is immune to illusionary magic of all kinds. The bond between the living tattoo and its bearer conveys this immunity to the bearer as long as the raven can witness the illusion, and thus see through it.

Winged Snake

The winged snake is a beautiful, multi-colored tattoo that normally is placed along the bearer's back with the snake wrapping around one arm or leg.

In battle the winged snake receives a –3 bonus to its initiative due to its speed. The poisonous bite of a tattoo-snake does 1d4 points of damage. The next round its acidic poison does an additional 1–8 points of damage to its foe. The winged serpent can also attack with its breath weapon, a small shower of burning sparks. The sparks do 2d4 points of damage to anyone within ten feet of the serpent. The winged serpent can use this attack only once per turn. Winged snakes are immune to electrical attacks.

Lycanthrope, Loup-garou

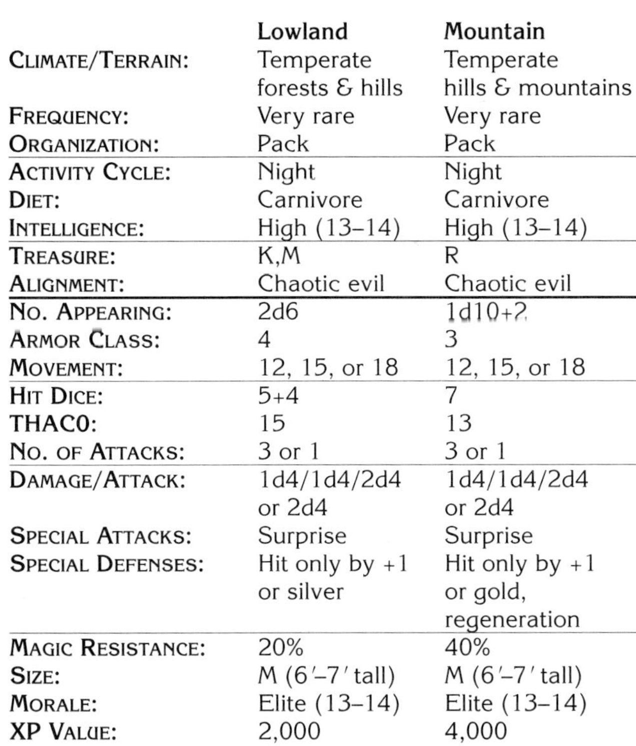

	Lowland	Mountain
CLIMATE/TERRAIN:	Temperate forests & hills	Temperate hills & mountains
FREQUENCY:	Very rare	Very rare
ORGANIZATION:	Pack	Pack
ACTIVITY CYCLE:	Night	Night
DIET:	Carnivore	Carnivore
INTELLIGENCE:	High (13–14)	High (13–14)
TREASURE:	K,M	R
ALIGNMENT:	Chaotic evil	Chaotic evil
NO. APPEARING:	2d6	1d10+2
ARMOR CLASS:	4	3
MOVEMENT:	12, 15, or 18	12, 15, or 18
HIT DICE:	5+4	7
THAC0:	15	13
NO. OF ATTACKS:	3 or 1	3 or 1
DAMAGE/ATTACK:	1d4/1d4/2d4 or 2d4	1d4/1d4/2d4 or 2d4
SPECIAL ATTACKS:	Surprise	Surprise
SPECIAL DEFENSES:	Hit only by +1 or silver	Hit only by +1 or gold, regeneration
MAGIC RESISTANCE:	20%	40%
SIZE:	M (6′–7′ tall)	M (6′–7′ tall)
MORALE:	Elite (13–14)	Elite (13–14)
XP VALUE:	2,000	4,000

Loup-garous are powerful cousins of the common werewolf. Like most true werewolves in Ravenloft, they can assume three forms: human, man-wolf, and wolf. The human form is completely normal.

The loup-garou always looks the same in its human form, just as it looks the same in its wolf or man-wolf form. In this shape, the beast has a movement rate of 12.

As a man-wolf, it stands about 7′ tall and is extremely muscular. The body is fur-covered and has a short tail, canine legs, and a wolf's head. The creature walks erect and can manipulate things with its hands. In this form, the creature can talk, although its voice is low and raspy. The man-wolf shape is also faster than its human guise, having a movement rate of 15.

As a wolf, a lowland loup-garou looks just like a worg wolf while its mountain cousins are larger. The creature is swiftest in this form, having a movement rate of 18, but cannot handle tools or weapons, and cannot talk.

Combat: The tactics and weapons that a loup-garou employs in combat depends wholly upon the shape that it employs. The creature needs a full round to change from one form to another.

The human can belong to any character class and may have any experience level, although most loup-garous tend to be warriors or thieves. The experience level never affects Hit Dice or hit points. Werewolves without a character class are treated as 1st level fighters. In this form, the creature depends upon weapons to defend itself.

In man-wolf form, the loup-garou can attack 3 times per round, once with each clawed hand and with a bite. It can use a weapon, but then only gets one attack per round. The creature has a Strength of 18/00 in this form, and gains the appropriate combat bonuses (+3 on attacks and +6 to damage).

In wolf form, a loup-garou can attack only once each round by biting. This form has the advantage of speed and surprise, however. Because of its keen senses, a loup-garou in wolf form imposes a –2 penalty on its enemies' surprise rolls. The wolf form is also less conspicuous than the man-wolf, appearing as a normal animal rather than a supernatural creature.

In any form, the lowland loup-garou has some natural resistance to magic. Its mental capacity remains the same regardless of shape.

The creature can be harmed only by silver or magical weapons. Silver weapons do normal damage, but magical weapons only do as much damage as their bonus. For example, a *sword +1* can inflict no more than 1 point of damage per successful hit, regardless of the damage roll. A character's Strength bonus does not apply. A blessed weapon (or other specialty weapon with a bonus) inflicts 1 point of damage per hit.

Habitat/Society: Lowland packs wander the Ravenloft domains in search of prey, preferably humans. In the wild, lowland packs often use a cave or ruined building as a den. They also have been known to travel as humans and stay in inns. They hate other lycanthropes and especially wolfweres (see the *MONSTROUS MANUAL*).

Ecology: The werewolf's most fearsome aspect is the infection its bite can cause. Any infected human or humanoid can become a werewolf when the condition is triggered (frequently by the 3 days of a full moon). The infected werewolf can be controlled by the true werewolf that infected him. In animal form, the infected creature is a semi-intelligent (2–4), raging beast. It takes a full turn for an infected werewolf to change from man to wolf or vice versa.

Mountain Loup-garous

This larger species is as big as a dire wolf when in wolf form. It can only be hurt by gold or magical weapons. It is more magic resistant than many types of werewolves, and can regenerate 1 hit point per turn. Mountain loup-garous are more likely to hunt alone than other forms of werewolf.

Lycanthrope, Werejackal

Climate/Terrain:	Har'Akir
Frequency:	Rare
Organization:	Solitary
Activity Cycle:	Night
Diet:	Carnivore
Intelligence:	Average to High (10–14)
Treasure:	K
Alignment:	Lawful evil
No. Appearing:	1
Armor Class:	5
Movement:	15
Hit Dice:	6
THAC0:	15
No. of Attacks:	3
Damage/Attack:	1d6/1d6/1d10
Special Attacks:	See below
Special Defenses:	Hit only by +1 or better weapons
Magic Resistance:	Nil
Size:	M
Morale:	Steady (12)
XP Value:	True: 975 Cursed: 420

Werejackals originated in the ancient land that gave birth to the island domain of Har'Akir. There, they were priests of a strange god called Anubis. Once in Ravenloft, the jackals sought out followers to worship their now-distant deity.

The werejackal resembles a tall, thin humanoid with a dog like face locked in a perpetual sinister smile. Behind the evil grin is a row of sharp ebony teeth. Its hands and feet are long paws tipped with black nails capable of rending an unarmored man.

Werejackals have two forms. The first is that of a normal human while the second is a humanoid shape with the fur, head, and claws of the jackal. When in human form, the creature generally seems surly and snarls at insulting comments. His nails are long and darker than usual. The creature's clothing remains unaffected by the change to either form.

Werejackals speak the language of Har'Akir, but are also said to know a secret tongue sacred to the god Anubis. The latter is said to sound much like the barking and howling of wild dogs, but this may be only rumor.

Combat: Werejackals rely on their minions and fearful spells more than their own natural weaponry. When pressed, the fiends can defend themselves with slashing claws and tearing teeth. The werejackal's claws cause 1d6 points of damage each. If either of these hits is successful, the lycanthrope has drawn close enough to attempt a bite with its black teeth, causing 1d10 points of damage if it hits.

True werejackals can cast priestly spells as if they were 6th level priests with a Wisdom of 18. During day to day activities, the priest tends to pick spells that will awe his followers and keep them happy, or terrify rebellious and as yet uninfected villagers into acquiescence. *Call lightning, cause disease, plant growth* (used on crops), *summon insects,* and *water walk* all fit this description. If the werejackal is aware of imminent confrontation and has time to prepare, his spells tend toward controlling poisonous snakes via *snake charm* or *sticks to snakes,* or any of the above that might still be appropriate.

As priests, werejackals can control undead as described under "Evil Priests and Undead" in the *Player's Handbook*. Strangely, werejackals don't tend to like taking advantage of this power. They prefer to let their armies of lesser werejackals and followers prove their devotion instead. Only in the direst circumstances or when undead are used against them will werejackals attempt to exercise this ability.

As is the case with all lycanthropes, werejackals can only be hit by +1 or better weapons. While most lycanthropes can be hit by silver weapons, these are no threat to the cursed priests of Har'Akir. Their weakness lies in a vulnerability to things made of bronze, for all weapons of that type can harm them.

Jackals have a natural cowardice that the Dark Powers have twisted into a dark curse on their lycanthropic namesakes. When confronted by an obviously superior force, the cowardly werejackal must make a Morale Check every round. Failure indicates that the creature must retreat for 5–20 (5d4) rounds. The werejackal will usually not return, but begin to plot some fiendish scheme of retribution instead.

Habitat/Society: A true werejackal tries to transform a small population of beings into cursed versions of itself. Once infected with lycanthropy, the new werejackal must make a saving throw vs. spell at –4 or become permanently enslaved to his creator's will. This link is not telepathic, so the priest will have to verbally command his lesser minions. Those that remain free-willed are still under the werejackal's control whenever they assume their humanoid form. Troublesome resisters are usually slain after a single incident raises the priest's ire.

One of the first tasks the werejackal demands of his pack is the creation of a temple dedicated to Anubis, the god he serves. The minions practice the priest's religion routinely, gradually becoming enthralled by the werejackal's tales of the mysterious god's deeds and goals.

Ecology: Werejackals are cunning and cold. They seek to dominate all those around them by creating a state of fear and helplessness. Then the true savagery of the lycanthrope emerges as they cruelly taunt their foes through a long and agonizing death.

Lycanthrope, WereJaguar

CLIMATE/TERRAIN:	Jungle
FREQUENCY:	Rare
ORGANIZATION:	Tribal
ACTIVITY CYCLE:	Any
DIET:	Carnivore
INTELLIGENCE:	Average to high (10–14)
TREASURE:	Nil (I)
ALIGNMENT:	Lawful neutral
NO. APPEARING:	1, 3–18 (3d6)
ARMOR CLASS:	5
MOVEMENT:	18
HIT DICE:	5
THAC0:	15
NO. OF ATTACKS:	3
DAMAGE/ATTACK:	1d4/1d4/1d6
SPECIAL ATTACKS:	Nil
SPECIAL DEFENSES:	+1 or better weapons to hit
MAGIC RESISTANCE:	Nil
SIZE:	M
MORALE:	Elite (14)
XP VALUE:	True: 650 Cursed: 420

Werejaguars lurking in the darkest hearts of jungles, usually living in and around old ruins long ago forgotten by locals. They venture from their secluded homes only to hunt and patrol their wilderness territories.

Werejaguars have but a single form, that of a hybrid humanoid / jaguar. This allows the creature to walk upright like a man or on all fours for running. Their pelts are spotted like their namesake and fur covers all areas but the face and palms. Their clothing tends to be strange to most of Ravenloft's denizens, featuring brightly covered loincloths and wraps that cover a single shoulder and the chest area. Werejaguars often use tools of obsidian, but prefer their teeth and claws in combat.

In addition to the common tongue of men in their area, werejaguars speak a growling, hissing language of their own.

Combat: Werejaguars are silent, deadly hunters. They move through even the thickest of brush with hardly a sound and strike without warning. Because of their natural hunting prowess, anyone attacked by a werejaguar in a jungle or similar setting suffers a –3 penalty on his surprise check. Further, the creature's own keen senses of smell, hearing, and eyesight make it impossible to surprise without magical aid of some sort.

The fearsome claws of these deadly beasts are employed in a pair of slashing attacks that inflict 1d4 points of damage each. In addition, the creature can bite its enemies for 1d6 points of damage. Because they are not true cats, werejaguars have no raking attack.

As with other lycanthropes, werejaguars are immune to weapons of less than +1 enchantment. They are unafraid of silver, however, for their bane is the hard wood of the ebony tree. Weapons fashioned from this material are able to strike the creature even if they are not enchanted in any way.

Werejaguars are unusually vulnerable to fire, suffering 1 extra point of damage per die of any such attack. As such, they greatly fear flames used against them in combat. Werejaguars confronted with torches or similar flames must make a successful saving throw vs. paralysis to attack. Larger flames or multiple sources force the creatures to save with a –4 penalty. Failure prevents the creature from coming within 10 feet of the fire. If a werejaguar suffers damage from flames, it must make an immediate Morale Check with a –4 penalty or flee for 5–20 (5d4) rounds.

Habitat/Society: Werejaguars form tightly knit communities carefully hidden from the eyes of humanity. They do not normally hunt intelligent creatures, even those of an evil nature, but will kill those who threaten their pack without mercy.

When outsiders enter their lands, werejaguars will often hunt them for sport. A victim will be toyed with, catching only fleeting glimpses of the lightning quick cats as they dart to and fro in the jungle. This torment can continue for hours or day, depending upon how fearful the prey is. Only when the cats tire of their fun will they move in for the kill. When that happens, they strike quickly and without mercy.

Werejaguar groups of 10 or more always have a 6-Hit-Die leader. There is a 20% chance that the leader is lawful evil. If that is the case, the pack will tend to roam far outside of its territory, hunting down all sentient species it comes across.

Ecology: Werejaguars live on a diet of meat, usually taken from the dense jungles in which they live. In truth, many of the lycanthropes dislike the taste of sentient flesh. They say these creatures taste bitter and unhealthy.

As territorial as they are, werejaguars serve as the custodians of their jungle homes. Much as a druid or ranger character might oversee an expanse of forest or wilderness, they strike quickly against any force that might upset the balance of nature around them.

Lycanthrope, Wereleopard

Climate/Terrain:	Arid prairies and mountains
Frequency:	Uncommon
Organization:	Tribal
Activity Cycle:	Any
Diet:	Carnivore
Intelligence:	Low to high (5–14)
Treasure:	K (I)
Alignment:	Lawful neutral to evil
No. Appearing:	3–18 (3d6)
Armor Class:	5
Movement:	18
Hit Dice:	5
THAC0:	15
No. of Attacks:	3
Damage/Attack:	1d4/1d4/1d6
Special Attacks:	Hamstring
Special Defenses:	Nil
Magic Resistance:	Nil
Size:	M
Morale:	Steady (12)
XP Value:	True: 650 Cursed: 420

Wereleopards are a race of ferocious hunters. They tend to keep to themselves until led by the paka, an intelligent race of humanoid cat people. Under the influence of that evil race, they are often involved in sinister acts against the folk of the realm.

Wereleopards have only one form, almost a direct cross between a feline and a human. The creature can fight from all fours or upright as it chooses. Either way, its terrible claws can rake foes while its powerful jaws lock in on the prey's throat. They dislike clothing, but have a thick spotted coat that protects them from the elements. Female leopards are almost exclusively black with slightly lighter spots throughout. Males have orange fur with black spots.

Wereleopards speak their own language, a growling tongue almost impossible for men to learn, as well as that of the paka. They disdain the languages of men and never learn to speak them.

Combat: Wereleopards are faster than other lycanthropes, and they use this speed to great advantage in combat. Their favored attack form is to race behind a fleeing foe and bite at the tendons in the back of the leg. When it strikes in this way, the creature receives a +4 bonus to its attack roll (in lieu of the normal +2 for a rear attack). Any modified roll of 18 or better which strikes the target indicates that the victim becomes painfully hobbled until healed. While so injured, the victim can move at only half its normal rate. Whether or not the victim was hobbled, the attack does its usual 1d6 points of damage.

Once the prey has been slowed, the wereleopards circle as a pack and try to herd them in one direction or another. As the targets become separated and confused, the creatures close in for a quick and violent kill. Only after the entire group of prey has been slaughtered will the pack allow itself to return for the feast.

Wereleopards can only be hit by silver or magical weapons of +1 or better, or by magic, acid, fire, or other special attacks.

If unable to employ its preferred method of attack, the wereleopard will tend to avoid combat. If that is not possible, the creature slashes with its claws, making two attacks for 1d4 points of damage each, and bites at its victim, inflicting 1d6 points of damage with a successful attack.

Their only real weakness is their fear of lightning. When confronted with natural or magical lightning, they must make an immediate Morale Check with a –4 penalty or flee for 5–20 (5d4) rounds. Loud noises that resemble thunderclaps also frighten them and require a Morale Check, although a +4 bonus is allowed in this case.

Habitat/Society: Wereleopards come from a hot, arid place where stark mountains rise majestically above vast plains. In Ravenloft, they usually settle in areas similar in appearance and temperature. On their world, the creatures were true leopards who were led into acts of evil by an unknown creature. When they made their way to the Demiplane of Dread, they were cursed with lycanthropy and their shapes forever twisted. Only 40% of wereleopards are true lycanthropes, and only they are capable of transmitting lycanthropy to their victims.

Cursed wereleopards, those who are not true lycanthropes, are often created by the pride to help defend against a particular local threat, such as settlements, adventurers, or even the evil creatures that sometimes threaten them. After the curse takes effect, the victim develops near-animal intelligence and strictly follows the orders and whims of the true lycanthropes that rule the community. Unfortunately for members of this worker class, when their usefulness is at an end, so is their life.

When the full moon rises across the plains, cursed wereleopards transform back into their human shape until the sun rises the next morn. After transformation, the victim is dazed and confused. He remembers both his wereleopard pride and human life and usually attempts to flee to sort the conflicting emotions of loyalty. The leaders of the pride exploit the moment of weakness and bring them down with savage delight. The transformed humans do not last long naked and unarmed against the ferocious felines. Not all of the transformed are eaten, but most are. Some may even be allowed to escape as the others know they'll come back when the sun rises and the transformation reverses itself.

Ecology: Wereleopards eat strictly meat, preferably freshly killed. Their catlike origins show in every aspect of their life. They lounge in the limbs of tall trees, lick their fur clean, and even roll in the grass with the innocence of kittens. When it's time to hunt, however, few can mistake their true natures.

Lycanthrope, Wereray

Climate/Terrain:	Sea of Sorrows
Frequency:	Uncommon
Organization:	School
Activity Cycle:	Any
Diet:	Carnivore
Intelligence:	Average (8–10)
Treasure:	(D)
Alignment:	Chaotic evil
No. Appearing:	3–18 (3d6)
Armor Class:	5
Movement:	Sw 12
Hit Dice:	5
THAC0:	15
No. of Attacks:	2
Damage/Attack:	1d6/1d8
Special Attacks:	Sting
Special Defenses:	+1 or better weapons to hit
Magic Resistance:	Nil
Size:	M
Morale:	Steady (11–12)
XP Value:	True: 650 Cursed: 420

Wererays live in the warm and salty waters of the Demiplane of Dread. They prey on fishermen and others who wander too close to the surf and sting them with their long, whiplike tails. The terrible creature then watches as its paralyzed victim drowns, feasting on the remains only after enjoying its agonizing death.

Wererays are one of the strangest lycanthropes. From the top, they look much like giant manta rays with mammoth wings of rubbery gray skin. Underneath is the humanoid portion of the beast. The creature has arms and legs, but the legs are seemingly attached to the winged shell by tenuous membranes. The arms are free and can be used to manipulate tools or weapons. The head and the rest of the body are attached to the shell like the legs and cannot separate. The skin of the creature's head and belly is a sickly, glistening white, while the arms, legs, and sides are the same rubbery gray as the shell. The tail of the thing is long and gray, but ends in a jet black barb. Its eyes are similarly black with two dull slits of yellow for pupils.

Cursed wererays, those created by true lycanthropes, are only transformed when the moon is full. During other times, their skin takes on a slight grayness and seems rubbery and tight. The iris of the eye is always black after infection.

Wererays have no language of their own, but often speak one or more human tongues.

Combat: Wererays are one of the most malicious of all lycanthropes. They enjoy cursing others with their terrible condition, so only 40% of wererays encountered are true lycanthropes. The rest are stricken fishermen, unfortunate swimmers, or even unlucky sailors who happened to garner the attentions of these lurkers.

Wererays often lurk beneath a thin layer of sand, making them effectively *invisible* unless a careful search is made for the creature. When an unsuspecting victim disturbs the ray, it strikes with its whiplike, barbed tail. Anyone hit by this attack suffers 1d6 points of damage and must make a saving throw vs. poison. Failure indicates that the character has been injected with a deadly neurotoxin that not only paralysis the victim for 1d4 turns but also causes excruciating pain. A paralyzed victim will usually be left to drown. Only after it has enjoyed watching the poor creature die in this way will the wereray return to devour it.

The wereray can also deliver a dangerous bite that inflicts 1d4 points of damage. However, it seldom uses this form of attack, preferring to rely upon its deadly tail and stinger.

Like other lycanthropes, these creatures are immune to injury from weapons with less than a +1 enchantment. Arms fashioned from silver pose no special threat to them, but those made from coral or sea shells will harm them even if not enchanted in any way.

Habitat/Society: Wererays live in packs of 3d6 creatures in caves deep below the surface of the sea. These caverns are often filled with the bones and treasures of their prey.

They are less intelligent than most other lycanthropes, but their cunning more than makes up for it. From time to time, they construct artificial reefs and the like to wreck ships and bring them new victims.

Ecology: Wererays prefer to eat humanoid flesh, but fish and other sea creatures are their usual diet. Capturing prey from the surface usually consists of burying themselves beneath the sand in a shallow area and stinging anyone who ventures too close.

Mist Ferryman

CLIMATE/TERRAIN:	Mists and fog banks
FREQUENCY:	Rare
ORGANIZATION:	Solitary
ACTIVITY CYCLE:	Foggy days or nights
DIET:	Carnivore
INTELLIGENCE:	Low (5–7)
TREASURE:	Nil
ALIGNMENT:	Neutral evil
NO. APPEARING:	1
ARMOR CLASS:	3
MOVEMENT:	12
HIT DICE:	4
THAC0:	17
NO. OF ATTACKS:	3
DAMAGE/ATTACK:	1d6/1d6/1d8
SPECIAL ATTACKS:	Disease
SPECIAL DEFENSES:	+1 or better weapons to hit
MAGIC RESISTANCE:	Nil
SIZE:	M (6′ tall)
MORALE:	Average (8–10)
XP VALUE:	420

Some call these spectral ambassadors of Ravenloft grim reapers, confusing them with those sinister creatures (see *MONSTROUS COMPENDIUM, RAVENLOFT Appendix*).

The mist ferrymen are frightful beasts, appearing as skeletal parodies of normal humans. Their mouths are full of sharp incisors which often have bits of rotting flesh caught between them. An unwary traveler can almost never see their full form, because swirling clouds of mist hide the shape of the creature, allowing only glimpses of its horrifying figure.

Mist ferrymen seem unhindered by language, apparently having the ability to speak with any sentient creature they encounter. Their hollow, sinister voices give an instant impression of death, however, which none can deny.

Combat: Mist Ferrymen are foul creatures of the Ravenloft Mists, haunting the Misty Borders of the Core and the Islands. They prey on the travelers in the mists, occasionally cooperating to bring down the more powerful specimens. They are mostly solitary creatures and attack any interlopers in their territory, including other Ferrymen and even an occasional Vistani tribe.

When one of these creatures needs help to defeat an invader it issues a strange, ululating howl, sounding like the sobbing of a frightened woman. This attracts all other ferrymen within 2 miles (usually 1d8 + 1). These arrive in five rounds, traveling through the mists with preternatural speed.

Their method of travel is somewhat unclear, as no one has ever seen one in transit. Perhaps they assume the form of fog and speed through the mists which surround them, re-forming when they reach their destination. They never use this ability in combat, so there is no proof they use this method of transit.

When they appear, they fall upon their victims, tearing at them with their sharp claws and powerful teeth. Any who receive damage from these must successfully save vs. poison or suffer from a debilitating disease. The victims lose 1 point of Constitution per week unless a *cure disease* spell is cast upon them. Lost Constitution points are regained at a rate of 1 point per day. If a victim reaches 0 hit points, he becomes a mist ferryman himself after three days.

Ferrymen attempt to keep their victim alive as long as possible, for they relish the flow of the living blood as well as the flavor of the struggling flesh and muscle. They often attempt to overbear their victims, overwhelming them with sheer numbers, at which point they take turns eating.

Mist ferrymen can be turned as ghasts and have the usual undead resistance to spells like *charm, sleep,* and *hold.* Holy water does not harm them but contact with a lawful good holy symbol will inflict 1d4 points of damage to them.

Habitat/Society: Although usually solitary creatures, mist ferrymen occasionally band together for hunting purposes.

It seems that they have somehow acquired the ability to travel anywhere they desire in the Mists, but it is not known just what gives them this power.

If one subdues a ferryman in combat, it is possible to force the creature to lead the way to a desired destination within Ravenloft. There is no way to make a ferryman take someone out of the demiplane, although there are those who say that the secret of escape from Ravenloft is known to these undead creatures.

Ecology: It is sometimes said that mist ferrymen are manifestations of the Mists themselves, lesser forms that sometimes serve the whims of the lords. Their ability to cause the mists to work for them lends credence to this theory, but there are many factors that count against it as well.

Moor Man

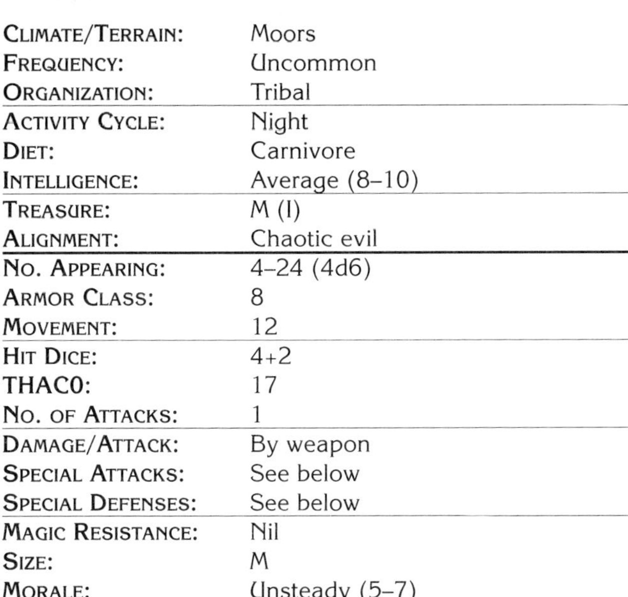

Climate/Terrain:	Moors
Frequency:	Uncommon
Organization:	Tribal
Activity Cycle:	Night
Diet:	Carnivore
Intelligence:	Average (8–10)
Treasure:	M (I)
Alignment:	Chaotic evil
No. Appearing:	4–24 (4d6)
Armor Class:	8
Movement:	12
Hit Dice:	4+2
THAC0:	17
No. of Attacks:	1
Damage/Attack:	By weapon
Special Attacks:	See below
Special Defenses:	See below
Magic Resistance:	Nil
Size:	M
Morale:	Unsteady (5–7)
XP Value:	270

Moor men are a race of wild humanoids that live in the most dismal fens of Ravenloft. They hunt by ambushing unwary travelers by night and feasting on their steaming remains.

Moor men look like short humans with oversized eyes. They are completely hairless, and wear little more than a loincloth, or, for females, leather shirts made from the skins of their victims. Males very rarely wear shirts, preferring to decorate their bare flesh in tattoos made of mud, the blood of small animals, or any other ready stain.

Combat: Moor men have an acute sense of infravision that allows them to see heat emitting targets up to 300 yards distant on the cold moors. Unfortunately for them, this fantastic ability makes bright sunlight extremely painful. Moor men discovered in daylight or exposed to *continual lights* or other illumination of high intensity are blinded until the source is removed, and fight with a –4 to all Attack and Damage Rolls.

Most moor men (50%) use short swords taken from their past victims. Another quarter (25%) use axes, and the rest use clubs or daggers. Ten percent of the tribe will have short bows as well.

Moor men decorate themselves in a variety of tattoos that give them temporary abilities or powers. The tattoo is actually an amalgamation of several designs painted on key parts of the body, so no moor man can ever have more than one tattoo in effect at one time. When moor men are encountered, the DM should roll to see which tattoo each individual is wearing. The tattoos can not be made permanent, and must be replaced after any sort of combat or strenuous engagement.

1. **Defense.** This tattoo contains images of shields and mystical symbols. It gives the wearer a +1 to all saving throws, and imposes a 1-point penalty on the Attack and Damage Rolls of any enemy.

2. **Luck.** The designs of this tattoo are made of various flowers and other symbols that speak of good luck to the moor men. This allows the moor man to reroll a single die roll once per round, though the second roll supersedes the first.

3. **Veil of Darkness.** This tattoo is always black and contains images of eyes and suns. Moor men who wear it do not suffer from sunlight or other bright light.

4. **Invulnerability.** This tattoo automatically repels the first successful attack to hit the wearer in any given round, regardless of its nature. The design of this tattoo is the most distinctive. The moor man must draw a skeletal figure over his flesh that mimics his own. The coloration of the stain is always white.

5. **Berserking.** This tattoo shows axes and swords. During combat, it drives the wearer into a frenzied state that doubles the number of attacks he makes and his hit points. A moor man is mortally wounded when he loses his original hit points; the tattoo simply keeps him from realizing it.

6. **Bedazzlement.** These spiralling designs capture the attentions of anyone who gazes at the moor man and fails a saving throw vs. spell. The effect continues until the moor man or target is slain. A bedazzled victim may attempt an additional saving throw every round to shake off the effect. While under the tattoo's spell, a character cannot attack and loses any Dexterity bonuses to Armor Class.

Habitat/Society: Because of their aversion to sunlight, moor men spend most of their time in a state of quasi-hibernation buried in shallow pits by grasses, limbs, or other natural camouflage. As the sun sets, the clan emerges from its lair and members begin marking themselves with ceremonial tattoos. When that is done, the clan roams the moors looking for anyone unfortunate enough to cross their path.

Ecology: Moor men eat the meat of their prey. Usually they have to settle for marsh rats, raw fish, and the like, but it is humanoid flesh that they crave. Since few men dare to venture outdoors at night, the moor men's desire for this meat often overwhelms their fear of superior numbers or even their aversion to light.

Obedient

CLIMATE/TERRAIN:	Dementlieu
FREQUENCY:	Common
ORGANIZATION:	See below
ACTIVITY CYCLE:	Any
DIET:	Omnivore
INTELLIGENCE:	Average to high (10–15)
TREASURE:	M
ALIGNMENT:	See below
NO. APPEARING:	1
ARMOR CLASS:	10 (by armor type)
MOVEMENT:	12
HIT DICE:	Varies
THAC0:	Varies
NO. OF ATTACKS:	1
DAMAGE/ATTACK:	By weapon
SPECIAL ATTACKS:	Nil
SPECIAL DEFENSES:	Nil
MAGIC RESISTANCE:	Nil
SIZE:	M
MORALE:	Elite (14)
XP VALUE:	Varies

The Obedient are those unfortunate souls who have been mesmerized into lifelong servitude by the lord of Dementlieu, Dominic d'Honaire. They help their evil master hatch plots against their neighbors and keep nosy outsiders from discovering too much about their cursed land.

The Obedient are normal townspeople living in and around the land of Dementlieu. Many of them are the wealthier and more influential persons about town, for Dominic finds their positions useful in fulfilling his complex schemes.

All members of the Obedient speak the elegant language of Dementlieu. Those among them who have traveled or are well educated will know other tongues as well.

Combat: Most of the Obedient are simple fishermen, shopkeepers, and the men and women who work at the inns, taverns, stables, and other places where visitors are likely to stop. Dominic has often provided these persons with poisons to kill or render unconscious anyone he suspects of causing trouble. If forced into direct conflict, the Obedient wield a variety of weapons from long swords to simple daggers. Characters who realize that the Obedient are under the control of another but opt to slay them anyway are subject to a powers check.

Escaping the control of d'Honaire is a difficult thing without outside help. Spells such as *command, emotion,* or the like can be used to shatter the hypnotic blocks that the lord of Dementlieu has established. If one of the Obedient is freed from the influence of the master hypnotist, however, Dominic will know immediately. The former servant will despise d'Honaire for enslaving his mind and usually help a party defeat him if possible.

Habitat/Society: The primary purpose of the Obedient is to inform Dominic d'Honaire about current events in the villages of Dementlieu. One of the most powerful servants is Lord-governor Marcel Guignol. In public, Dominic pretends to be the Lord-governor's adviser, but in truth, Guignol is the hypnotist's puppet. Other important persons under Dominic's control are the constables in the towns of Port-a-Lucine and a Chateaufaux, most of the wealthier merchants, and even the captains of Port-a-Lucine's fishing fleet.

Characters operating within Dementlieu will not go unnoticed by these servants, and word will reach d'Honaire's ears within hours of any strangers' arrival. Particularly powerful visitors, especially warriors and wizards, might attract Dominic's personal attentions as he attempts to mesmerize them and gather them to his flock of guardians and protectors.

Female characters with high Charisma scores (14 or better), will almost certainly attract Dominic's attentions, and may even be invited to dinner at the adviser's elegant chateau. Characters aware of Dominic's weakness for beautiful women may use this as a way to get to the hypnotist, but if they should discuss their plans while in Chateaufaux or Port-a-Lucine, there is a strong chance that they will be overheard by the Obedient and relayed to their master. Dominic has turned the tables on do-gooders more than once, transforming a dinner at his chateau into a deadly trap for his guests.

If visitors to town are particularly vocal about their attitudes toward Dominic or even the Lord-governor, the hypnotist will dispatch several of his more powerful servants to do away with the troublemakers. These servants are typically of the same average level as the character party, and are made up of two warriors, a wizard, and a priest. If extra villains are needed, Dominic can send more warriors of 1–2 levels lower than the party's average to fill the ranks. The DM should generate the characters as an NPC party of the appropriate levels, including the possibility of magic items and so forth.

Though d'Honaire often uses brute force as described above, most of the Obedient are everyday folk who live and work in the villages of Dementlieu. When not delivering messages to the hypnotist's minions, they go about their everyday lives exactly as if nothing was going on.

A member of the Obedient's alignment is normal until he must report to his master or take some action to protect him. At that point it switches to lawful evil, returning to normal only after the task is complete.

Ecology: The Obedient live, eat, and sleep like normal men and women. Dominic prefers human servants over elves, dwarves, or other humanoids, because other races aren't usually trusted anyway, and the illusion of trust and normality is an important facade for the Obedient.

Climate/Terrain:	Any land
Frequency:	Very rare
Organization:	Solitary
Activity Cycle:	Any
Diet:	Nil
Intelligence:	Very (13–14)
Treasure:	Nil
Alignment:	Chaotic evil
No. Appearing:	1
Armor Class:	N/A
Movement:	9
Hit Dice:	N/A
THAC0:	N/A
No. of Attacks:	1
Damage/Attack:	Nil
Special Attacks:	Domination
Special Defenses:	Immune to physical damage
Magic Resistance:	See below
Size:	N/A
Morale:	Fearless (19–20)
XP Value:	1,000

An odem is an undead spirit that moves into living bodies and takes control of them.

This creature is invisible to normal sight. Characters who can perceive ethereal objects see the odem as a white vapor when it is outside a body. When it is inside a body, they see a white aura about the face, which is concentrated at the eyes and mouth. The creature also appears as a white vapor on the ethereal plane.

Odems do not speak except when in control of a host. When that happens, they know the languages that they did in life, but not necessarily those of the host.

Combat: When it is outside a living body, the odem does not fight. In this state, it is invisible, ethereal, and immune to any form of physical or magical attack. Any spells designed to force extraplanar creatures to retreat or leave the prime material plane (*banishment, dismissal,* etc.) will indeed function normally. In the demiplane of Ravenloft, these spells only drive it from the host body and make it flee the region. This assumes that the person casting the spell can see the odem. An odem cannot be turned by a priest.

The odem inhabits a body by entering an orifice such as the mouth, nose, or ear. It can inhabit any living humanoid creature. Once inside the body, the odem is immune to any spell except *wish* or *magic jar,* which can drive it from the host body and repel the wizard's spirit back into the receptacle.

The inhabited body is quite vulnerable to harm while inhabited by the odem. Since the mind in control is that of the odem, spells affecting the mind don't work. If the host body is killed, the odem flees the body and must find a new victim.

An odem can pass through any physical object, but not through a magical restraint. A spell such as *trap the soul, temporal stasis,* or *imprisonment* will trap the odem in its current host.

Habitat/Society: The odem wanders the border of the ethereal plane, and peers into the Prime Material plane. It searches for victims with great potential for fear, anger, or hate.

An odem does not kill its victim or deaden his or her thoughts. If the victim's body were a coach, and the mind its driver, the odem would bind and gag the driver and take the reins himself. Like the poor driver who sits bound and gagged in the coach, the person whose body has been hijacked is completely aware of everything the odem is doing. He simply is helpless to act. He can even communicate telepathically with the odem if he wishes. If the odem is driven out, the character returns to normal.

Ecology: The odem is an evil undead spirit. Vicious or murderous characters of great willpower may become odems when they die.

The goal of the odem is always to cause mayhem and destruction. It feeds on the fear, anger, and hate of those around it. Since it is not harmed by the death of its host, it considers the host quite expendable. Typically, it attempts to start fights with insults or even physical abuse. It also may steal from one person and plant the goods on another.

Paka

Climate/Terrain:	Ravenloft
Frequency:	Rare
Organization:	Pride
Activity Cycle:	Day or night
Diet:	Carnivore
Intelligence:	Average to supra-genius (8–19)
Treasure:	U
Alignment:	Chaotic evil
No. Appearing:	3d6
Armor Class:	6
Movement:	15
Hit Dice:	Varies
THAC0:	By class
No. of Attacks:	2
Damage/Attack:	1d6/1d6 or by weapon
Special Attacks:	Springing
Special Defenses:	Healing
Magic Resistance:	20%
Size:	M
Morale:	Steady (11–12)
XP Value:	1,000

Paka are an ancient and sinister race of shapechanging feline humanoids who prey upon the settlements of humankind. Able to pass easily for human, they can spend years sowing evil before their true nature is discovered.

The appearance of a paka is that of a slender and fit but otherwise normal human. They are lithe, supple, and capable of amazing feats of agility, though they will never let non-paka who see these displays live. Female paka almost always have orange hair that turns dark gray as they age. Male paka may have any color hair except dark brown. The eyes of a paka shine red if caught in the light.

Paka can change their shape to more resemble their feline origins, but they are not lycanthropes and cannot transmit their powers in any way. When transformed, the paka's face becomes much more catlike, developing a smaller blackish nose, whiskers, and sharp teeth.

In either form, paka have sharp claws on their hands. These are retractable, however, and only a careful examination of the creature will reveal them when they are not extended.

Paka are skilled linguists who will almost always be able to speak half a dozen human languages in addition to their own tongue. Many of these creatures can also converse with lycanthropes such as wereleopards and weretigers.

Combat: Paka, or *cat people* as the Vistani call them, are supple and malicious fighters who love to torment their prey before finally killing it.

Paka can leap great distances, up to 40′ in a horizontal direction with a running start, 15′ without, or 15′ straight up. They often use this ability to spring at their opponents and catch them by surprise. Paka who attack with surprise double their damage in the first round.

Most paka like to use their natural claws to slice their victim's flesh, but many have acquired powerful weapons from past victims and have learned to use them effectively. A paka that attacks with its claws may strike twice in any combat round, inflicting 1d6 points of damage with each successful hit. Their weapons cause their normal damage, but paka may attack twice per round with any small or medium weapon due to their amazing agility. These claws are retractable in either the humanoid or feline form.

Any normal feline within 50 feet can be telepathically commanded by a paka. The paka can see through the animal's eyes and hear through its ears. The only way to break this link is via an *anti-magic shell* or similar barrier.

Paka will often torment those they dislike by commanding a horde of angry felines to physically attack someone. Such a cat swarm is generally made up of 5–10 (1d6+4) Hit Dice worth of animals. In towns and villages, these will be domesticated pets. In a wilderness setting, they will be more deadly beasts.

Paka have an innate healing ability. By licking a wound clean, paka can regain 2d4 lost hit points per day. They may lick the wounds of others once per day as well as their own.

Habitat/Society: The paka's control of cats also allows it to create dangerous traps or incite malicious behavior. Gossip overheard through the cat's ears can be repeated to make one person think another has violated their trust. The trouble that such a simple action can cause is often overwhelming.

Finally, paka can use their feline friends to set simple traps that will maim or kill their masters. Typical tricks include dragging a quilt into the fire to burn down a house, pushing a heavy vase or other object off a mantle and onto someone's head, or simply dragging things onto steep staircases to trip someone.

One method for detecting a paka is through dogs and other canines. Domesticated animals will bark and raise their hackles; feral canines will attack. Even werewolves (in human or wolfen form) will take an instant disliking to a paka. This doesn't necessarily mean that the lycanthrope will know a cat person for what it truly is, but something about it will just seem wrong.

The most vicious racial trait of the paka is a deep-rooted desire for revenge. Whenever someone crosses its path, harms another paka, or foils one of its plans, the creature and its closest friends will plot together to bring the offender to his knees. If a paka is ever killed, the entire pride will plan and cause the killer's slow and agonizing death.

Within the settlements of humankind, paka stay publicly separate from one another, but secretly form a very tight-knit pride within their community. If any individual is threatened, he can usually call on 3d6 others for help within an hour. Paka cannot exercise their telepathic abilities between one another, but they can send messages through any other feline.

Paka can be any class, though many are multi-classed as thieves. The only classes closed to the paka are paladins, bards, specialist wizards, and druids.

Paka who opt to be thieves may advance to the 10th level of experience. Such characters add +20% to their climb walls ability, but suffer a –10% penalty to pick pockets and open locks.

Paka wizards may advance to 11th level, and always have a cat familiar. Their spells tend to lean toward those that affect the mental faculties, with only a few offensive spells such as *fireball* or *lightning bolt*.

Priests of this race may advance to 8th level and gain all the benefits thereof. They worship a strange figure they refer to as the "Cat Lord," though even they admit they know little about him or his origins. Paka priests cannot control or turn undead.

Warriors have unlimited advancement, and may specialize and gain all other benefits available to their class. Rangers are common, but their species enemy is always humans. When the ranger is eligible to gain followers, 2d6 wereleopards will be the creatures that flock to his side.

Every community of 5 or more paka has a priest of at least 5th level that serves as a leader. He cannot really force any paka to do his will any more than any other, but others generally respect the priest's decisions as being handed down from the Cat Lord. The priest looks no different from any other disguised paka, but many of them pose as "good" clerics in the village. This amuses the evil beings and they often use their special status to cause far more harm than good.

Their purpose in life seems one of sheer revenge for some wrong done to their species in older times. No paka has ever admitted knowing what this wrong was, or even if it occurred in Ravenloft or elsewhere, but they are sure it was the human race that caused it. For this they have infiltrated the people of the land and consciously work to cause them suffering and hardship.

Ecology: Paka eat only meat. This has occasionally been used as a method of identification by perceptive adventurers.

Paka do not mate for life, preferring to remain allied to the pride instead. A female paka can bear young once per year, though most bear but a single litter of 1–6 kittens in their lifetime. The paka have no concept of a father, but ties to the mother are very strong. She and all other paka in the pride are responsible for teaching the children their heritage and the ways in which they keep their identity secret from their neighbors.

Plant, Bloodrose

Climate/Terrain:	Ravenloft core domains
Frequency:	Uncommon
Organization:	Patch
Activity Cycle:	Any
Diet:	Blood
Intelligence:	Non- (0)
Treasure:	U
Alignment:	Nil
No. Appearing:	3–36 (3d12)
Armor Class:	10
Movement:	0
Hit Dice:	10
THAC0:	11
No. of Attacks:	1
Damage/Attack:	1d2 + target's AC
Special Attacks:	Blood drain
Special Defenses:	Nil
Magic Resistance:	Nil
Size:	S (4′)
Morale:	NA
XP Value:	2,000

The bloodrose is a foul plant that feeds upon the blood of the living. Its keen thorns easily cut unprotected flesh, spilling precious blood into the soil where its roots can absorb it.

Bloodroses have dark green stems ending in flowers of purest white. Thin tendrils covered with sharp thorns hang limply from the base of the flower, looking much like the branches of a weeping willow. After feeding, the flowers begin to turn crimson with traces of blood etching their alabaster petals.

Bloodroses are unintelligent plants, unable to communicate in any way.

Combat: To someone not familiar with the bloodrose, the plant looks much like any other wild flower. Indeed, this illusion is the key to the plant's feeding habits and is maintained until a wandering animal reaches the center of the patch. At that point, the plant suddenly springs to life. Without warning, the thorny tendrils lash out like whips, tearing into unprotected flesh and spilling life-giving blood on the earth below.

A bloodrose patch has a diameter in feet equal to the number of plants within it. Thus, a patch of 20 plants would be 20 feet wide. When an attack begins, each plant is entitled to one attack roll with a hit indicating that a number of damage points equal to the target's Armor Class has been inflicted (with a minimum of 1 point). A patch of bloodroses is able to attack a number of man-sized creatures equal to the number of plants that make it up.

Escaping the patch can be a difficult process. The whirling vines of these plants have the same effect as an *entangle* spell. The saving throw for this is modified by the number of plants above or below 10 in the patch. Thus, a patch with 13 plants imposes a –3 penalty on the save while a patch with 8 plants allows a +2 bonus.

If the patch is attacked as a whole it is assumed to have the total hit points of all its flowers. The same is true for determining its attack and saving throws. Thus, a patch of 10 plants attacks and saves as a 10-Hit-Die creature. If individual plants are targeted, they have only their own Hit Dice.

Blunt or piercing weapons cause but a single point of damage on a successful attack. Slashing weapons, fire, or other attack forms generally have their normal effect. Bloodroses are exceptionally vulnerable to salt water. Every gallon of salt water poured on a patch will cause 1d10 points of damage. Characters who coat themselves in salt will be attacked once. After that the plant recoils with pain and will not attack that individual again.

Habitat/Society: Bloodroses live in the high mountains or rocky badlands, places where most plant life is reduced to desperate weeds or tiny pockets. In these desolate areas the bloodrose thrives as local animals are forced to try their luck in eating them. Only creatures with the thickest of skins are successful, other hunters quickly become the hunted.

It is said that some creatures of the Demiplane of Dread actively cultivate the bloodroses in the high mountains to cover cave entrances and the like from prying adventurers.

Ecology: Bloodroses reproduce like most other plants, by pollen collecting insects that can approach the patch unmolested.

If a bloodrose can be collected while pure white, it is said to be able to ward off the attacks of certain types of undead, namely vampires. Bloodroses can only survive 1d4 days after being pulled from the vine. Even artificial feedings or replanting cannot help—the plant needs its patch to survive.

Plant, Fearweed

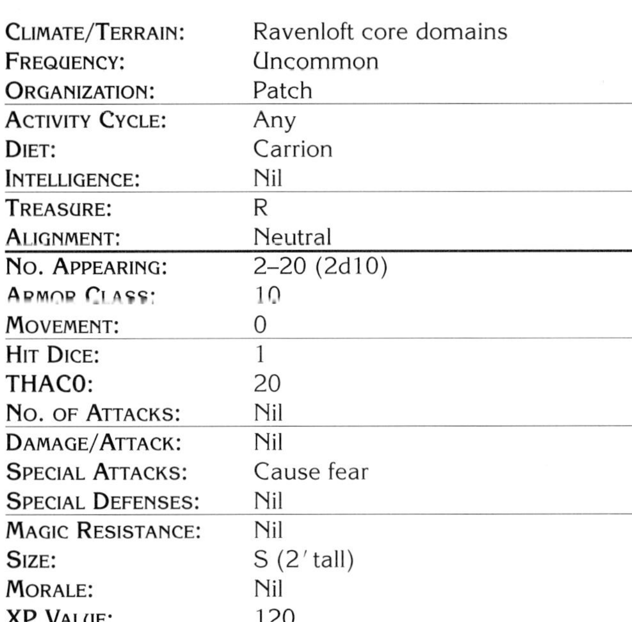

CLIMATE/TERRAIN:	Ravenloft core domains
FREQUENCY:	Uncommon
ORGANIZATION:	Patch
ACTIVITY CYCLE:	Any
DIET:	Carrion
INTELLIGENCE:	Nil
TREASURE:	R
ALIGNMENT:	Neutral
NO. APPEARING:	2–20 (2d10)
ARMOR CLASS:	10
MOVEMENT:	0
HIT DICE:	1
THAC0:	20
NO. OF ATTACKS:	Nil
DAMAGE/ATTACK:	Nil
SPECIAL ATTACKS:	Cause fear
SPECIAL DEFENSES:	Nil
MAGIC RESISTANCE:	Nil
SIZE:	S (2′ tall)
MORALE:	Nil
XP VALUE:	120

Fearweeds are terrible plants that use mind-numbing terror and confusion to defend themselves. Anyone exposed to their pollen risks confrontation with nightmares worse than any they have ever imagined.

These strange horrors look like a milkweed plant and are indistinguishable from them by anyone but druids and rangers. In both cases, white flowers and broad green leaves top a short, thick stem. The only real difference is in the weed's root structure. Fearweed has a much broader system composed of spongy fibers designed to soak up the blood and decayed nutrients of those who fall prey to its manipulations.

Like nearly all plants, fearweed has no ability to communicate.

Combat: The extensive root system of the fearweed plant serves to alert it to the proximity of living creatures. Whenever an animal (including humans and the like) comes within 20 feet of it, the fearweed releases a cloud of invisible and odorless gas. These vapors quickly form a cloud that surrounds the plant at a distance of roughly 20 feet. Any creature within this cloud must make a saving throw vs. poison with a –2 penalty. Those who fail this roll are overcome with paranoid fear. Friends become evil dopplegangers, trees become twisted and evil terrors, and every dark shadow contains threatening horrors. Few things make sense to the victim any more, but it is clear that anything moving is a threat.

Dispel magic will not cure the effects of the gas, but *remove curse* or *neutralize poison* will. Also, whenever a character falls unconscious or dies, all companions may attempt a second saving throw to realize just what has occurred. Characters who succeed in this secondary attempt become shaken and act as if hit by the *confusion* spell.

Habitat/Society: Fearweed originated in harsh climes where the soil was nutrient-poor. Instead of developing mobility and other carnivorous traits, fearweed instead sought to cause creatures to die and decay in its vicinity. In this way, their nutrients seep into the soil where the hungry plant can collect it.

Over time, fearweeds were transplanted throughout the realm, but retained their deadly method of enriching the environment.

Liches, powerful undead, or other creatures immune to biological phenomenons often cultivate patches of fearweed around their lair to keep out intruders.

Ecology: Fearweeds multiply by producing pollen from their flowers. Strangely, milkweeds have occasionally been known to turn into fearweeds, possibly after being fertilized by insects carrying fearweed pollen. Most realms in Ravenloft have milkweeds, so there is a 5% chance that any patch of overgrown area will develop fearweeds as well. This usually happens in places that receive little gardening attention, such as fallow fields, cemeteries, or even certain areas around castle walls and gardens.

Radiant Spirit

CLIMATE/TERRAIN:	Ravenloft
FREQUENCY:	Very rare
ORGANIZATION:	Solitary
ACTIVITY CYCLE:	Night
DIET:	Nil
INTELLIGENCE:	Genius (17–18)
TREASURE:	E, S
ALIGNMENT:	Lawful evil
NO. APPEARING:	1
ARMOR CLASS:	8
MOVEMENT:	9
HIT DICE:	10
THAC0:	11
NO. OF ATTACKS:	1
DAMAGE/ATTACK:	1–10
SPECIAL ATTACKS:	Blinding rays
SPECIAL DEFENSES:	See below
MAGIC RESISTANCE:	Nil
SIZE:	M (5′–6′ tall)
MORALE:	Special
XP VALUE:	1,000

A radiant spirit is the ghost of a powerful paladin or lawful good cleric killed while pursuing a holy cause. The anguish that fills his heart traps his spirit on the demiplane and taunts him with the failure of his quest.

The spirit is near impossible to see as it appears in a blinding, brilliant flash of white light. The few who have somehow managed to penetrate this aura say that the spirit inside is a figure wracked in constant agony of the deeds he is forced to perform.

Radiant spirits retain the same knowledge of languages that they had when alive. When they speak, however, their voices are remorseful and tortured, full of sorrow and grief.

Combat: Radiant spirits are forced to haunt the grounds on which they died. They can operate within a mile of the site, but often remain in a ruin or other fixed location.

Creatures who simply look at the brilliant image of the radiant spirit must make a save vs. spell or be blinded for 1d4 rounds.

The spirit can use this power actively as well. In this case, the ghost concentrates its energies and sends them out in pulses that permanently blind those looking at it. It may use this ability once per round, affecting all creatures within 25 feet who are looking directly at it. A save vs. paralysis will negate the attack, but failure means permanent blindness. An eerie aftereffect of the attack is white scarring on the pupils that looks like laughing human skulls. A character who has been blinded in this way suffers a –2 penalty to his Charisma score when checking NPC reactions. The folk of Ravenloft, especially the Vistani, won't normally consort with someone so marked by the horrors of the world.

Radiant spirits can only be harmed by magical weapons of +1 or better. Silver weapons can also hurt them, but do only half damage. They can be turned as ghosts, and holy water splashed on them does 2d4 points of damage.

The only way to release the tortured spirit is to complete the quest it was on at the time of its death. Usually the obstacles encountered during the quest are far worse than the radiant spirit. If this is done, however, the spirit appears as it did in life, thanks the characters, and vanishes into the nether regions.

Habitat/Society: Radiant spirits often haunt a ruin or site somehow involved in the completion of the quest they were on at the time of their death. They will generally allow lawful good characters to come and go in these places without interference, but will hinder others (especially those of evil alignment) who trespass there. Characters of any alignment who discover the spirit's corpse and are in some way disrespectful to it are certain to be attacked.

Discovering the spirit's cause is often as difficult as completing it, but the rewards are often threefold. Heroes can release the tortured spirit, gather treasure and experience during the quest, and the quest itself almost always results in the setback of some greater evil. The spirit will do what it can to aid those attempting to complete its quest, but is forbidden to answer direct questions on the subject, even under magical compulsion.

Ecology: A priest or paladin who dies while pursuing a just cause may rise as a radiant spirit 2–8 (2d4) months after his death. In order for a radiant spirit to be formed, however, the quest that the character was on must be one of extreme importance. As a rule, the failure of this mission must result in something as terrible as the utter collapse of the character's church.

Climate/Terrain:	Ravenloft
Frequency:	Uncommon
Organization:	Uncommon
Activity Cycle:	Any
Diet:	Omnivore
Intelligence:	Very to exceptional (11–16)
Treasure:	K
Alignment:	Neutral
No. Appearing:	1
Armor Class:	10
Movement:	12
Hit Dice:	3
THAC0:	17
No. of Attacks:	1
Damage/Attack:	1d4
Special Attacks:	Haunting
Special Defenses:	Nil
Magic Resistance:	Nil
Size:	M
Morale:	Unsteady (5–7)
XP Value:	35

Recluses are female Vistani who have decided to forego their clan and commune with the spirits that thrive on the Demiplane of Dread. Now they cackle gleefully at dark shadows flitting past their campfires and speak long-dead languages to ancient spectres only they can see.

Recluses dress in the bright gypsy garb common to all Vistani. Their constant communication with the cryptic and often dangerous spirits of Ravenloft makes their eyes and attentions jump randomly, behavior most simply see as eccentric or insane.

The typical recluse speaks the Vistani tongue, as well as a half dozen or so languages of normal men. It isn't uncommon for a recluse to have learned three or four long-forgotten languages from the spirits she communicates with.

Combat: Recluses are physically decrepit creatures. As such, the thought of one entering melee combat is almost laughable. Indeed, if a recluse is attacked, she will take no action to defend herself. This does not mean, however, that the recluse is defenseless.

Recluses are masters of the Vistani evil eye. Anyone who kills a recluse will be instantly stricken with a deadly curse. For example, any enemy who attacks the character will always do maximum damage or any saving throw the character is called on to make will always fail.

In addition, the character will become a magnet for spiritual activity. Within 24 hours after the death of the recluse, a ghost, spectre, or other incorporeal undead will begin to torment the murderer. As each day passes, another spirit will arrive. Eventually, the character will be surrounded by spirits determined to cause him harm. Only by restoring the recluse to life can the character escape these hauntings.

All recluses have mastered the Vistani art of tarokka casting. By means of these prophetic cards, the recluse may cast any spell from the sphere of Divination or the school of Lesser/Greater Divination. All of these spells are assumed to have a casting time of 1 round and require no material components other than the old woman's tarokka deck. All of these spells are cast as if the recluse were a 13th level character.

Habitat/Society: Recluses live solitary lives communing with spirits that are as maddening as they are insightful. As the years pass, they drift farther and farther out of touch with the real world. Eventually, they will pay little or no attention to the affairs of man, giving themselves wholly over to the world of spirits.

Those who seek out the recluse in hopes of learning some important fact will be required to pay for the service. Most frequently, the fee will take the form of some action that benefits one of the spirits with whom the recluse is in communication. For example, the characters might be asked to solve a murder so that the victim's spirit could rest easily in his grave. Only when this task is done will the gypsy answer their questions.

Because of the rambling nature of a recluse's thought patterns, making sense of an answer may be as hard as getting one. After all, these women are considered by most to be utterly mad. Any questions asked of a recluse are likely to be answered with metaphors, riddles, and other difficult to fathom answers.

Ecology: Recluses tend to eat strange things such as boiled bat wings and lizard tongues. It may be that these things heighten their perception of the spirit world, but no one can say for sure. It might just be that these are the most easily available foodstuffs in the strange places recluses pick to inhabit.

Remnant, Aquatic

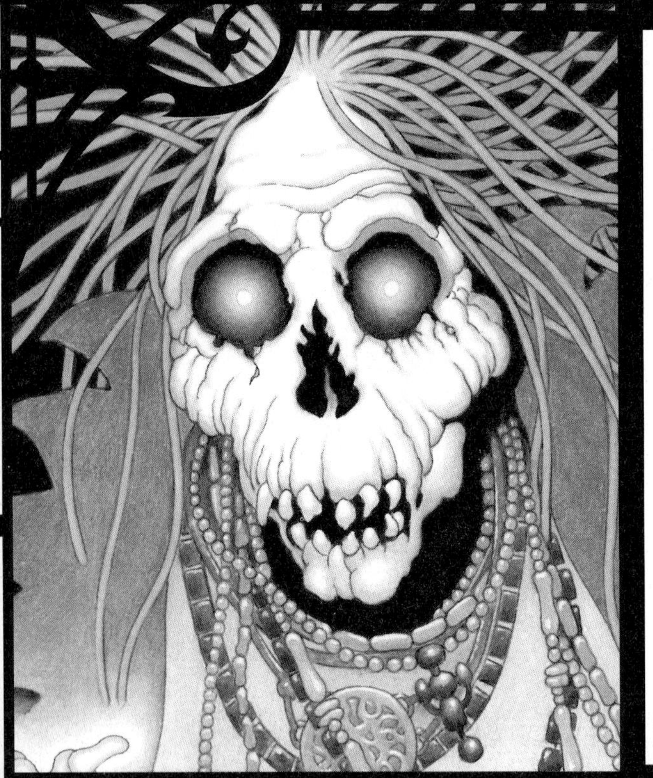

Climate/Terrain:	Any aquatic
Frequency:	Rare
Organization:	Solitary or group
Activity Cycle:	Any
Diet:	Nil
Intelligence:	Average (8–10)
Treasure:	Nil
Alignment:	Chaotic neutral
No. Appearing:	Varies
Armor Class:	0 or 8
Movement:	Sw 36
Hit Dice:	3
THAC0:	17
No. of Attacks:	1
Damage/Attack:	See below
Special Attacks:	See below
Special Defenses:	See below
Magic Resistance:	Nil
Size:	S
Morale:	Average (8–10)
XP Value:	3,000

Remnants are the spirits of humans and humanoids whose former bodies have been thrown into an unconsecrated, watery grave after they have died of acute stress and exhaustion. The callous way in which they have been disposed of after a torturous and miserable life leaves them in a state of such sorrow that they cannot completely leave the material world behind, and they lurk in the pools and rivers where their bodies were abandoned.

Aquatic remnants appear as melancholy faces with eyeless sockets and pale floating hands. Their bodies seem to fade away into the depths, leaving no sight of their legs.

Without the aid of magic it is impossible to communicate with these tragic spirits.

Combat: Remnants are related to ghosts (see "ghost" in the *Monstrous Manual*) and as such, are ethereal monsters that can be seen by non-ethereal creatures.

At will, their cold, wet touch chills a corporeal being to the bone, inflicting no damage, but draining 1 point of Dexterity per successful attack. Any creature whose Dexterity reaches 0 succumbs to acute hypothermia and dies. Lost Dexterity points return at the rate of 1 per hour. Victims of remnants do not become remnants themselves.

In order to attack a corporeal creature, remnants' hands must become semimaterialized, during which time their Armor Class drops to 8. Semimaterialized remnants can be hit only by silver weapons, which inflict half damage, or magical weapons. While fully ethereal, they can only be attacked by others in a similar state.

Remnants are turned as ghosts and can be damaged by holy water while in their semimaterial form. Each vial of the precious liquid that strikes them does 1d6 points of damage.

Habitat/Society: Remnants are confined to bodies of water connected to their graves. If a living creature looks into the water where a remnant resides, it has a 10% chance to spot the creature. Knowing of the remnant's presence raises this chance to 80%. Remnants are flickering, elusive creatures, who prefer to stay out of sight until they can approach creatures in the water.

Remnants are not always hostile, and they may even help those who fight the creatures that mistreated them in life. Remnants can even convey what amounts to *water breathing* upon corporeal creatures by grasping their hands, pulling them under the water, and briefly performing "mouth-to-mouth resuscitation." (Actually, the remnant is drawing the living creature partly into the Border Ethereal.) Thereafter, so long as the corporeal creature holds the semimaterial hand of the remnant, it will not drown.

Ecology: Remnants remain trapped in the Border Ethereal until ritual burial services are performed over their remains. They do not hate material life as their ghostly cousins do, but they will not hesitate to attack any member of the race that caused their condition.

Rushlight

CLIMATE/TERRAIN:	Ravenloft
FREQUENCY:	Uncommon
ORGANIZATION:	Solitary
ACTIVITY CYCLE:	Night
DIET:	Nil
INTELLIGENCE:	Average (8–10)
TREASURE:	Nil
ALIGNMENT:	Chaotic evil
NO. APPEARING:	1
ARMOR CLASS:	4
MOVEMENT:	Fl 18 (A)
HIT DICE:	6
THAC0:	15
NO. OF ATTACKS:	1
DAMAGE/ATTACK:	Nil
SPECIAL ATTACKS:	Ignition
SPECIAL DEFENSES:	Spell resistance
MAGIC RESISTANCE:	30%
SIZE:	S (2′ diameter)
MORALE:	Steady (11–12)
XP VALUE:	1,400

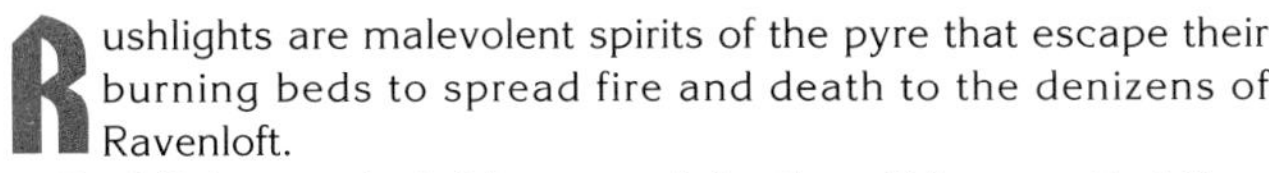

Rushlights are malevolent spirits of the pyre that escape their burning beds to spread fire and death to the denizens of Ravenloft.

Rushlights are invisible most of the time. When spotted they appear as flickering globes of flame. Inside the near-transparent ball are the face and hands of an evil, tortured spirit.

Rushlights cannot speak. However, they seem to be able to understand the languages that they knew in life.

Combat: Rushlights can only be seen from the corner of the eye. Anyone who attempts to look right at one sees nothing, though they may soon feel its fiery touch. Only if a player announces that his character will attempt to use his peripheral vision will the creature be fairly visible. Even this is difficult, and attackers suffer a –2 penalty on their attack rolls. Certain spells, a *detect invisibility* for instance, can make the creature fully visible.

The rushlight attacks by slamming into the victim and his belongings, often setting the latter alight. Although the flame of a rushlight emits little light and no perceived heat, it is one of the most deadly things a character is likely to encounter. A successful Attack Roll by the rushlight indicates that it has struck its target, inflicting 3d4 points of damage. In addition, every item the character is carrying must make a saving throw vs. magical fire or be utterly destroyed.

Once a character has been hit by a rushlight, his very flesh will smoulder and burn. Each turn after the successful attack the character will take 2d4 points of damage. Extinguishing the magical fire of the rushlight is no easy matter, requiring a *dispel magic* or similar enchantment. Normal means of fire fighting, such as immersion in water or attempting to smother the flames with a leather cloak, will prove ineffective.

Rushlights can only be hit by magical weapons or creatures with 4+1 Hit Dice. They are immune to any spells that affect the body or the mind, as well as spells of cold or fire.

Although they might be technically classed as undead, rushlights cannot be turned. Curiously, however, they are very vulnerable to holy water and suffer 2d6 points of damage per flask that strikes them.

Habitat/Society: Rushlights are formed when an evil being is burned alive on a funeral pyre. The soul flees the smoldering shell and attempts to escape into the night. Before the spirit can break free of its earthly bonds, it merges with the all-consuming fires and acquire their power.

When not active, the thing sinks into the earth near the site of its death. At night, it roams up to twenty miles from its "lair" searching for travelers to torture and kill. Something in the tortured psyche of these creatures tells them that by destroying living things, they will ease their own suffering.

Ecology: A rushlight seems to feed on the fear and pain it creates. After the first few victims have been ignited, the thing moves more energetically. Though they do not rest, the rushlight must remain buried in the earth where its body was cremated during the daylight hours.

Sea Spawn, Master

Climate/Terrain:	Sea of Sorrows
Frequency:	Rare
Organization:	Solitary
Activity Cycle:	Any
Diet:	Carnivore
Intelligence:	Average (8–10)
Treasure:	J
Alignment:	Lawful evil
No. Appearing:	1
Armor Class:	5
Movement:	9, Sw 9
Hit Dice:	10
THAC0:	11
No. of Attacks:	3
Damage/Attack:	1d6/1d6/1d10
Special Attacks:	See below
Special Defenses:	Nil
Magic Resistance:	Nil
Size:	M (7′)
Morale:	Steady (11–12)
XP Value:	4,000

The master sea spawn is one of the most horrid creatures to lurk beneath the oceans of the Demiplane of Dread. They infiltrate coastal villages with their disgusting spawn and then use them to take control of the minds they come into contact with.

The master is a large humanoid with great black claws that match its dark, pupilless eyes. A series of thick fins runs down the length of its head and spine. These are almost always covered with wafting fungus, weeds, or scraps of torn flesh. The rest of the body is covered with sickly green scales and sheathed in a toxic mucus. The webbed hands and feet are oversized to help with swimming. The creature's viciousness is evident from the double rows of sharp, jagged teeth that jut from the master's tremendous jaws.

Sea spawn masters speak no known language, but are able to telepathically communicate with their sluglike spawn and the creatures they control without regard for such things.

Combat: Sea spawn masters cannot leave the water. If forced to do so, they will asphyxiate in 10+1d6 rounds. In the meantime, of course, the creature will try to escape or kill whatever is keeping it from the sea. This means characters who want to deal with the thing will have to travel beneath the murky sea, incurring all the usual penalties and problems thereof.

When confronted, the master usually uses its telepathic abilities to summon help from fishes and other creatures of the depths. This functions as a *monster summoning IV* spell but applies only to aquatic creatures. Each monster summoned arrives 1d4 rounds later. The spawn master may use this ability twice per day.

Though the spawn prefers to let others fight its battles, it is not completely helpless. Its jagged claws cause 1d6 points of damage per hit, and its frightening maw of jagged teeth inflicts 1d10 points. Those bitten by the creature may also contract a rotting disease that infects a wound and keeps it from healing. Anytime a character takes damage from the thing's bite, he must make a saving throw vs. poison. Should he fail, the bite's damage is permanent until healed by a *cure disease* spell.

The skin and scales of sea spawn masters are notoriously slimy and covered with bits of rotting flesh. This functions as an *oil of slipperiness*, making it nearly impossible to grab or otherwise hold the beast. Webs, nets, and other devices are equally ineffectual. The beast often uses this advantage to slip in and out of fishermen's nets and steal their catch. Many a confused fisherman has been puzzled by the slimy residue that is the only prize of a once-heavy haul.

Habitat/Society: By day, the sea spawn master lurks in shallow caves, reefs, or thick tangles of seaweed near the target of its latest attack. Here it spends most of the day in a sort of trance, coordinating the movements of its less intelligent minions.

The lair of the thing is usually littered with bones, scraps of clothing, and a few coppers and other artifacts, but little else. There is a very small chance that the thing has feasted on more powerful folk, however, so the lair has a 20% chance of containing treasure type W as well as J.

Ecology: Sea spawn masters are born from minions that somehow escape back into the sea. The survival rate for these tiny, vicious things isn't high, so there is only a 1% chance that they will survive long enough to develop into masters.

The spawn matures similarly to a tadpole. As it grows larger on a diet of fish and the like, tiny legs and arms grow and elongate. Over a period of twelve months, the minion rapidly develops into a full-grown spawn master. Four months into this change, the spawn develops its telepathic powers and can summon other creatures to protect it. The slippery coating of scum and rot is well developed by the time the thing reaches maturity.

Once a master, the spawn survives on a diet of fish and other sea creatures. But seafood is poor fare for this horror of the deep. The taste of human flesh drives it to seek a seashore community to provide it with bloody fodder.

CLIMATE/TERRAIN:	Coastal (Sea of Sorrows)
FREQUENCY:	Rare
ORGANIZATION:	Group
ACTIVITY CYCLE:	Any
DIET:	Carnivore
INTELLIGENCE:	Low (5–7)
TREASURE:	Nil
ALIGNMENT:	Lawful evil
NO. APPEARING:	3–18 (3d6)
ARMOR CLASS:	5
MOVEMENT:	3, Sw 3
HIT DICE:	1
THAC0:	19
NO. OF ATTACKS:	1
DAMAGE/ATTACK:	1 point of damage
SPECIAL ATTACKS:	See below
SPECIAL DEFENSES:	See below
MAGIC RESISTANCE:	Nil
SIZE:	T (6″ long)
MORALE:	Steady (11–12)
XP VALUE:	35

The minions of the sea spawn (q.v.) are tiny creatures that seek to inhabit the skull of a coastal villager and control his will and body. Their sole purpose is to provide living flesh for their horrid master.

The minions look like disgusting, slimy, six-inch-long slugs. Unlike their landborn cousins, the minions have a circular mouth, much like that of a lamprey, which they use to bore into their victim's flesh. Their skin is much thicker than that of normal slugs as well, probably as a means of keeping out the salt of the water that would kill regular slugs.

Sea spawn slugs do not speak, but are in constant telepathic contact with their masters.

Combat: The only physical attack that sea spawn minions possess is their bite. By itself, this inflicts an insignificant wound and causes only 1 point of damage. However, the bite of the minion injects a powerful poison that renders a victim paralyzed for 1d4 turns unless a saving throw vs. paralyzation is made. Long before the paralysis has worn off, the spawn will bore a tunnel for itself through the soft flesh behind and below the skull of the victim. The gruesome thing then coils around the brain stem and takes control of the host's higher functions.

A sea spawn host retains all memories, spell abilities, and proficiencies, and can use these powers normally. The only noticeable difference is in personality. A spawn's victim becomes detached from his family and friends. Indeed, the thing is waiting for its slimy brothers to come in the following nights and dominate the rest of the town.

Removing a spawn minion is difficult and requires the magical touch of a priest. *Cure* spells have no effect except to heal the spawn and its host of normal damage. *Cure disease* or *restoration* are the only spells that will force the creature out of the victim, though even this will cause 3d6 points of damage as the thing writhes and chews its way back out.

Each day that a slug spends in the skull of a victim lowers that person's Intelligence score by 1 point. If the creature is driven out of its host, the newly liberated mind will be far less alert than it was previously. Nothing short of a *wish* spell will repair this damage.

The sea spawn minions have a telepathic link with all other slugs produced by the same master, so the moment one of them becomes cornered or harmed it will summon 3–18 (3d6) other hosts to help it. The things also have mental contact with the sea spawn master, so it too might send allies to the minion's aid.

Most hosts are villagers with 1 Hit Die. Occasionally the things will find more powerful victims. There is a 25% chance that the spawn have found adventurers generated from the rules presented in the *MONSTROUS MANUAL*.

Habitat/Society: When a sea spawn master spies a coastal village it thinks will provide it with fresh fodder, it ejects 3d6 minions. These foul creatures make their way to the shore. From that time until an entire village has become dominated, the spawn master will continue to release its slimy children once per night. While at sea, the slugs swim like eels. On shore, they are forced to slither like worms or snakes. The slime that coats their bodies is sticky, allowing them to climb up walls and ceilings to drop down on their victims. From there the spawn bite and paralyze their prey, bore into the skull and take up residence in the brain. In this manner, the creatures gradually take control of whole communities.

Not all of a sea spawn's slugs will reach the shore. About 1 in 10 of them are swept out to sea by currents and the like. Most of these die, but about 1% of them grow to become sea spawn masters after about a year.

Sea spawn begin feeding their master mere hours after inhabiting their first victim. Their preferred method is to abduct the young or helpless from the homes of their hosts and toss them into the sea by cover of night. Their malicious master waits greedily for the tender flesh of surface dwellers. If this isn't possible, one of the minions will deliver its own host to the master to sate its hunger for a time.

Ecology: Sea spawn minions are born in a sack above the master's gut. From there they are spewed into the sea and forced to swim ashore. Once on the land, they seek out places where they can lurk undiscovered and strike without fear of detection.

The things mature inside their hosts, feeding on brain tissue. Each day that passes sees the mind of the victim partially destroyed by the hunger of the sea spawn. Their life span is short, however, for when the entire village is taken over, they hurl their hosts into the sea where both parties are consumed by the sea spawn master.

Shadow Asp

CLIMATE/TERRAIN:	Har'Akir
FREQUENCY:	Rare
ORGANIZATION:	Special
ACTIVITY CYCLE:	Any
DIET:	Nil
INTELLIGENCE:	Animal (1)
TREASURE:	A
ALIGNMENT:	Neutral
NO. APPEARING:	5d6
ARMOR CLASS:	2
MOVEMENT:	0
HIT DICE:	½ (1–4 hit points)
THAC0:	20
NO. OF ATTACKS:	1
DAMAGE/ATTACK:	1d2
SPECIAL ATTACKS:	Shadow poison, surprise
SPECIAL DEFENSES:	Piercing attacks do half damage
MAGIC RESISTANCE:	Nil
SIZE:	T (6″–12″ long)
MORALE:	Fearless (19–20)
XP VALUE:	65

In all of Ravenloft, no place reveres the tombs of its dead more highly than Har'Akir. Recently, the priests of this desert realm have found deadly wardens for the tombs of their pharaohs: shadow asps.

Shadow asps appear to be slender snakes composed of pure darkness. They seem to have no physical form, but look as if they are nothing more than an extension of the shadows that give them their name. Although these creatures are barely intelligent, they instinctively lash out at those who intrude upon the tombs they live in.

Shadow asps make no sound, not even a hiss or slithering, as they move.

Combat: Shadow asps are very hard to spot as they slide silently through the darkness of a tomb or temple. Because they make no sound and are utterly black, they often surprise their victims when they strike. To reflect this, shadow asps impose a –5 penalty on their victim's surprise roll. It is important to note that shadow asps do not radiate body heat and are thus well hidden from all infravision.

In combat, a shadow asp strikes with its needlelike fangs, just as normal asps do. Although the bite inflicts only minor injuries (1–2 points of damage), it injects an insidious toxin. Those who are bitten must save vs. poison. Failure to save indicates that the victim has been injected with the essence of darkness and gradually begins to become a shadow. This transformation takes five rounds, during which time the character gradually grows darker and darker. At the end of the fifth round, the character must make a system shock roll. Failure indicates that the victim breaks up in the process of becoming a shadow and is lost, with no chance of resurrection. Success means that the victim has become a shadow. Shadows created by this process are bound to the area guarded by the shadow asps and join them as wardens of that place. At any time during the transformation, but not afterwards, a *remove curse* or *dispel magic* spell can be cast on the victim to halt the change.

Those who strike at a shadow asp with weapons will find it difficult to harm. Although it can be injured by any normal weapon, the snake's agility makes it very hard to hit (hence its low Armor Class). A *hold monster* spell used to immobilize one would make it AC 8. Although bludgeoning and slashing weapons inflict full damage to shadow asps, piercing attacks (such as from arrows, spears, etc.) do only half damage.

Any single shadow asp can be instantly slain by the casting of a *light* or *continual light* spell that has been directly targeted on the creature. No saving throw is allowed. Illuminating spells used to destroy shadow asps provide no additional light for vision, being cancelled out at once.

Shadow asps are not undead and cannot be turned by priests or harmed by holy water. They are summoned creatures and can be held back by spells like *protection from evil.*

Habitat/Society: Shadow asps are magical creatures summoned by the priests of certain gods worshiped in Har'Akir (Osiris, Set, or Nephythys). The ceremony by which these creatures are called into existence is a tightly guarded secret.

Shadow asps are very territorial. They slither about the place where they were summoned and maintain a constant vigil against the intrusions of potential grave robbers or defilers.

Because they turn their victims into shadows, there is a 40% chance of finding 1d6 shadows (see the *MONSTROUS MANUAL*) with any group of shadow asps.

Ecology: Shadow asps are not a part of the physical world. Because of their extradimensional origins, they play no part in the grand scheme of nature apart from bringing death to their victims and creating undead shadows.

Shattered Brethren

CLIMATE/TERRAIN:	Bluetspur
FREQUENCY:	Rare
ORGANIZATION:	Fraternal
ACTIVITY CYCLE:	Any
DIET:	Varies
INTELLIGENCE:	Low (5–7)
TREASURE:	I, K, M
ALIGNMENT:	Neutral evil
NO. APPEARING:	5d6
ARMOR CLASS:	Varies
MOVEMENT:	Varies
HIT DICE:	3
THAC0:	17
NO. OF ATTACKS:	Varies
DAMAGE/ATTACK:	Varies
SPECIAL ATTACKS:	See below
SPECIAL DEFENSES:	Regeneration, psionics
MAGIC RESISTANCE:	Nil
SIZE:	M (4′–7′ tall)
MORALE:	Unsteady (5–7)
XP VALUE:	250

The shattered brethren are the result of the cruel experiments by the mind flayers of Bluetspur. The main difference between the brethren and their cousins, broken ones, is that these creatures have developed innate defenses that prevent psionic intrusions. They also possess random wild talents (see *The Complete Psionics Handbook*).

Bluetspur's broken ones resemble the animals that they have been magically and genetically linked with. Without exception, they favor their animal half over their human half. They include a wide variety of animal types because the mind flayers are constantly looking for combinations that make useful slaves.

These pitiful creatures know the languages they spoke before their conversions, but they also speak a secret dialect peculiar to them.

Combat: Bluetspur's broken ones are stronger than their common counterparts because natural selection is so fierce among them. Also, while common broken ones are the result of failed experiments, these were purposely altered, so they are more *successful.* Therefore, they always have a minimum of 7 points per Hit Die and regenerate 3 hit points per round.

They wield weapons if they can get their hands on them, but usually use combat techniques relating to their animal traits. A lionlike broken one may claw and bite while a spiderlike one may use a poisonous bite.

Habitat/Society: Bluetspur's broken ones are the lucky few who have developed ways to avoid the mind flayers' psionic control over them. They escaped their former masters and fled into the fissures that honeycomb Bluetspur. Here they have formed their fraternity. One of the few tenets that binds them together is a mutual desire to survive. Their shared skills allow them to steal goods and scavenge sustenance from the illithids.

Their mutual hatred of their mind flayer captors also brings them together. Given the chance, they will ambush a lone illithid and murder him, but whether they derive more pleasure from exacting revenge or from having a good dinner is hard to tell. The brethren aid enemies of the mind flayers as they can, but remain fearful and distrustful of all strangers.

Thirty broken ones live in the fissures of Mt. Makab—though their numbers shift as more escape from the mind flayers and others die in numerous ways.

Bluetspur's broken ones tend to forget their former lives and take new names that reflect their condition. For example, a lionlike broken one might be named "Snarler."

Ecology: The dietary needs of Bluetspur's broken ones are largely dictated by their animal natures. The limited access to vegetables in the caves results in better survival rates, and thus larger numbers, of carnivores and omnivores. They eat anything they can steal, but a captured illithid is considered a delicacy.

Skeleton, Archer

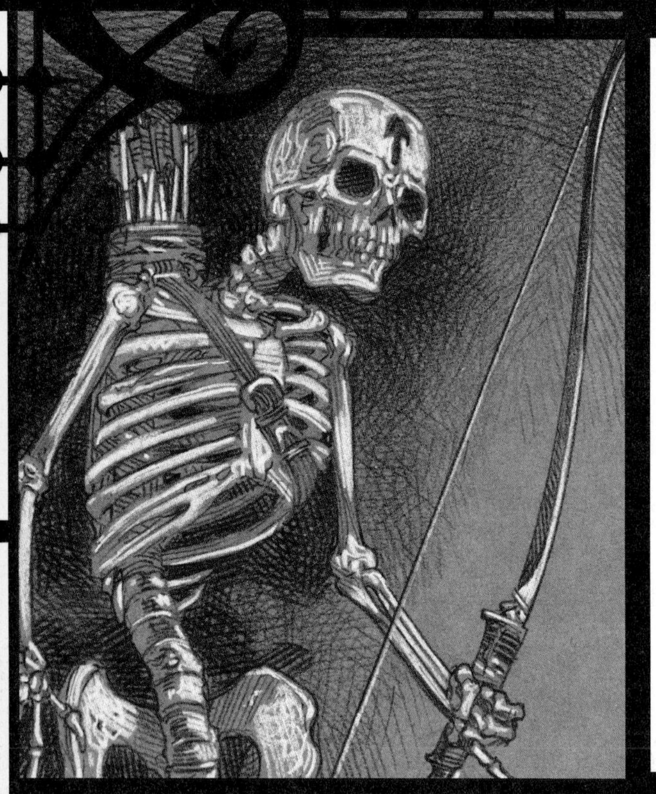

Climate/Terrain:	Ravenloft
Frequency:	Very rare
Organization:	Band
Activity Cycle:	Any
Diet:	Nil
Intelligence:	Non- (0)
Treasure:	Nil
Alignment:	Neutral
No. Appearing:	2–20 (2d10)
Armor Class:	7
Movement:	12
Hit Dice:	2
THAC0:	19
No. of Attacks:	1
Damage/Attack:	1–6
Special Attacks:	Skeleton creation
Special Defenses:	Damage resistance & spell immunity
Magic Resistance:	Nil
Size:	M (6′ tall)
Morale:	Fearless (19–20)
XP Value:	175

Archer skeletons are magically animated humanoid undead monsters created as guardians or warriors by powerful evil wizards and priests. Such creatures are crafted from the bones of dead archers using an *animate dead* spell. The creator must also bond a blooded arrowhead to the skull of each skeleton. During the animation process the arrowhead fuses with the skeleton's skull.

These skeletal monsters are identical in appearance to normal skeletons, being formed from the bones of humans and demihumans, save for an arrowhead-shaped black mark on their skulls. These monsters are always armed with long bows made of ash wood and human sinew, and bone arrows carried in hide quivers.

The bowmen of the night cannot speak and are utterly unable to communicate. They can understand simple commands from their master, but these must be clearly worded and very short.

Combat: In battle, an archer skeleton almost always attacks with its sinister bow and bone arrows. A skeleton can attack once per round and each arrow does 1–6 points of damage. Although these arrows do no extra damage, they are considered magical weapons and can affect those creatures protected from nonmagical weapons.

Each archer skeleton carries 20 such arrows. A skeleton can create new arrows simply by robbing graves and sharpening other bones into arrows.

It is, however, when the archer skeleton's arrows miss their target that they prove most devastating. Whenever an arrow fails to hit its target, the DM should make a saving throw vs. crushing blow for the arrow. If the saving throw fails the shaft simply breaks and becomes useless. If it is successful, however, the arrow remains intact and rapidly (1 round) grows into a skeleton with all the normal abilities of those undead (see the *Monstrous Manual*). Such skeletons are hideous automatons of death and destruction that will immediately attack the closest living target.

If forced into close combat, the archer skeleton wields its bow as a weapon, attempting to bludgeon opponents for 1–4 points of damage per hit. An archer skeleton will resort to this method of attack only if it is impossible to fire its arrows. If its bow is destroyed, the creature will claw at its enemies for 1d3 points of damage.

Archer skeletons are immune to *sleep, hold, charm,* or *fear* spells. They need never check morale, usually being magically commanded to fight to their destruction. They are also immune to all cold-based attacks, as are normal skeletons. Similarly, edged and piercing weapons do only half damage to these creatures, while blunt weapons, being designed to crush bone, do full damage. Holy water inflicts 2–8 points of damage per vial.

Habitat/Society: Archer skeletons are said to have first been created by a zealous necromancer named Karakin. Karakin wished to murder all the people of his land so that he would be the only human living there. Once this was accomplished, Karakin would surround himself with undead courtiers far more loyal than any living vassals. Creating a vast army of archer skeletons and other undead, Karakin prepared to march, but the sheer force of his malice proved virulent enough to carry him instead through the mists and into Ravenloft.

Where Karakin resides now is unknown, but his skeletal archers and the secret of their construction have come into the hands of a growing number of nefarious individuals.

Archer skeletons are most often employed as the vanguard of an evil force ranging in size from 2–20 skeletons to a full army. They are also commonly used as guards and sentinels by their foul masters. The lich lord, Azalin, is said to have a large number of these minions under his control.

Ecology: As with all lesser undead, these creatures have no place in the natural ecology. They are abominations of evil, twisted into foul mockeries of life, and exploited by those persons who have turned from light and virtue.

Although the skeletons themselves turn to dust and ash when destroyed, the longbows and arrows of these monsters remain intact. It is thus possible for a character to pick up and use these weapons. The arrows have the same effect for player characters that they do when fired by archer skeletons. However, any time an arrow fired by a character creates a new skeleton, the character must make a powers check as he adds to the corruption of the world.

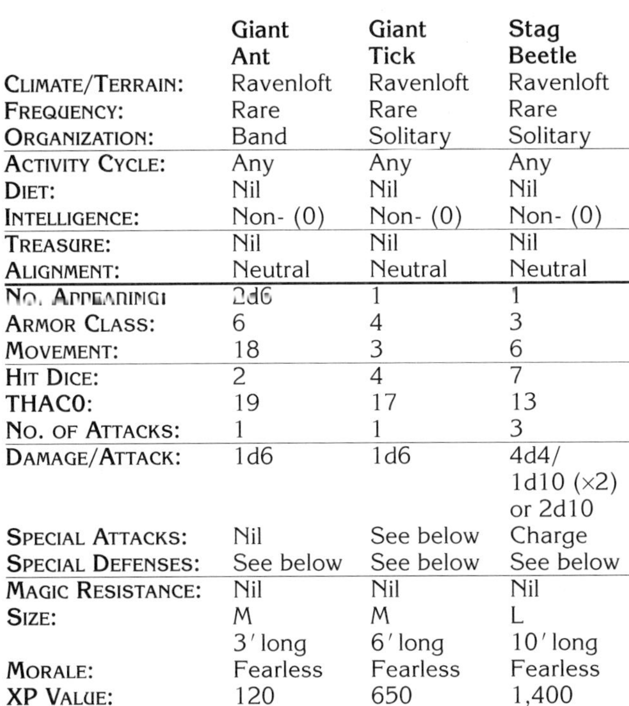

	Giant Ant	Giant Tick	Stag Beetle
Climate/Terrain:	Ravenloft	Ravenloft	Ravenloft
Frequency:	Rare	Rare	Rare
Organization:	Band	Solitary	Solitary
Activity Cycle:	Any	Any	Any
Diet:	Nil	Nil	Nil
Intelligence:	Non- (0)	Non- (0)	Non- (0)
Treasure:	Nil	Nil	Nil
Alignment:	Neutral	Neutral	Neutral
No. Appearing:	2d6	1	1
Armor Class:	6	4	3
Movement:	18	3	6
Hit Dice:	2	4	7
THAC0:	19	17	13
No. of Attacks:	1	1	3
Damage/Attack:	1d6	1d6	4d4/ 1d10 (×2) or 2d10
Special Attacks:	Nil	See below	Charge
Special Defenses:	See below	See below	See below
Magic Resistance:	Nil	Nil	Nil
Size:	M 3′ long	M 6′ long	L 10′ long
Morale:	Fearless	Fearless	Fearless
XP Value:	120	650	1,400

These nightmarish automatons are the animated exoskeletons of dead insects. Evil priests and wizards, bent on manipulating nature for their own nefarious purposes, create these chitinous monstrosities with *animate dead* spells in a process almost identical to that used in the creation of normal skeletons.

Insectoid skeletons are, from a distance, easy to mistake for their still-living brethren. However, upon closer examination it quickly becomes obvious that these creatures are no longer living. As a rule, their eyes and bellies are missing, and their exoskeletons are often chipped or cracked in several places. Most insectoid skeletons make harsh clicking and grinding sounds when they move.

Insectoid skeletons cannot speak or comprehend spoken languages. Simple orders from their master, however, are instantly understood and obeyed.

Combat: Most insectoid skeletons retain the physical attacks they had while living. The exception to this is that they do not retain any venom or poison they might have had in life, although a stinger could still do piercing damage.

There are many different types of insectoid skeletons. All such skeletons are immune to the effects of *sleep, charm, hold,* and *fear* spells, as well as all cold-based attacks. Edged and piercing weapons do only half damage to them, since they no longer have vital organs to pierce or blood to spill.

Habitat/Society: These undead insects have no true habitat or society. They are only capable of understanding the simplest of orders and are thus normally employed as guards, advance warriors, or as tireless excavators, pack animals, and the like.

Ecology: Insectoid skeletons are created with the use of a special version of the *animate dead* spell. It is believed that this spell was created by a drow necromancer, but the truth of that supposition is unknown.

Giant Ant

Skeletal giant ants are always animated in groups. Such groups of undead ants most commonly attack by swarming their victims, with no fewer than three ants attacking a single creature. In combat these monsters attack with their mandibles, doing 1–6 points of damage per attack.

Giant Tick

The carapace of a giant tick skeleton is unique among the undead exoskeletons in that it is still capable of storing fluid within its chitinous form. Such creatures attack their victim with their mandibles, digging into the unfortunate's flesh and draining his blood at a rate of 1d6 hit points per round.

Once a tick has successfully hit, it can automatically drain blood from its victim, doing an additional 1d4 points of damage each round. Unlike living ticks, the skeletal tick can drain more than its own hit points worth of blood. Indeed, as the vital fluid merely pours out of the creature and onto the ground once it has filled the carapace, there is no limit to the "appetite" of this foul thing. Fortunately, this creature does not transmit the diseases its living counterparts do.

For every 10 points of blood within its carapace, a skeletal tick may spit a stream of blood up to 10 yards. If the tick hits its target the target must make a saving throw vs. paralysis or be blinded for 2–8 (2d4) rounds.

Stag Beetle

The undead stag beetle attacks with its pair of 8-foot-long horns and its hideous mandibles, doing 1d10, 1d10 and 4d4 points of damage respectively. If the monster can get up a running charge of at least 25 feet it does an additional 2d10 points of damage as it tramples its opponent.

Skeleton, Strahd

Climate/Terrain:	Barovia
Frequency:	Very rare
Organization:	Pack
Activity Cycle:	Night
Diet:	Nil
Intelligence:	Non- (0)
Treasure:	Nil
Alignment:	Neutral
No. Appearing:	2d10
Armor Class:	7
Movement:	12
Hit Dice:	2
THAC0:	19
No. of Attacks:	3 per 2 rounds
Damage/Attack:	1d6
Special Attacks:	Nil
Special Defenses:	Turn as wights
Magic Resistance:	20%
Size:	M (6′ tall)
Morale:	Special
XP Value:	420

Strahd skeletons are magically animated undead monsters, created as guardians or warriors by Count Strahd Von Zarovich, the vampire lord of Barovia.

Unlike common skeletons, Strahd's creatures still bear bits of leathery flesh, as well as shreds of clothing. Otherwise, they are nothing but bones. Their motions are swift but jerky. In the blink of an eye, they can attain full speed from a dead stop. They have no odor other than the faint suggestions of dust and freshly dug earth.

Strahd skeletons cannot make vocal sounds, but when they move, their bones clatter softly.

Combat: Strahd skeletons always wield a weapon of some sort, even if it is just a table leg for a club. Regardless of the weapon, they can only inflict 1d6 points of damage per attack. They have long since forgotten their fighting skills, but their unusual speed does allow them three attacks every two rounds.

Piercing weapons, such as spears or arrows, slide harmlessly between the bones of these creatures, inflicting no damage. Polearms, spears, and such can be used like a quarterstaff. Edged weapons and blunt, smashing weapons are effective against these creatures, but they only do half damage. Any magical blunt weapon inflicts full normal damage.

These monsters can detect invisible creatures within 30 feet. The highly magical nature of Strahd skeletons gives them a 20% magic resistance. Like all undead, they are immune to *sleep, charm, hold,* and other mind control spells. Being Strahd's creatures, they are as difficult to turn as wights. They have no flesh to speak of, so cold-based attacks cannot harm them.

Habitat/Society: Strahd skeletons lurk in dungeons, graveyards, or anywhere in Castle Ravenloft. The Count has been known to post them anywhere in Barovia where they may be of service. A band of skeletons supposedly lies in waiting somewhere beneath the surface of the River Ivlis.

As mindless undead, these creatures have no society. They obey any orders given to them by their master. These commands must be simple—a single sentence of no more than a dozen words.

While in Barovia, they can report back to Strahd if it is a part of their orders. It takes a full turn to establish communication, assuming he bothers to respond. They can only communicate a simple feeling of success or failure.

Ecology: Strahd skeletons are not a part of nature. Only Strahd Von Zarovich knows the arcane ritual that brings about their creation. For raw material, he requires human skeletons that still include the skull and 90% of the bones. What other foul components might be required are known only to the dread master of Ravenloft.

Skin Thieves

CLIMATE/TERRAIN:	Ravenloft
FREQUENCY:	Rare
ORGANIZATION:	Clan
ACTIVITY CYCLE:	Night
DIET:	Carnivore
INTELLIGENCE:	Low (5–7)
TREASURE:	Q (I)
ALIGNMENT:	Chaotic evil
NO. APPEARING:	3–12 (3d4)
ARMOR CLASS:	7 (10)
MOVEMENT:	12
HIT DICE:	2+2
THAC0:	19
NO. OF ATTACKS:	3
DAMAGE/ATTACK:	1–6/1–6/1–4
SPECIAL ATTACKS:	Nil
SPECIAL DEFENSES:	Disguise
MAGIC RESISTANCE:	Nil
SIZE:	M (5' tall)
MORALE:	Steady (11–12)
XP VALUE:	120

Skin thieves are bizarre beast men who scuttle through the wastelands of Ravenloft in small clans searching for unsuspecting victims to rob. As their name implies, skin thieves kill their victims in order to steal their skins. Once in possession of their hideous trophies, the skin thieves don these hides and assume the outward appearance of their victims.

In their natural form skin thieves appear as shuffling humanoids with bearlike faces and dark, heavily furred bodies. Their arms are unusually long and their hands are gnarled, eight-fingered appendages that end in wickedly pointed nails ranging from 8–16 inches in length. Skin thieves adorn themselves with various items of clothing and jewelry taken from their past victims. They are particularly fond of rings, bracers, and any other items that draw attention to their long nails.

Skin thieves have no language of their own. Instead, they communicate in an unusual dialect assembled from fragments of dozens of other languages.

Combat: Although not exceptionally intelligent, skin thieves possess a great deal of low cunning, almost always attacking at night and attempting to isolate their intended victims.

If in their natural forms, these creatures often separate into several small groups, one of which makes distracting noises while the other groups attack from the flanks. If one or more of the skin thieves is currently wearing a skin, the disguised creatures will attempt to use this advantage to isolate a victim.

Once the skin thieves attack, they do so with abandon. They lash out with their long claws (doing 1d6 points of damage each) and bite with their rows of sharp teeth (inflicting 1d4 points of damage).

The transfiguring skin worn by a skin thief is fairly delicate. Every time it is struck in combat the skin must save (as thin wood) vs. crushing blow. If it fails the saving throw, the skin rips apart and exposes the creature's true nature. Once ripped, the skin is destroyed and can no longer be used as a disguise.

When attacking, the creatures make an eerie, moist, snuffling sound. Skin thieves always try to attack only victims they believe are weaker than themselves. Skin thieves usually run from a fair fight, preferring to be predator rather than prey.

Habitat/Society: Skin thieves are nomadic creatures who travel the uninhabited sections of Ravenloft, often hovering near the outskirts of civilization. They are particularly fond of trade routes or areas of sparse habitation. Such areas often give them the opportunity to attack small groups of humans, their favorite source of food, disguises, and adornment (rings, bracers, etc.).

Clans of skin thieves consist of two to three families. Such clans are led by whichever skin thief can best intimidate the other members of the clan. Such "chiefs" rarely stay in power for more than a few months, and the leadership of a skin thief clan is almost always in flux.

Skin thieves have no true homes. Instead, the creatures build small lean-tos or shelter in caves for up to a month at a time before moving on.

Skin thieves are also fond of killing the members of small caravans or farmsteads and then living in these quarters for a period of time. In such cases, the skin thieves will don the skins of their victims and perform a twisted parody of human activity, even to the extent of interacting with other humans in an attempt to lure more unsuspecting victims. However, the true nature of the monsters inevitably becomes obvious in their behavior and crude speech patterns.

Ecology: Skin thieves are vicious and petty creatures that prey on those weaker than themselves. It is uncertain where such fiends originated, but most scholars believe them to be humans whose ancestors turned to cannibalism and whose progeny bore the mark of their bestiality.

Skin thieves steal almost all of their belongings, making little if anything for themselves. The only items of any appreciable value they will have is the jewelry they covet.

Spirit, Psionic

CLIMATE/TERRAIN:	Ravenloft
FREQUENCY:	Very rare
ORGANIZATION:	Solitary
ACTIVITY CYCLE:	Night
DIET:	Nil
INTELLIGENCE:	Exceptional (15–16)
TREASURE:	Nil
ALIGNMENT:	Neutral evil
NO. APPEARING:	1
ARMOR CLASS:	0
MOVEMENT:	9
HIT DICE:	9
THAC0:	11
NO. OF ATTACKS:	0
DAMAGE/ATTACK:	Nil
SPECIAL ATTACKS:	Psionics
SPECIAL DEFENSES:	+1 or better to hit
MAGIC RESISTANCE:	Nil
SIZE:	M (6′ tall)
MORALE:	Fearless (19–20)
XP VALUE:	7,000

Psionics Summary:

Level	Dis/Sci/Dev	Attack/Defense	Score	PSPs
9	3/5/14	PsC/All	15	300

Psychometabolic - Devotions: Aging, cause decay.
Psychokinetic - Sciences: Telekinesis, project force. **Devotions:** Animate object, control body, control sound, control light.
Telepathy-Sciences: Mindlink, mindwipe, probe. **Devotions:** Attraction, aversion, contact, ESP, false sensory input, phobia amplification, post-hypnotic suggestion, psychic crush.

The psionic spirit is an unusual form of ghost with great psionic abilities that it employs instead of the normal magical abilities most often associated with such creatures. Although perhaps more subtle in its methods than some ghosts, the psionic spirit is still a dangerous foe.

Always found in ectoplasmic form, the psionic spirit usually appears as a faintly shimmering human or demihuman. The limbs of the psionic spirit are indistinct, trailing off into wispy, ectoplasmic tendrils. Occasionally, an ectoplasmic tendril drifts away from the spirit. Such pieces gradually solidify into a putrid, jellylike substance.

Psionic spirits know only the languages that they did in life. As one might expect, psionicists can use psychic means to communicate with them.

Combat: The psionic spirit's sole source of pleasure is tormenting the minds of living creatures. It particularly detests psionicists and will go out of its way to first destroy the psionicist's mind and finally his body.

Before attacking more directly, the spirit will often use one or more of its psionic disciplines to frighten and confuse its intended victims. Only when it feels its foes are sufficiently disoriented and terrified will the spirit attack more directly.

When attacking, the psionic spirit usually uses its *control body* devotion to cause confusion among its enemies. The spirit will then attack spell users or psionicists with its *psychic crush* or *aging* powers.

The spirit can also attempt to drive a character mad. Whenever the ghost successfully uses its telepathic *probe* it can force a character to look inside its demented mind. The character must then make a madness check. The psionic spirit can cause madness in a character of any class, not just psionicists.

A psionic spirit can only be hit by weapons of +1 enchantment or greater. It is immune to *sleep, charm, hold,* poison, and cold-based attacks. A priest can turn the spirit as a ghost. Holy water harms the creature doing 2–8 (2d4) points of damage per vial.

Habitat/Society: A psionic spirit is more likely than most spirits to roam from place to place. It spends much of its time searching for, and attempting to destroy, the psionicists it loathes.

Two theories exist as to the origin of psionic spirits. The first states that such monsters are actually psionicists who somehow become trapped within their *shadow form.* Eventually the torment of their hideous half-existence drives such individuals into madness, evil, and at the last into the arms of the Dark Powers, who grant the psionicist its ghostly form. The second theory simply asserts that psionic spirits were once evil psionicists who suffered a violent death while using their mental powers. Somehow the spirits of such psionicists remain in the world in the form of psionic ghosts.

Ecology: Psionic spirits care little for treasure or other material possessions. Treasure found in such a spirit's lair will simply be the incidental goods of previous victims.

Psionicists who use *retrospection* while in Ravenloft would do best to take care, for psionic spirits can sense the use of this power. Any psionicist using *retrospection* has a 5% chance of calling such a spirit to himself.

Unicorn, Shadow

Climate/Terrain:	Ravenloft forests
Frequency:	Rare
Organization:	Solitary
Activity Cycle:	Night
Diet:	Omnivore
Intelligence:	Very (11–12)
Treasure:	D
Alignment:	Neutral evil
No. Appearing:	1
Armor Class:	2
Movement:	24
Hit Dice:	6
THAC0:	15
No. of Attacks:	3 or 1
Damage/Attack:	1–8/1–8/1–12 or 3–36 (3d12)
Special Attacks:	Charge, flaming horn, cause fear, surprise.
Special Defenses:	Immune to poison, *charm, hold* and *death* spells, +1 or better weapons needed to hit, *blink*.
Magic Resistance:	Nil
Size:	L (6′ tall at shoulder)
Morale:	Champion (15–16)
XP Value:	2,000

The shadow unicorn is a terrifying creature of pure evil that roams the wilds of Darkon and Falkovnia, intent only on glorying in the fear and pain of those it encounters.

The shadow unicorn is a blurred copy of its cousin, the normal unicorn. The coat of such a steed is always some form of dappled gray. The depth of color varies from the deepest coal to the palest steel, while the mane and tail are always very long, silky, and utterly black. Its eyes are a smoldering, malevolent red and its ebon horn, which is 2 to 3 feet in length, is sometimes illuminated by a corona of crimson flames. The cloven hooves of the shadow unicorn are the color of scorched earth and are always sharpened in order to add to the pain their blows inflict. Mares and stallions are distinguishable in that the stallion has a tangled black beard that the mare lacks.

Shadow unicorns speak their own language as well as those of nightmares, and several creatures from the outer planes.

Combat: Shadow unicorns have no one preferred way of approaching combat. In general these intelligent, dark steeds will attempt to attack in whichever way will cause their foes the most heart-rending fear, pain, and horror.

These evil unicorns can magically hide within the shadows and are capable of moving with absolute silence when they desire. When within the shadows and moving silently the monsters are almost undetectable, requiring a *detect invisible* spell or like ability to discern. Even when not hidden within the shadows, the dark unicorns can move so quietly their opponents receive a –6 penalty to their surprise rolls.

Sometimes, however, a shadow unicorn will choose to let its hooves make noise. This is a favored tactic when the unicorn wishes to sow terror among those who see it as the hooves will make a thunderous pounding when the creature gallops along. Anyone hearing the hammering of the shadow unicorn's unsilenced hooves or the shrieking wail of its terrible whinny must make a saving throw vs. spell (with a –2 penalty for the whinny) or be overcome by *fear* (as per the wizard spell). In addition, every time a character fails this saving throw there is a 5% chance that his hair will immediately turn permanently white as a result of the sheer horror of the experience.

In combat, the shadow unicorn attacks with its sharpened front hooves, which do 1d8 points of damage each, and its ebon horn, which does 1d12 points of damage. Due to the horn's magical nature, the shadow unicorn always receives a +2 bonus when attacking with it. Three times per day the evil unicorn can cause its horn to emit an eerie red flame which lasts for 8 rounds. While the horn is aflame, victims of its attack take an additional 2d4 points of damage per hit.

A shadow unicorn can also lower its horn and charge at an enemy if it has at least 20 feet of open space between itself and its target. Opponents struck by a charging shadow unicorn take 3d12 points of damage. A shadow unicorn cannot attack with its hooves in the same round it charges.

A shadow unicorn is also capable of using a short range teleportation ability known as a *blink* (as per the wizard spell) three times per day. However, the unicorn can only use this power when it is engulfed in shadows. More than one victim has been frightened nigh unto death by the sound of a galloping shadow unicorn pounding closer and closer behind him only to have the actual beast rear up in front of the terror-stricken traveler seconds later with its horn blazing, eyes glowing, and piercing shriek ripping through the night air. This is truly one of the most frightening sights in all of Ravenloft and an event that few live to relate to others.

Shadow unicorns are immune to all forms of poison, *charm* or *hold* spells, and death magic, and all of their saving throws are made as if they were 9th level wizards.

Habitat/Society: It is said the first shadow unicorns were the result of a foul mating between a unicorn drawn into the mists of Ravenloft and the nightmare who first corrupted him.

As the Vistani tell the tale, the nightmare first appeared to the unicorn, Addar, in his dreams. Appealing to his vanity and great sense of self-importance, the nightmare claimed that there was a vast wood desperately in need of protection. Further, she said that all the denizens of that forest would be appropriately thankful and respectful of the unicorn lord were he to become their guardian—and master. Wooed by the nightmare's dark promises and his own hubris, Addar agreed to make his way to the misty forest where the nightmare waited.

Out of this dark alliance were born twin foals, the first shadow unicorns. It is here the tales diverge. Some say the twins slew their father, while others insist that Addar is still trapped in his darkly wooded domain, demanding worship from all who pass through his dead forest. Still others claim that the birth of the twins shattered the spell the unicorn had fallen under, and that he wanders his domain to this day driven mad by grief and self-loathing. Only the Land itself knows the truth of the matter.

What is known is that there are now shadow unicorns living in the wilder regions of both Darkon and Falkovnia. Extremely territorial, no two shadow unicorns will work together, instead fighting tenaciously to guard their own lands. The only exception to this is during the spring mating season. After a gestation period of fourteen months, such a union always results in twins.

In approximately 5% of these births, one member of the twins is actually a unicorn. Such throwbacks have the same initial coloration as young shadow unicorns, but both their abilities and temperaments match those of true unicorns (see the *MONSTROUS MANUAL*). Such animals will grow up to become the mortal enemies of shadow unicorns if they survive. Fortunately for these unicorns, their mothers are incapable of distinguishing the youthful unicorns' true nature until the creature's near adolescence. At this point the unicorn's coat grows in far too white for even the palest of shadow unicorns and, more importantly, the unicorn is incapable of causing its horn to flame. Most such unicorns flee their homes by this time, venturing out into the world to do what small measure of good they can for the forest and its denizens.

The woodlands dominated by a shadow unicorn tend to be even gloomier than most of the forests found in the domains of Ravenloft. This is in part due to the constant hush of the forest, caused by the fear that smaller denizens feel for the master of the woods.

There is, however, a more direct reason for this preternatural melancholy. A shadow unicorn can carve a special *glyph of gloom* with its ebon horn.

Such a glyph serves two purposes. The first is to warn other shadow unicorns of the dark steed's claim to the forest in question. If the glyph is carved into a living tree while the horn is flaming, the second purpose is also served, as the glyph causes a magical gloom to descend on everything within 100 yards of the glyph. This gloom causes the light in the area affected to never rise above the level of twilight. A *light* spell can temporarily reverse this effect, while a *continual light* spell will provide a continuing oasis of light—at least until the shadow unicorn happens upon the area and removes or destroys the focus of the spell.

Any tree that has such a *glyph of gloom* placed on it will wither and die within a year, mute evidence of the shadow unicorn's twisted presence and power. Once the tree has died, a new *glyph* must be placed on another tree in order to keep the gloom in that section of the forest. Thus, a single shadow unicorn can easily destroy many of the trees within its domain over the course of its lifetime (which can be up to 1,000 years in length).

Travelers who pass through a shadow unicorn's forest are well advised to do so as swiftly as possible, since shadow unicorns delight in terrifying such intruders. Once the shadowy steed has noticed the travelers, it may or may not kill them outright. Why such a creature allows some to survive while it brings other unfortunates to their untimely ends is unknown. Certain peoples, in particular the Vistani, swear that speaking loudly of the shadow unicorn as a powerful lord, making obeisances to the forest, and leaving jewelry and other trinkets hanging from the branches of glyph-marked trees will gain safe passage, at least on most occasions. The Vistani even have several songs that are sung only while travelling through the woodlands claimed by a shadow unicorn, all of which show honor and reverence to the dark steeds.

The actual lair of a shadow unicorn is most often formed from tangled limbs and hanging vines, sheltering an area of ground strewn with mosses and various pieces of jewelry. Such lairs are always found at the heart of a dark steed's territory.

Ecology: Shadow unicorns are a blight upon the already cursed lands of Darkon and Falkovnia. Whole forests have slowly withered and eventually been destroyed under a shadow unicorn's vile ministrations, while much of the wildlife abandons the area in terror. In addition, over half the animals that do reside within a shadow unicorn's woods do not reproduce, thus cutting population levels drastically. All in all, these vile creatures are abominations, foul mockeries of their virtuous cousins, and the cancerous heirs of their ancestors' twisted desires.

Shadow unicorns are omnivores, although they particularly enjoy feeding upon treants and other sentient plants. The evil treants found in the land of the mists loathe shadow unicorns and are rarely found in the same forests with them. Occasionally, a grove of such creatures will come to an uneasy understanding with a particular shadow unicorn, but such an alliance rarely lasts.

If the shadow unicorn's horn is powdered it can be used by an alchemist in the creation of 2–12 (2d6) applications of *oil of fiery burning*.

CLIMATE/TERRAIN:	Subterranean
FREQUENCY:	Very rare
ORGANIZATION:	Solitary
ACTIVITY CYCLE:	Night
DIET:	Special
INTELLIGENCE:	Exceptional (15–16)
TREASURE:	Ix2
ALIGNMENT:	Chaotic evil
NO. APPEARING:	1
ARMOR CLASS:	0
MOVEMENT:	12
HIT DICE:	8+3
THAC0:	13
NO. OF ATTACKS:	1 or 2
DAMAGE/ATTACK:	1d4+4/1d4+4
SPECIAL ATTACKS:	Spells, cause awe, drain fluids, poison, and see below
SPECIAL DEFENSES:	Spells, +1 or better to hit, immune to poison, regeneration, and see below
MAGIC RESISTANCE:	25%
SIZE:	M (5′ tall)
MORALE:	Elite (13–14)
XP VALUE:	7,000 (+1,000 per 100 years of age)

Unlike most races, the drow consider it an honor to be granted the *Kiss of Lolth,* as they refer to vampirism. The dark elves view vampires with both awe and trepidation, believing undeath to be a state of being that brings an elf closer to a true understanding of the powers that surge through the universe. Such knowledge brings immense power, which the dark elves both crave and respect.

The vast majority of drow vampires are female, although a such a creature occasionally honors a male with the transformation. Drow vampires are almost identical in appearance to the living members of their race. They are of slight build, approximately 5′ in height with long, pale hair and dusky skin. The features of such vampires are almost radiantly beautiful in their refinement. Even the vampires' skin emanates a faint, pearlescent glow. This radiance can only be seen out of the corner of the viewer's eye and its near-visibility is often distracting. Drow vampires normally dress in luxurious, but somber, garments and carry both an adamantine dagger and short sword.

Drow vampires retain their knowledge of the languages of intelligent underworld creatures as well as their own language of gestures and body movements. In addition, these vampires can communicate with all animal species who make their home in the underworld.

Combat: Drow vampires, like their living counterparts, are skilled in battle. These vampires are extraordinarily fond of causing pain and consider battle an art form in which the object is to cause their victims to suffer as much as possible before granting them the release of death. The vampires view each slice of anguish as an offering to Lolth.

The transformation to vampiric form grants the undead drow an 18/76 Strength. This gives the creatures a natural bonus of +2 on all melee attack rolls and +4 to the damage caused by any physical attacks. This bonus is separate from the +2 a drow receives when using its adamantine short sword and dagger. When using these weapons, drow vampires can attack with both weapons in a single round.

As in life, drow vampires can see the heat emitted by living bodies up to 120 feet distant. Similarly, they can detect sliding or shifting walls, stonework traps, or their distance underground five times in six.

Drow vampires retain a measure of their race's innate ability to cast spells. They can cast the following spells once per day: *darkness, continual darkness, levitate, know alignment, detect magic, dispel magic,* and *suggestion.* They cast these at the 8th level of ability.

Additionally, drow vampires retain a portion of their race's powerful magic resistance. Drow vampires have a 25% resistance to magic. Sages theorize that the magic resistance of drow vampires must lower somewhat in order for the creature to manifest its unlife. However, as the creatures age and their connection to the negative material plane strengthens, their magic resistance begins to increase (see **Habitat/Society** below).

A drow vampire can *cause awe* with its merest gaze. Anyone looking into the vampire's pale eyes must make a saving throw vs. spell. Failure means the character stands awestruck before the vampire for 2d4 melee rounds. Awestruck characters automatically drop anything they are holding. Affected victims will not attack or even approach the drow vampire unless the creature attacks them. As the drow ages it becomes more difficult for victims not to become awestruck by the monster's imperious gaze (see **Habitat/Society**).

The dread touch of the vampire drow drains the very fluids from its victim's body. Each successful unarmed melee attack enables the undead drow to drain 1d6+1 hit points from its victim. Each time the vampire uses this hideous attack, the victim permanently loses 1 hit point. Such draining is excruciatingly painful and leaves a small welt where the drow touched its victim's flesh. Only the *heal* spell will remove these angry welts that the drow refer to as *Lolth's caress.* The vampire can absorb any hit points it drains from its victims in this manner, although the creature will never have more than its maximum number of hit points. Any drow brought to 0 hit points by this attack becomes a vampire. Victims of other races merely die in unendurable agony, sacrifices to Lolth and her vampire minion.

A vampire drow can only be hit by weapons of +1 or greater enchantment. Unenchanted weapons pass through the monster as if it were vapor. The monster regenerates 3 hit points per round when in absolute darkness.

If reduced to 0 hit points a vampire drow is not slain. Instead, the monster is forced to take its *poisonous vapor* form (see below). If the drow cannot reach the safety of its stony tomb within 12 turns the vapors dissipate and the vampire is destroyed. If it does reach its tomb the vampire must rest for eight hours, after which the foul creature is fully restored.

Although a vampire drow is unaffected by holy water, water drawn directly from a waterfall does 2d4 points of damage to the monster. If the creature is held completely within the downpour of a waterfall itself, the vampire will be destroyed when it reaches 0 hit points. Holy symbols have no effect on a vampire drow.

Like all vampires, these monsters are immune to all manner of mind-affecting spells. These include, but are not limited to, *sleep, charm,* and *hold*. They are also immune to poisons and cannot be suffocated or drowned. Spells that depend upon cold or electricity do only half damage to drow vampires.

Of all vampires, the drow are the most adversely affected by light. A vampire drow will almost never emerge onto the surface of Ravenloft as even one ray of sunlight will instantaneously destroy it. Even moonlight does damage to the monster, doing 2d4 points of damage per round. The 5th level priest spell *moonbeam* does similar damage to the vampire. Starlight does not damage the vampire, but the creature is incapable of regeneration while touched by starshine. Magical illumination, such as *light* or *continual light,* does 1d4 points of damage per round that the vampire is exposed to such illumination. The vampire cannot regenerate under these conditions and will do everything in its power to destroy the light source.

Drow vampires can take the form of giant spiders. While in this form, such vampires can control 10d10 Hit Dice of spiders. The creatures will arrive within 2d10 rounds of summoning. The exact type of spiders summoned depends on the nature of the spiders in the immediate area. In normal form, drow vampires can control up to four driders. Driders worship vampire drow, seeing the monsters as Lolth's chosen ones.

A drow vampire can change into *poisonous vapors* at will. This ability is similar to a normal vampire's *gaseous form,* save that any creature that breathes in any portion of these vapors must make a saving throw vs. poison with a –2 penalty. Failure means the victim takes 2d6 points of damage. Those who make this saving throw take only half damage from the fumes. While in this form, the vampire can only be hit by weapons of +3 or greater enchantment.

A vampire drow cannot cross a line of salt (even when in vaporous form). The vampire finds pure salt repugnant and can only act indirectly to break such a barrier. For instance, the vampire might summon spiders to scatter the salt or use a *suggestion* spell to get someone else to break the line. If there is even the slightest break in the line the vampire drow can cross with impunity.

Because of their strong connection with the spider goddess, Lolth, vampire drow are more difficult for priests to turn than most undead, being turned as ghosts.

A vampire drow can be immobilized by impaling the monster through the heart with a stake made of rock salt, although this in itself will not permanently destroy the monster. Once the stake is removed, the monster will immediately begin to regenerate. Only exposing the creature to the rays of the sun, immersing it in the pounding torrent of a waterfall, or binding the corpse with cords woven of silver thread, smearing it with oil, and burning the body for at least twelve hours will ensure the vampire's destruction.

Habitat/Society: Vampire drow rarely ever leave the deepest levels of their caverns, and it is almost unheard of for such creatures to appear on the surface itself. Instead, these vampires spend years within elaborate underground tombs constructed by drider slaves. Such tombs are exquisite yet disturbing works of art with carvings ranging from twisted masses of limbs to horrifying faces fighting to swallow themselves. These tombs often serve as temples to Lolth as well as homes for the vampires.

Aloof and convinced of its superiority, the vampire drow is perhaps the most reluctant of all undead to create progeny. Only rarely does the drow vampire feel the loneliness of its existence, and it enjoys keeping its place in Lolth's heart as exclusive as possible.

Ecology: The vampire drow revels in its great power and ability to cause pain. Such a monster is perhaps one of the cruelest creatures found on the Demiplane of Dread. The monsters are said to particularly enjoy torturing dwarves and drow of different noble factions than the vampire's own.

The surface of the dark and twisted tomb-homes of drow vampire are often coated with a contact poison that burns fiercely, causing much pain but doing only 1 point of damage per dose. Drider are known to purposely poison themselves with this substance to show their loyalty to Lolth and her vampire servant.

Vampire drow truly believe themselves the favored of Lolth. They occasionally speak with Lolth's priestesses, but otherwise remain aloof from drow society save when they wish a new victim to torture for their own perverse amusement.

As the centuries pass, the vampire grows more and more powerful. The following chart details this advancement:

Age	HD	Drain	Attack	Awe	MR
0–99	8+3	+1	+1	0	25%
100–199	9+3	+1	+1	–1	30%
200–299	10	+2	+1	–1	35%
300–399	11	+2	+2	–2	40%
400–499	12	+3	+2	–2	45%
500+	13	+4	+2	–3	50%

HD indicates the number of Hit Dice a vampire has at a given age.

Drain indicates the amount of hit points worth of fluid the vampire can drain. At 200, the vampire drains 3–8 (1d6+2).

Attack indicates the level of enchantment necessary for a weapon to hit the vampire.

Awe shows the modifier to the victim's saving throw vs. the vampire's awe.

MR indicates the vampire's level of magic resistance.

Vampire, Nosferatu

Climate/Terrain:	Ravenloft
Frequency:	Very rare
Organization:	Solitary
Activity Cycle:	Night
Diet:	Blood
Intelligence:	High to genius (13–18)
Treasure:	F
Alignment:	Any evil
No. Appearing:	1
Armor Class:	1
Movement:	12, Fl 18 (C)
Hit Dice:	8+3
THAC0:	11
No. of Attacks:	1
Damage/Attack:	1d6+4
Special Attacks:	See below
Special Defenses:	+1 or better weapon to hit
Magic Resistance:	Nil
Size:	M (6′ tall)
Morale:	Champion (15–16)
XP Value:	2,000

Nosferatu are variants of the common vampire (see the *Monstrous Manual*). Like other vampires, they can be of any humanoid stock, although the powers of demihuman nosferatu have been known to vary from those of their human cousins (see the *Monstrous Compendium, Ravenloft Appendix*).

During the night hours, a nosferatu looks like a normal member of its race, though its skin is unusually pale. At sunrise, however, the nosferatu falls into a deathlike coma. If it has fed within the last 2 hours, its complexion appears slightly flushed. If cut or stabbed at this time, the creature bleeds. As the day wears on, the body begins to lose its fresh appearance. By nightfall, the face becomes gaunt and the flesh turns gray.

Nosferatu remember all the languages they learned in life and may even have mastered a few other tongues in their long unlife.

Combat: While the common vampire drains life energy levels, the nosferatu drains Constitution points instead. Except as noted below, Nosferatu have all of the other strengths and weaknesses of a common vampire.

The nosferatu has no obvious melee attack. It can use the punching and wrestling system, or throw dangerous and heavy objects. Otherwise, it must use weapons or spells just like normal humans. Its great strength does give it a +2 attack bonus and a +4 on damage inflicted. Smart or powerful nosferatu always have some sort of magical weapon available.

The nosferatu only attacks weak or *charmed* prey. To drain Constitution, it must bite its victim—usually on the neck—and drink his blood. If the victim is resisting, this action requires an attack roll. Armor protects a victim normally, but shields offer no defense.

Once a bite is successful, the draining is automatic on subsequent rounds. Usually the victim loses 1 point of Constitution per round, allowing the nosferatu to savor the slow death of its prey. If necessary, however, a nosferatu can drain blood at a rate of 3 points per round.

While draining its victim, this vampire's only attack or defense is its *charm* gaze. It can, of course, elect to stop the drain. The nosferatu's victim regains lost Constitution points at a rate of 1 point every 2 days. Those who die from the nosferatu's bloody kiss rise again as half-strength creatures subject to the will of their creator.

Using a form of *telepathy,* a nosferatu can *charm* from afar any person it has bitten. Once *charmed,* the victim is subject to the vampire's will for the rest of his life, or until a *remove curse* is cast upon him by a priest of 14th level or higher. This telepathic communication is one way. The nosferatu gives instructions to its victim, but the victim cannot relay anything to the vampire. The nosferatu must be within 360 feet to command his unwilling subject.

Habitat/Society: Most nosferatu live in cemeteries or other abandoned places. They hunt at night and return to their coffins during the day. Usually, a nosferatu maintains a minimum of 3 or 4 coffins, each in a different location.

Ecology: Unlike the common vampire, a nosferatu needs blood to survive. Unless it can drain at least 3 Constitution points from a victim each night, it loses 1 Hit Die. The loss is cumulative and continues every night until enough blood is consumed or the nosferatu is reduced to 4 Hit Dice. At 4 Hit Dice, the creature ceases to decline further, but it goes berserk if it is within 40 feet of a viable victim.

If attacking a humanoid victim is impractical, a nosferatu can restore nearly all of its Hit Dice by drinking the blood of animals. Animal feedings, no matter how frequent, always leave the creature 1 hit die below normal.

Nosferatu also need sleep. They lose 1 hit die for each day without proper rest. "Proper rest" requires lying in its coffin with a handful of soil from its original grave for at least 8 hours. A tired nosferatu can regain 1 hit die after a day of proper rest, provided it has drained at least 6 Constitution points during the previous night. To regain all lost Hit Dice, it may need to gorge itself several nights in a row.

Vampire, Oriental

CLIMATE/TERRAIN:	Rokushima Táiyoo
FREQUENCY:	Very rare
ORGANIZATION:	Solitary
ACTIVITY CYCLE:	Night
DIET:	Special
INTELLIGENCE:	High (13–14)
TREASURE:	F
ALIGNMENT:	Chaotic evil
NO. APPEARING:	1
ARMOR CLASS:	1
MOVEMENT:	12, Fl 6 (C)
HIT DICE:	9+3
THAC0:	11
NO. OF ATTACKS:	2
DAMAGE/ATTACK:	1d4+4/1d4+4
SPECIAL ATTACKS:	Energy drain, *hold* victim
SPECIAL DEFENSES:	Invisibility; +1 weapon to hit; immune to *hold, sleep, charm;* see below
MAGIC RESISTANCE:	Nil
SIZE:	M (6′ tall)
MORALE:	Elite (13–14)
XP VALUE:	9,000

The oriental vampire is very similar to its common, western cousin. There are, however, differences in culture, abilities, and appearance that distinguish the two strains of undead.

While the oriental vampire appears human at first glance, slightly feral features and faintly luminous skin make it appear slightly inhuman. What is most remarkable about the creature's appearance is its fingernails, which are always from 5 to 12 inches in length; any of them that are cut or broken regenerate as the vampire sleeps. Although most oriental vampires have dark hair and eyes, rare examples of this race have lighter hair and western features. It is the *strain* of vampirism that is eastern, not necessarily the individual vampire.

Oriental vampires speak all of the languages that they knew in life. Further, these creatures often acquire several other tongues in the centuries following their deaths.

Combat: The oriental vampire is a fearsome opponent in combat, possessing a Strength of 18/76, which affords a bonus of +2 on all attack rolls and +4 on all melee damage rolls.

It is almost unheard of for an oriental vampire to use a weapon other than its wickedly sharp fingernails. The nails function as +1 magical weapons, and they can hit even foes normally hit only by enchanted weapons. Hence, the creature attacks twice per round with its nails, inflicting 1d4+5 points of damage per attack (including Strength and "magical" nail bonuses).

Three times per day the vampire can gaze at an individual and thus attempt to *hold* him. The victim must make a successful saving throw vs. spell with a –4 penalty (due to the strength of the vampire's gaze). This ability is extremely useful when the vampire wishes to feed quietly or render a guard immobile.

The oriental vampire is a creature of both the Positive and Negative Energy Planes. The eastern vampire can drain energy levels, but only by biting its opponent. If the this happens, the monster drains *two* life energy (experience) levels from its victim and inflicts 1d4 points of damage. The bonuses for the vampire's exceptional strength do not apply when it bites an enemy.

Oriental vampires can only be struck by weapons of +1 or better enchantment. Normal weapons pass through the vampire's body, actually corroding and becoming useless in the process unless they successfully save vs. disintegration. Even when struck by a magical weapon, the oriental vampire regenerates at the rate of 3 hit points per round.

If reduced to 0 hit points, the vampire is forced to fade into *invisibility*. Once invisible, the vampire attempts to flee to its coffin to rest for eight hours, after which it regains its normal form and all hit points. If necessary, the invisible vampire can also use its innate ability to *passwall* to aid in its escape. If the vampire cannot reach its coffin within 12 turns, it breaks up and is truly destroyed. The monster does regenerate 3 hit points per round once it has been reduced to this state.

Sleep, charm, and *hold* spells do not affect oriental vampires. They are neither harmed by poisons nor susceptible to paralysis. Spells that are based on cold or electricity inflict only half damage upon them.

Oriental vampires cannot assume *gaseous form,* but they can use *passwall* at will. When the vampire uses this ability, it leaves no mark on the wall to betray its passing.

An eastern vampire is also capable of fading into *invisibility* at will, requiring one full round to disappear completely. While invisible, opponents attack the vampire with a –4 penalty. Thereafter the vampire remains invisible until it attacks another creature, at which time the *invisibility* is dispelled, just like the spell of the same name. Anyone who witnesses the oriental vampire's gradual fade into invisibility must immediately make a fear check if the true nature of the monster was not previously known.

An oriental vampire can summon an *insect swarm* at will, which appears in 1d4+1 rounds and aids the vampire in any way possible within the limits of the spell of the same name. If in the wilderness, the vampire can also summon 1d4+1 great cats for assistance. The type of cats called depends upon the area. The summoned animals will appear in 2d6 rounds.

An eastern vampire may transform into a tiger at will. When in this guise, the monster has all of the natural abilities of such beasts, including their keen senses. In addition, the vampire retains all of its own natural defenses and its gaze attack while in this state.

Although the oriental vampire is incapable of climbing walls, as its western cousin can do, it can *levitate* at will, drifting at a steady movement rate of 6 even in the stiffest of winds.

The oriental vampire has its share of weaknesses as well. Like the western vampire, the eastern variant can be held at bay by a mirror or a lawful good holy symbol, presented with courage and conviction. This does not drive the vampire away, but merely keeps the creature from attacking. On the other hand, garlic does not bother the eastern vampire, but a garland made of rosemary and ivy will prevent it from attacking an individual or entering an area warded by the garland. (The vampire attempts to overcome such hazards indirectly, ordering a summoned cat to attack the person bearing the holy symbol, or tricking an intended victim into removing a garland, for example.)

The oriental vampire can be slain by those brave and knowledgeable enough to face the inherent dangers in such an effort. If the oriental vampire is exposed to direct sunlight, it is instantly rendered powerless, and two rounds later the creature perishes, turning to dust. If a hunter can find all the resting places of the vampire and scatter rosemary and myrrh on the earth within, the soil becomes anathema to the vampire. Since the vampire must rest on at least a cubic foot of the soil in which it was buried, such a tactic can kill it—if the vampire goes without sleeping upon such soil for nine days in a row, it is forever destroyed. Unfortunately for hunters, the oriental vampire is amazingly crafty in hiding caches of such soil, and it is almost impossible to find every one of those hiding places.

An oriental vampire can also be neutralized by driving a bamboo shaft through its heart, yet if the stake is removed the vampire will soon recover. In order to truly be rid of the creature, the hunter must place a piece of *blessed* rosemary in the vampire's mouth and then sew the creature's eyes and mouth shut with a silver needle, threaded with gold.

Unlike the western vampire, the oriental version of the monster can enter a home without invitation. However, burning incense of rosemary and myrrh keeps the creature from entering a dwelling.

As with western vampires, the oriental vampire casts no reflection in glass, casts no shadow, and moves in complete silence. As Doctor Rudolph van Richten remarked in his treatise on vampires, such observations are often the simplest way for a vigilant observer to spot a vampire.

Any human slain by the life draining attack of an oriental vampire is doomed to become such a creature himself. The victim rises the night after burial, a powerful pawn to its evil creator. If the victim is never buried, he will not become a vampire. This is the reason it is traditional to cremate the bodies of those suspected to have lost their lives to a vampire.

Vampires lose almost none of the abilities and knowledge they possessed during life. There are vampire wizards capable of wielding their powerful magic as well as the innate powers of a vampire. Such creatures are incredibly dangerous to even the most powerful of hunters.

Habitat/Society: Oriental vampires prefer to live in austere and lonely abodes. They are particularly fond of living near sweeping moors, jagged mountain peaks, desert wastes, and other powerful but bleak natural formations. Unlike their western counterparts, oriental vampires are not particularly attached to graveyards, churches, or the like, so long as they have enough of their burial soil available to sleep upon. Although their homes are austere in nature, these vampires never live too far from trading roads or an area of human habitation, as they prefer not to have to travel too far in their pursuit of sustenance. Eastern vampires are most commonly encountered in Rokushima Táiyoo and Sri Raji. However, such creatures have been found in several of the core domains as well.

Several oriental vampires have claimed to be mortal sages, thus inspiring frequent pilgrimages to their lairs. Many such wisdom seekers find only their deaths at the end of these journeys.

Although oriental vampires are solitary creatures, preferring to spend the vast majority of their time in meditation or pursuing intellectual studies, such creatures do have a rigid social hierarchy. Exactly how a vampire comes to have status among its fellow vampires is unclear to all save the vampires themselves. The monsters display their ranks by painting and affixing jewels to their long fingernails. The more austere and minimal the decoration, the higher the vampire stands in its society—apparently those of lower status feel the need to display their wealth and artistic abilities in a more blatant manner.

In general, oriental vampires care little for the world of mortals, viewing such creatures as cattle. Pleas for mercy inevitably fall on deaf ears, for why should the vampire show mercy to what it perceives to be an animal?

Ecology: Regardless of the vampire's alignment in life, within weeks of its transformation the newly created undead becomes chaotic evil. This change is simply in the nature of the essence that gives a vampire unlife.

The nails of oriental vampires may be cut and taken from an immobilized vampire. Such nails can be used to create +1 arrowheads, dagger tips, and other small weapons.

An oriental vampire's ties to the Negative Energy Plane grow stronger with the passing of the years. As such, its powers increase as well. The following table shows the changes in a vampire's abilities with the passage of time.

Age	HD	Drain	Attack	Gaze	Str
0–99	9+3	2	+1	0	18/76
100–199	10+3	2	+1	–1	18/90
200–299	11+3	2	+2	–1	18/00
300–399	12+3	2	+2	–2	19
400–499	13+3	3	+3	–3	20
500+	14+3	3	+3	–4	20

HD indicates the number of Hit Dice a vampire has at a given age.

Drain is the number of life energy levels that a bite victim loses.

Attack dictates the level of enchantment necessary for a weapon to hit the vampire.

Gaze provides the modifier to the victim's saving throw vs. the vampire's *hold* gaze.

Str indicates the vampire's Strength score at any given age.

Virus, General Information

The magical viruses of Ravenloft are microscopic horrors that are invisible to the naked eye, but deadly in their effect. These magical strains are similar to their mundane counterparts in several ways: Both magical and mundane viruses lie dormant until they contact living cells, and once such contact is made, both types of virus become active and begin to spread through the host's body.

Background

An elderly, embittered mage named Phagius first introduced magical viruses to the Land. His wife bore him six children before dying in childbirth. Although Phagius paid little attention to his brood, he demanded from them absolute obedience, verging upon worship. Phagius grew more cruel, petty, and tyrannical over the years, refusing to allow his children to marry or to become apprentices to any other wizard than himself. Eventually, his offspring grew desperate and mixed a lethal poison into his meal, hoping to rid themselves of their evil sire. In this they succeeded, but not before Phagius had his revenge.

Phagius was working on a series of potions designed to spread infection throughout his homeland, Invidia. Only he would know the cures, and he planned to use his knowledge to control the domain. Realizing that his death was but moments away, Phagius cursed his children and drank the six virulent potions he had created.

As the aged wizard collapsed onto his bed, his body transformed. When Phagius's children crept upstairs to witness the result of their dread deed, one of them touched the body, which immediately collapsed into dust. Choking, the children fled the room and the keep, taking with them their evil inheritance: six magical viruses. Each child of Phagius became the carrier (see **Transmission**, below) of a different disease, spreading an evil legacy.

Description

Viruses are microscopic and thus are invisible to the naked eye, but even *eyes of minute seeing* are incapable of spotting them. They are not revealed by a *detect invisibility* spell either, for their invisibility is due to their minuscule size, not any magic. A *detect magic* spell will reveal the presence of these minute menaces when they are highly concentrated, as is the case in an infected person.

Combat

Viruses do not participate in combat *per se*. Rather, the virus waits in a state of suspended animation until it comes into direct contact with living tissue, at which time it activates and attempts to invade the tissues of the body. Once the virus is inside the body, symptoms of infection appear.

Magical viruses can affect living beings in three ways. A magical virus can imprint its own genetic patterns over those of the host tissue, forcing the original tissue to die, leaving virus-patterned tissue in its place. Other viruses cause such frenetic activity in the tissue that it grows out of control, causing excruciating pain before death. Perhaps most horribly, some magical viruses affect the victim's psyche, twisting and warping the mind instead of the body.

Transmission

Phagius's viruses exist in two states: dormant and active. They are contracted through physical contact with their dormant forms. When a dormant virus contacts living flesh, it attempts to infect the body. If the virus successfully infects the victim it becomes active. An active virus perishes immediately if exposed to any elements outside the body, so, ironically, an infected individual cannot spread the infection to others. The active virus spreads aggressively within the host, however, never ceasing its attack until the victim's death. Once a victim dies, the virus falls dormant. Thus, anyone touching the body of a deceased victim risks infection.

Viruses may also spread by means of a carrier. A carrier is not himself affected by the virus, but carries the dormant virus within his body. Such a carrier can infect others by touch, saliva, or any other direct physical contact. Whole villages have perished when just one member became a carrier for such a virus.

A character who comes into contact with a magical virus must roll a saving throw vs. spell with a –2 penalty. Failure indicates the character contracts the virus. If successful, the character does not contract the virus, but must immediately make a saving throw vs. death magic. Failure this time indicates the character is now a carrier. He continues to be a carrier until the virus is purged from his system.

A *periapt of health* and similar items prevent the bearer from either becoming infected or carrying the virus to others. *Dispel magic* or *cure disease* kills any dormant or active viruses within a 15-foot radius of the caster.

Diagnosis

Diagnosis of Phagius's magical viruses is very difficult. Initial symptoms appear within 24 hours of contamination, often including fever and irritability. Each virus has its own unique signs, but relatively few physicians or priests are yet trained to recognize these early symptoms. If the sick individual is isolated and all magic removed from him, a *detect magic* spell may reveal the infection. If the spell is successful, parts of the infected victim's (or carrier's) skin will faintly glow a sickly greenish-yellow.

The Vistani are adept at recognizing the signs of Phagius's viruses. They also have several potions said to cure victims, but rarely give such potions to giorgios. The Vistani are not immune to the viruses, but seem to be resistant to them. When a Vistana becomes infected, prompt medical attention is always provided, although many of the gypsies died before they developed their cures for these terrible viruses.

Treatment

There are two main ways to treat victims of Phagius's viruses without the help of the Vistani.

Magical Healing: The *heal* spell is the most effective magical treatment. As long as it is cast before the victim's death, it destroys the virus. The *cure disease* spell is also effective. Unfortunately, it is not always completely reliable unless cast on the victim within 24 hours of infection. After that time, the virus has made significant changes in the victim's body and psyche, and the cure becomes less certain. For every 12 hours after the first day, the chance of success decreases by 10%. Hence, a priest has a 90% chance to kill the virus within 36 hours of the infection, but a few hours later the chance of success drops to 80%. On the seventh day, the virus can no longer be cured in this manner. A priest may only try once to cure the victim (although another priest is free to attempt a cure if the first fails). *Dispel magic* and *purify food and drink* can prevent infection by killing any dormant viruses in the area, but they are of no use to an infected individual.

Psionic Healing: The psychometabolic devotion absorb disease can be used to cure Phagius's viruses. However, the technique is dangerous because the psionicist must roll his power score or become infected himself. If, however, the psionicist is immune to the virus in some way, this is a safe option. Suspend animation delays any effects of the virus for as long as it is in effect. Certain other psionic sciences and devotions might affect particular viruses as well. The psychometabolic science complete healing does not affect the viruses, due to their magical nature.

Experience Points

The experience point values indicated for the various viruses indicate the reward that a character receives for curing (or aiding in the successful treatment of) a character that has contracted one of these dread diseases.

Virus, Combustion and Crystal

	Combustion	Crystal
CLIMATE/TERRAIN:	Ravenloft	Ravenloft
FREQUENCY:	Very rare	Very rare
ORGANIZATION:	N/A	N/A
ACTIVITY CYCLE:	Any	Any
DIET:	Nil	Nil
INTELLIGENCE:	Non- (0)	Non- (0)
TREASURE:	Nil	Nil
ALIGNMENT:	Neutral	Neutral
NO. APPEARING:	N/A	N/A
ARMOR CLASS:	N/A	N/A
MOVEMENT:	0	0
HIT DICE:	special	special
THAC0:	Nil	Nil
NO. OF ATTACKS:	0	0
DAMAGE/ATTACK:	Nil	Nil
SPECIAL ATTACKS:	Combustion	Crystallization
SPECIAL DEFENSES:	See below	See below
MAGIC RESISTANCE:	Nil	Nil
SIZE:	T (microscopic)	T (microscopic)
MORALE:	N/A	N/A
XP VALUE:	650	420

Combustion Virus

The magical combustion virus causes the cells of its victim's body to continually increase their levels of activity, growing wildly out of control. If left unchecked, the victim will spontaneously burst into flame and quickly die an agonizing death.

The first symptoms of the combustion virus's infection are a high fever and sore skin. These symptoms appear within six hours of infection. Within 24 hours, the victim's skin becomes extremely tender; at this point the victim receives a –2 penalty to all attacks and saving throws. Over the next week, bloody lesions begin to break open on the victim's skin. The pain and fever grow worse, and by the end of the week the victim suffers a –4 penalty on all actions that call for dice rolls.

If the virus is not stopped, the victim dies a grisly death, spontaneously combusting in 1d6+10 days. Anyone within 10 feet of the victim must make a successful saving throw vs. breath weapon to resist the heat of this incineration. A failed roll indicates that the bystander suffers 3d6 points of damage. A successful roll reduces this injury by half.

The psionic science energy containment is useful against this virus. The psionicist must successfully use this science on the subject, once every eight hours for three days, in order to flush the agonizing energies from the victim's system. With the conclusion of the final treatment, the patient is cured.

When a victim of the combustion virus dies, all that remains is a gray mass of ashes. This pile of ash contains thousands of dormant virus particles, which can scatter easily in the winds and cause mass infection if they are not somehow contained. Evil priests and wizards have been known to preserve this dust, sprinkling it on their undead minions. Even a lowly skeleton so treated becomes a hideously dangerous foe.

Crystal Virus

The crystal virus spreads more slowly than other viruses, but its results are just as terrible. Victims of this bug slowly crystallize, dying in agony as their lungs become incapable of drawing oxygen from the air and their blood hardens in their veins.

The crystal virus works its way into its victim, forming increasingly complex crystalline threads that gradually bind the body's tissues together. The initial symptoms of the disease are aching joints, fever, and areas of numb or tingling skin. Within three days, patches of the victim's skin begin to crystalize. Exactly eight days following infection, the victim's eyes begin to solidify. Although disorienting at first, this actually alters the victim's eyesight, giving him the same abilities as *eyes of minute seeing*. At this time the victim's movement rate is halved and his Dexterity score is reduced by 4, due to the stiffness of his changing body. If the crystallization process is not halted, the victim dies exactly 18 days after the initial infection. Within hours of death, the victim's body crumbles into fine, blood-red sand.

Because of the relatively slow progress of the infection, a *cure disease* spell works normally within the two days following infection, instead of the usual one.

The crystalline remains of a dead victim are thick with the dormant virus. Curiously, they can be handled safely as long as care is taken to keep them dry. Even the smallest drop of water, however, dissolves the crystals and creates a highly contagious fluid. Because they are water soluble, the sandy remains of a crystal virus victim have been used by assassins on more than one occasion.

Virus, Petrification and Phobia

	Petrification	Phobia
CLIMATE/TERRAIN:	Ravenloft	Ravenloft
FREQUENCY:	Very rare	Rare
ORGANIZATION:	N/A	N/A
ACTIVITY CYCLE:	Any	Any
DIET:	Nil	Nil
INTELLIGENCE:	Non- (0)	Non- (0)
TREASURE:	Nil	Nil
ALIGNMENT:	Neutral	Neutral
NO. APPEARING:	N/A	N/A
ARMOR CLASS:	N/A	N/A
MOVEMENT:	0	0
HIT DICE:	N/A	N/A
THAC0:	Nil	Nil
NO. OF ATTACKS:	Nil	Nil
DAMAGE/ATTACK:	Nil	Nil
SPECIAL ATTACKS:	Petrification	Cause phobia
SPECIAL DEFENSES:	See below	See below
MAGIC RESISTANCE:	Nil	Nil
SIZE:	T (microscopic)	T (microscopic)
MORALE:	N/A	N/A
XP VALUE:	650	270

Petrification Virus

The petrification virus causes its victim's body to gradually harden and eventually turn to stone. What is truly horrifying is that victims who have survived this terrible transformation claim to have been conscious even when their bodies were completely petrified.

The petrification virus attacks its victim at the exact spot where physical contact was made, so a large percentage of infections begin on the hands. Unlike other viruses, the initial symptoms of petrification virus infection do not include fever. Instead, the victim notices a hard, marbleized patch of skin at the point of infection.

So quickly does this microscopic invader do its work that skin at the point of contact is noticeably harder within just a few minutes. Within half an hour, this area becomes completely inflexible and begins to change to a color resembling pearly-gray marble. The marbleized patch of skin continues to spread, covering an additional 10% of the victim's body with each passing day. As the transformation progresses, several changes occur in the victim's body—most noticeable is a daily 10% increase in weight. In addition, the victim loses 2 points of Dexterity per day, but gains a 1 point improvement in his base AC.

If the infection is not stopped, the victim completely petrifies when his base Armor Class becomes 0. A marbleized victim remains alive long after the transformation, although no sign of life can be detected without magical or psionic help. Several months (2d6) after the conversion to stone, the victim finally dies and the virus falls dormant.

A *stone to flesh* spell cast on the victim removes all traces of marbleization from the body, but the virus remains active in the character's system and immediately begins to spread anew. Fortunately, a *cure disease* spell can be fully effective if used quickly.

The statue created of a dead victim's body contains thousands of dormant petrification viruses. As such, it is extremely virulent, so the slightest contact can be deadly. At least one twisted individual is known to have created hideous sculpture gardens out of his enemies by contriving to infect them with the virus.

Phobia Virus

The phobia virus is the only magical virus that does not necessarily cause its victim's death. Once in the body, it attacks the host's mind, causing the character to develop a severe phobia. Although such a neurosis may weaken a character at a critical moment and lead to death, the virus itself is not fatal.

Within 12 hours of infection, the victim of a phobia virus begins to feel generally nervous. The character begins to sweat profusely and runs a fever for several days. He also begins to have vague, recurring nightmares. Although the fever fades, the victim's fearfulness increases. By the seventh night of infection, the victim is exhausted. The virus-driven nightmares become clear, and the victim's fear crystallizes into a phobia. The fear is always of something that never troubled the victim before, and may even be something with which he was quite comfortable. Nevertheless, when the infected victim is confronted with the object of his newly formed phobia, he suffers the results of a failed fear check.

Remove fear and similar magic temporarily aid the sufferer, but he succumbs to his irrational fear as soon as the magic wears off. The spell *true seeing* combined with a *cure disease* spell can permanently rid the victim of his phobia.

Psionic powers also can be helpful in the treatment of a phobia virus victim. The most notable of these is psychic surgery, which can repair the damage done by the virus. Unless this treatment is followed with a *cure disease* spell or the like, however, the still-active virus attacks the brain again and restores the phobia.

Victims of a phobia virus are extremely vulnerable to psionic attacks such as id insinuation or magical spells like *cloak of fear.* Anyone who suffers from a phobia virus and is confronted with a magical or psionic fear-inducing attack must make an immediate Madness Check. (See Chapter II of the *Realm of Terror* book in the RAVENLOFT *Campaign Setting* boxed set for rules on madness.)

Virus, Psionic and Shadow

	Psionic	Shadow
CLIMATE/TERRAIN:	Any	Any dark
FREQUENCY:	Very rare	Very rare
ORGANIZATION:	N/A	N/A
ACTIVITY CYCLE:	Any	Any
DIET:	Nil	Nil
INTELLIGENCE:	Non- (0)	Non- (0)
TREASURE:	Nil	Nil
ALIGNMENT:	Neutral	Neutral
NO. APPEARING:	N/A	N/A
ARMOR CLASS:	N/A	N/A
MOVEMENT:	0	0
HIT DICE:	N/A	N/A
THAC0:	Nil	Nil
NO. OF ATTACKS:	0	0
DAMAGE/ATTACK:	Nil	Nil
SPECIAL ATTACKS:	Psionic overload	Shadow rot
SPECIAL DEFENSES:	Nil	Nil
MAGIC RESISTANCE:	Nil	Nil
SIZE:	T (microscopic)	T (microscopic)
MORALE:	N/A	N/A
XP VALUE:	650	975

Psionic Virus

The psionic virus opens pathways in a victim's mind, granting the character tremendous psionic abilities whether or not he had them before the infection. Unfortunately, such abilities continue to grow stronger and stronger, until the character's overstimulated brain literally explodes under the unaccustomed psionic pressures.

For the first 24 hours following infection, the only noticeable symptom is a strange feeling of disorientation. This is generally perceived as a buzzing in the ears and a sense of light-headedness. On the second day of infection, the victim gains the abilities of a 1st level psionicist (or gains one level of ability if he already possesses such powers). The DM can either roll randomly for the victim's newfound abilities or simply choose what powers the character gains.

Every 24 hours thereafter, the victim gains another level of psionic ability. The victim will also begin to experience profound headaches, lasting approximately one hour per level of psionic skill gained. While suffering from these excruciating migraines, the character suffers a –4 penalty to all attack and damage rolls, saving throws, and proficiency checks.

Once the headaches have reached eight hours in duration, the victim must make a Madness Check each day. When they reach 10 hours, the victim must make a daily saving throw vs. death magic. Success means the character's brain continues to handle the psionic energies, while failure indicates his brain explodes from the massive psionic pressures. A cumulative –2 penalty is applied to both of these rolls for each day after the first.

In addition to normal treatment options, the psionic virus can be excised with a successful working of psychic surgery in combination with mindwipe. The affected character cannot actively participate in this cure.

The flesh of a deceased victim's body hosts the dormant form of the psionic virus, so any unprotected person who touches the victim's body risks infection. In addition, anyone who makes direct mental contact with an infected mind must make a successful saving throw vs. death magic or contract the virus as well.

Shadow Virus

A character contracts this infection through physical contact with the dormant virus, just as with other strains. However, it is the victim's shadow which the virus first attacks, causing it to rot away. A victim whose shadow is destroyed by the virus becomes a shadow himself.

The initial symptoms of this horrifying virus are deceptively mild: simply a slight tingling of the scalp and a low fever. At the end of the first day of infection, however, the victim's shadow shows distinct signs of fraying around the edges. As the days pass, the victim's shadow continues to unravel and, if the virus is not halted, disappears entirely on the seventh day. Once the host's shadow has been consumed by the virus, the infection begins to take its toll on the flesh of the body. Within a day, one of the victim's limbs grows insubstantial, and on each successive night another portion of the victim's body becomes shadowy. On the fourteenth night of infection, the victim fades away utterly and dies. Within minutes of his demise, the character rises as a shadow himself.

A psionicist with the shadow form science cannot use this ability while infected with the virus. If a *continual light* spell is placed upon a small *blessed* diamond and the victim swallows this stone within the first seven days of the infection, he is cured. The reaction of the virus to the gem destroys them both, so the diamond is lost.

Shadows created by this virus carry the disease with them, so anyone touched by a virulent shadow risks contamination. Unlike the other viruses, this one is not spread by living carriers.

Vorlog

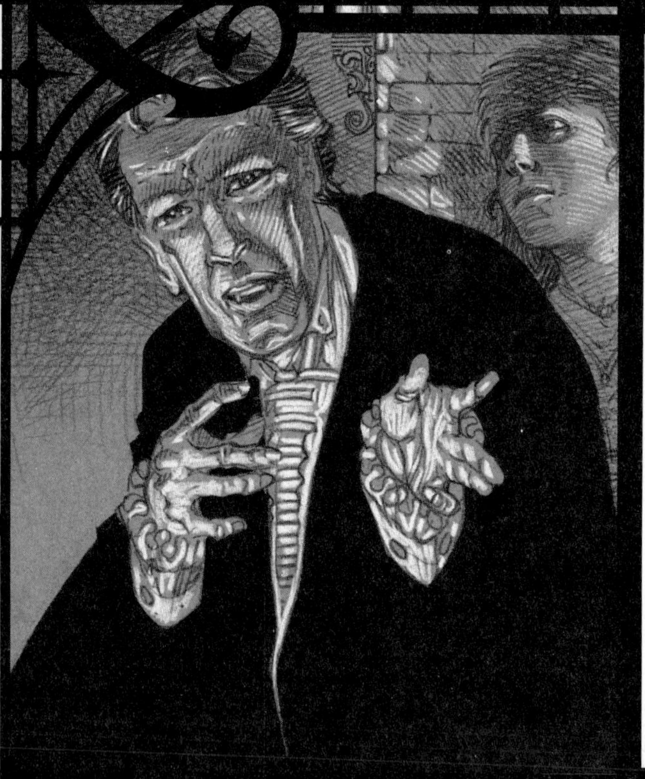

Climate/Terrain:	Any land
Frequency:	Very rare
Organization:	Solitary
Activity Cycle:	Night
Diet:	Special
Intelligence:	High (13–14)
Treasure:	C
Alignment:	Chaotic evil
No. Appearing:	1
Armor Class:	3
Movement:	12
Hit Dice:	6
THAC0:	15
No. of Attacks:	1
Damage/Attack:	5–10
Special Attacks:	*Charm*, sap Wisdom
Special Defenses:	+1 weapon to hit; immune to poison, *sleep, charm,* and *hold* spells; regeneration.
Magic Resistance:	Nil
Size:	M (5′–6′ tall)
Morale:	Steady (11)
XP Value:	3,000

One of a vampire's most vulnerable moments is when the evil creature is attempting to complete its *dark kiss,* its bonding with a new vampire companion, creating a vampiric "bride" or "groom." As elaborated upon by Doctor Rudolph van Richten in his great treatise on vampires, the process of creating a vampire bride or groom is quite elaborate, involving a great expenditure of both passion and blood on the part of the monster. For approximately one hour after the monster has poured all of its energy into the erstwhile companion, the vampire lies helpless beside the bride's or groom's transforming body. If the vampire is slain during this time period, its victim does not complete the transformation, but becomes a creature caught between the world of the living and that of the dead—a sorry being known as a vorlog.

Physically the vorlog appears no different from a normal human, save for the budding fangs visible when the monster speaks. A vorlog has pale skin and always wears an expression of terrible pain and longing on its ashen face. Although the vorlog casts a shadow (unlike a true vampire), the monster can be recognized by a careful observer who notes that the creature appears translucent in mirrors and makes no noise when it moves.

Vorlogs speak the languages they knew in life. Those who have existed for a long time may have acquired other tongues as well.

Combat: Vorlogs have the same raw physical strength as their vampiric creators. A vorlog enjoys a Strength score of 18/76 and thus receives a bonus of +2 on its attack rolls and +4 on its damage rolls. The blows of a vorlog's hands inflict 1d6+4 points of damage to opponents.

The vorlog also gains the ability to use *charm person,* although the vorlog's charm inevitably causes its victims to feel something more akin to pity and sympathy. Otherwise, the ability is identical to the 1st level wizard spell of the same name. The vorlog can charm at will, and often employs the power to convince its chosen victims to visit its lair.

Although it is incapable of draining energy (experience) levels, the vorlog taps into its victim's *spiritual* energies. Each time a vorlog strikes a character, the victim must make a saving throw vs. spell. Failure indicates the character loses 2 points of Wisdom. This loss is temporary, and the victim will regain Wisdom points at the rate of 1 per hour. Characters whose Wisdom scores fall below 3 become so dazed that they perceive the vorlog to be a powerful protector. Such characters desire nothing more than to rest in the supposed sanctuary of the vorlog's embrace.

The vorlog is not actually an undead creature, nor is it truly alive. Thus, neither spells that detect the undead nor spells that detect life will sense the vorlog. The vorlog cannot be turned by a cleric, either. However, as with a true vampire, the vorlog is unaffected by poison, *sleep, charm,* and *hold* spells. Furthermore, the vorlog is immune to normal weapons, being harmed only by those of +1 or greater enchantment.

Vorlogs are capable of regeneration. While this ability is much less potent than that of a vampire, it is still a useful defense. When resting, they regenerate at the rate of 1 hit point per hour. However, while in the company of a charmed *surrogate* (see below), vorlogs regenerate far more rapidly, at the rate of 1 point per melee round.

If a vorlog is reduced to 0 hit points, it issues a mournful wail and melts into a pool of its own tears. The vorlog then attempts to flee the area and return to its lair to recuperate. In this form, the vorlog can climb walls and seep through any crack, no matter how small. The vorlog cannot assume this form at will.

After eight hours of rest, the vorlog again assumes a human form. Unlike a vampire, the vorlog is capable of recuperating in any dark haven, yet it prefers the safety of its own lair.

A vorlog can, at will, touch the minds of any beast within 50 feet. The vorlog's mind is filled with such intense anguish and loss that mental contact drives animals into berserk rages. Affected animals either attempt to flee from the vorlog (50%) or violently attack the nearest creature (50%).

Garlic and holy water have no effect on a vorlog. A vorlog will not approach a character presenting a lawful good holy symbol with courage and conviction. Although it is a nocturnal creature, a vorlog is not destroyed by the sun's rays. Sunlight does, however, cause intense pain, and the vorlog suffers 1d6 points of damage per round of direct exposure. If reduced to 0 hit points by such contact, the vorlog immediately collapses into a pool of tears and seeks shelter from the sun's rays. If unable to do so, the creature quickly dehydrates and dies within 1d4 hours.

Habitat/Society: Vorlogs are often left alive by vampire hunters, for the creatures initially appear human. Many valiant hunters have falsely congratulated themselves for saving a poor wretch when they have actually condemned him to a semilife of eternal torment.

The focus of the vorlog's entire existence centers on its utter anguish and bereavement at the death of its vampire lover. The creature had already given itself over to the vampire, body and mind, when the newly wrought bonds were ripped away by the creature's sudden demise. The shattering combination of psychic and physical blows is so devastating that the creature can never truly recover. Instead, it spends its eternal existence attempting to recreate its lost companion.

A vorlog spends much of its time searching for humans who resemble—even in only a remote fashion—its vampiric creator. Once a vorlog fixates on a particular individual, the monster becomes more and more convinced that the person actually is the vampire, reincarnated or otherwise restored. This fixation becomes so powerful that the vorlog will attempt anything to have the object of its obsession.

Once the vorlog has captured or charmed the individual in question, it makes the new "companion" dress and act like the yearned-for vampire lover. The vorlog also exchanges a small amount of blood with its new companion for three consecutive running, attempting to re-create the original and satisfying bond. At this point, the companion becomes the vorlog's *surrogate*. The surrogate gains no advantages from this bonding, although the vorlog can regenerate faster (see *combat*) while in the presence of a surrogate. The vorlog also feeds on its surrogate's Wisdom regularly, so that the poor thing never has more than half of his or her normal Wisdom score at any time.

A vorlog can survive no more than three months without a surrogate to feed upon, and it is loathe to go for even a month without such a companion, as the loneliness of its existence is almost unbearable.

The vorlog can sense the location of its surrogate, no matter where he or she hides. Only an *amulet of proof against detection and location,* or a similar magical charm, can keep a vorlog from discovering its surrogate's whereabouts.

Over the course of a few weeks, or at most months, the vorlog grows dissatisfied with the hollow mockery of its original bonding. This dissatisfaction is inevitable, as no being can ever recreate the powerful relationship between the vorlog and its creator. The miserable creature grows bitter and anguished as it begins to restlessly search anew for its creator. Eventually, the creature finds a new object for its obsession, at which point the vorlog returns to its current surrogate and destroys him or her.

A vorlog is capable of bonding with only one surrogate at a time. It cannot create new vampires or even other vorlogs to ease the utter desolation of its existence.

Interestingly, when two or more vorlogs confront each other, they find no comfort in mutual commiseration or empathy. Instead, the creatures tend to fly into rages and attack one another or their surrogates. Even if such a fight does not occur, the vorlogs spend the bulk of their energies comparing their dead vampire masters, with each vorlog insisting that its beloved was far superior. Such petty and pointless rivalries consume the vorlogs, causing them to remain distant from the only other beings that might truly understand the anguish of their own existence.

Ecology: Only a mortal in the final stages of the transformation into a vampiric bride or groom (see *Van Richten's Guide to Vampires*—TSR product stock #9345) can ever become a vorlog. Other potential vampires merely recover or die as a result of the injuries inflicted upon them by their vampire attacker.

The vorlog must feed on both normal food and psychic energy to survive. The creature's body needs only one-tenth the amount of food it required while alive, and it can go months without being seriously affected by starvation. More important to the creature is the psychic energy it draws from its surrogates. Without such a surrogate, the vampire dies in three months.

The vorlog is a creature that was never meant to be. Caught on the razor's edge between life and undeath, the vorlog is trapped in a world of horror which no other being can truly understand. There is no known way to cure a vorlog; only death grants the monster any measure of release. The vorlog is a creature to be both pitied and feared.

Surrogate

Once bonded to a vorlog, a surrogate automatically becomes charmed by the creature. Once so affected, the pitiful minion is unable to escape its master's essence on its own. No additional saving throws or the like are possible unless an outsider interferes with the foul relationship.

While serving a vorlog, a surrogate serves as both a companion and a source of psychic sustenance. Thus, a surrogate never has more than a half-normal Wisdom rating, due to the constant draining of mental energy.

The bond between a surrogate and a vorlog is not particularly powerful. If the vorlog dies, the bond is broken and the former surrogate becomes *confused* (as per the wizard spell). The surrogate automatically recovers from this confusion in 1d4 weeks, or sooner if the creature is *blessed* at some point. The bond can also be broken by submerging the surrogate in holy water.

While the vorlog is alive and the surrogate is bound to it, the latter will do everything in his or her power to protect the former. Although often convinced that there is something terribly wrong with his or her sudden change in lifestyle and companion, the surrogate will usually decide that he or she is simply not worthy of the newfound love and that it is necessary to strive all the harder to embody the appearance and behavior the vorlog craves. Such is the terrible mental trap in which the vorlog ensnares its surrogates.

Except for their drops in Wisdom scores, surrogates maintain all the abilities and aptitudes they normally possess—they are mortal and can be killed as such. Surrogates receive only pain, confusion, and eventually death for their services to a vorlog lover. It is a terrible existence, but one from which there is at least some hope of escape, however small. A vorlog's only escape is death's final embrace.

Will O'Dawn

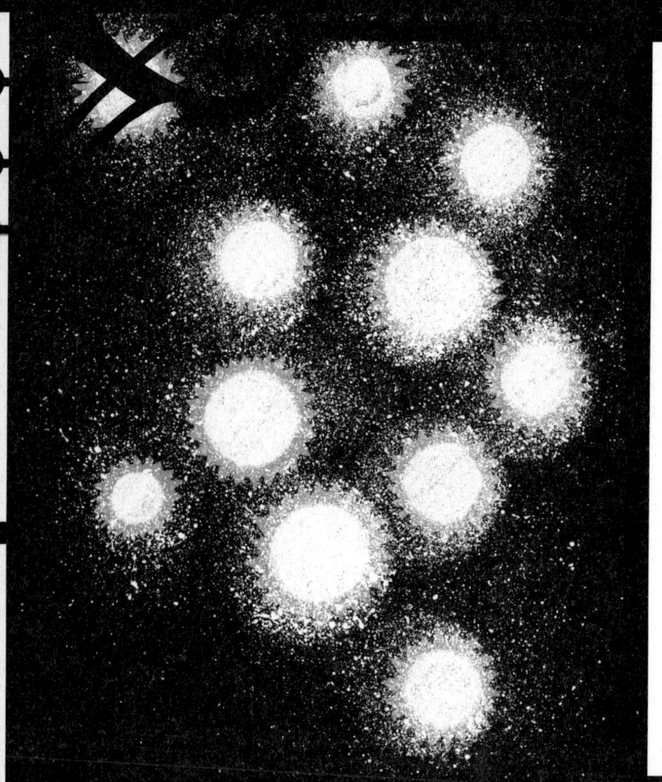

CLIMATE/TERRAIN:	Ravenloft
FREQUENCY:	Very rare
ORGANIZATION:	Solitary
ACTIVITY CYCLE:	Dawn
DIET:	See below
INTELLIGENCE:	Exceptional (15–16)
TREASURE:	Nil
ALIGNMENT:	Chaotic good
NO. APPEARING:	1 or 1–2
ARMOR CLASS:	–6
MOVEMENT:	Fl 18 (A)
HIT DICE:	6
THAC0:	15
NO. OF ATTACKS:	One spell
DAMAGE/ATTACK:	Nil
SPECIAL ATTACKS:	*Color spray, hypnotic pattern*
SPECIAL DEFENSES:	Spell immunity, invisibility
MAGIC RESISTANCE:	Nil
SIZE:	T (1'–2' diameter)
MORALE:	Champion (15–16)
XP VALUE:	1,400

The will o'dawn (or *feu follet,* as it is also called) is perhaps the most mysterious of all will o'wisp variants, and it is certainly the most helpful. The tiny energy form most frequently appears at dawn, and during this brief period it attempts to aid adventurers and others who are afraid, in pain, lost, or otherwise in trouble. In the dark and troubled land of the Mists, such a creature is truly remarkable.

A will o'dawn normally appears as a faintly glowing ball of light. Although generally smaller than its malevolent cousin, it is almost impossible to distinguish between the two. A will o'dawn can somewhat alter its shape and coloring and can easily be mistaken for a lantern, *light* spell, or other artificial illumination. The creature can become invisible at will, although it can only dampen its glow for 2d6 rounds at a time. A will o'dawn cannot cast its spells while invisible. Only beings that can sense invisible objects can spot a hidden will o'dawn.

Will o'dawns seem to communicate with each other via changes in color and brightness. Given enough time in the presence of these creatures, a person might interpret their language. In most cases, however, the best that can be achieved is a basic understanding of concepts like "red means danger" or "blue means safe."

Combat: Will o'dawns loathe combat. There are no known instances of a feu follet intentionally harming a living being. The only time will o'dawns enter battle is to protect themselves or those individuals who merit their assistance.

When in combat, a will o'dawn normally uses its *color spray* or *hypnotic pattern* to either stun or lull its opponents into quiescence. It can use either spell an unlimited number of times, but it can cast only one of either per melee round. The will o'dawn casts both spells and makes all saving throws as a 9th level wizard.

The will o'dawn is also fond of leading opponents on a merry chase, attempting to use the natural surroundings to delay or entrap its foes long enough for the will o'dawn, or those it is helping, to escape. The will o'dawn is not averse to miring its enemies in a bog or the like, but the creature will not purposely harm even its foes.

The will o'dawn is immune to all spells except *darkness* and *continual darkness.* The former stuns the creature for 1d6 rounds if cast directly at it, while the latter is instantly fatal unless a successful saving throw vs. death is made. The will o'dawn, like all will o'wisp variants, is vulnerable to normal weapons.

Habitat/Society: Will o'dawns are almost always encountered alone. On very rare occasions (5% chance per encounter), two such creatures are encountered together. The will o'dawn appears only during sunrise and remains active for no more than 20 minutes. After this time, the will o'dawn normally renders itself invisible and flees the area. On rare occasions when a will o'dawn has been captured, the creature's golden glow dims and slowly dissipates.

No one knows where the mysterious will o'dawn goes when it is not aiding others. What is known is that the will o'dawn aids anyone of good alignment that it meets, although it seldom stays with the beneficiary of its aid for more than a brief period of time. The will o'dawn can sense good creatures in pain or trouble and will attempt to aid them if at all possible. The aid a will o'dawn can offer includes leading adventurers to a treasure cache or secret door, helping lost travelers find their way out of a swamp, or distracting evil creatures in a fight. Unfortunately, many people that the will o'dawn attempts to help do not follow the creature, mistaking it for its evil cousin, the will o'wisp.

As mentioned above, will o'dawns communicate through rapid light flashes usually too subtle for humans and demihumans to understand. However, if a will o'dawn hypnotizes a subject, it can communicate directly with his mind. A will o'dawn can communicate in this manner with only one individual at a time.

Ecology: The will o'dawn seems to feed on the energies generated by excited, happy, or otherwise exhilarated minds. Thus, the will o'dawn attempts to create conditions which cause relief, excitement, or happiness. This apparent feeding on positive emotions renders the will o'dawn remarkably different from all other will o'wisp variants.

Will O'Deep

CLIMATE/TERRAIN:	Subterranean
FREQUENCY:	Rare
ORGANIZATION:	Clan
ACTIVITY CYCLE:	Night
DIET:	See below
INTELLIGENCE:	High (13–14)
TREASURE:	W
ALIGNMENT:	Neutral evil
NO. APPEARING:	1–4
ARMOR CLASS:	0
MOVEMENT:	Fl 12 (A)
HIT DICE:	5
THAC0:	15
NO. OF ATTACKS:	4
DAMAGE/ATTACK:	1d4 (×4)
SPECIAL ATTACKS:	Burning sparks
SPECIAL DEFENSES:	Spell immunity, invisibility
MAGIC RESISTANCE:	Nil
SIZE:	T (1′ diameter)
MORALE:	Champion (15–16)
XP VALUE:	1,000

The least powerful of all will o'wisp variants, the will o'deep is found only within the most remote tunnels and caverns. Whimsically evil, the will o'deep relishes leading unwary explorers into terrible predicaments far away from even the slight comfort and protection of the cloudy skies of Ravenloft.

The will o'deep is a tiny, flickering energy being. Normally golden or reddish in hue, the will o'deep can take on a variety of colors. Although capable of altering its shape, the will o'deep most commonly takes on a rippling, teardrop shape very reminiscent of the flames of a small torch. As with most will o'wisp variants, if the will o'deep does not attack it can temporarily dampen its glow for 2–8 (2d4) rounds, rendering the creature undetectable to all who cannot sense invisible objects.

These creatures communicate with each other through changes in color and intensity. Any human being able to survive in the company of these creatures for an extended period of time might be able to pick up their language, but so far there is no known case of this. There are reports. however, of drow and similar folk who have the ability to understand the conversations of these terrible monsters.

Combat: The will o'deep does not seek out direct combat, instead attempting to either trap its victims or lead them into ambushes and other dangers. Although not as physically dangerous as many of its cousins, the will o'deep is a crafty opponent and difficult to damage. Adventurers who find themselves the object of a will o'deep's attentions are wise to be on their guard or, better yet, retreat to the surface as soon as possible.

Will o'deep strategies often involves luring adventurers into complex labrynths or the lairs of dangerous creatures. Often found in small groups or clans, will o'deeps work together to accomplish such goals.

Although the results of the will o'deep's lure is often deadly, more often than not the creature is merely attempting to wear down the adventurers so that it can trap its victims deep underground. For example, a will o'deep might search out an area where only a small nudge is needed to cause a cave-in or trigger an old trap. Once this is done, the creature's victims are available for long-term feeding.

Will o'deeps can physically attack with a series of small, white-hot sparks. Such sparks have enough force to knock small rocks over or push doors closed. When used as an attack each spark does 1–4 points of damage. Will o'deeps can form up to four such sparks per round.

Additionally, a will o'deep often knows where small pockets of cave gasses have built up. If the will o'deep feels it is in danger it will attempt to lead its pursuers to such a pocket and use one of its sparks to cause an explosion. Anyone within 10′ of such an explosion takes 1–10 points of damage. Such explosions often cause cave-ins as well.

Will o'deeps are vulnerable to normal weapons; however, most magical attacks are useless against them. A *lightning bolt* or *chain lightning* spell will harm them, but all other known spells fail utterly against the will o'deep.

Habitat/Society: Will o'deeps prefer to travel and live in small clans of 2–4 individuals, but are also often encountered alone. Will o'deeps never appear above the surface, preferring to remain as far underground as their feeding needs allow.

The will o'deep is highly self-protective and will attempt to flee if reduced to 25% of its original hit points. If pressed, the will o'deep may lead its pursuers to some underground treasure in the hopes of distracting them while it makes good its escape.

Ecology: The will o'deep seems to feed on the energies given off by humanoid brains, particularly the impulses emitted by the brain when it is consumed by either fear or desperation. Will o'deeps can feed for weeks, even months, on humanoids they have managed to trap since the creatures sometimes go so far as to herd rats and the like to their captives' cells. They will keep their captives alive until apathy and despair set in, conditions on which the monsters seem incapable of feeding.

Will o'deeps have been known to turn such captives over to drow or other creatures of the darkness in return for gold, gems, or fresh victims.

Will O'Mist

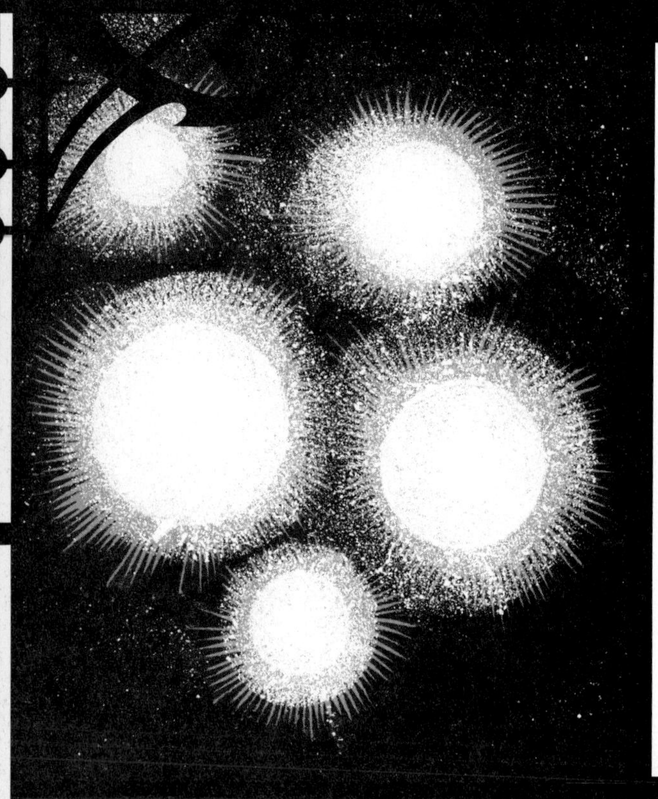

Climate/Terrain:	Ravenloft
Frequency:	Rare
Organization:	Solitary
Activity Cycle:	Night
Diet:	See below
Intelligence:	High (13–14)
Treasure:	Z
Alignment:	Chaotic neutral
No. Appearing:	1
Armor Class:	–6
Movement:	Fl 18 (A)
Hit Dice:	7
THAC0:	13
No. of Attacks:	1
Damage/Attack:	2–16 (2d8)
Special Attacks:	Electric burst
Special Defenses:	Spell immunity, invisibility
Magic Resistance:	See below
Size:	S (2'–4')
Morale:	Champion (15–16)
XP Value:	2,000

The will o'mist is a variant of the will o'wisp that makes its home only in the misty borders of Ravenloft. While most people have good cause to fear these creatures, the mysterious Vistani seem to have found some way of controlling them. This is an especially helpful skill when one considers the fact that a will o'mist is able to unerringly navigate the swirling vapors of Ravenloft's borders.

A will o'mist appears as a diffuse strip of radiant energy some 2 to 4 inches thick and 3 to 5 feet in length. Although normally icy blue in color, the will o'mist has been reported to range in color from golden-white to a very deep green. The will o'mist can alter its shape and size to some extent, and can easily be mistaken for a lantern, *light* spell, or similar source of illumination. If they do not attack, will o'mists are able to temporarily mask their glow, rendering them undetectable to all those who cannot sense invisible objects for 2–8 (2d4) melee rounds.

Unlike the other will o'wisp variants, the will o'mist does not seem to rely upon changes in color and intensity to communicate. However, the exact method by which they converse remains a mystery. Whatever this is, at least a few of the vistani seem to have mastered it.

Combat: Capable of travelling through the mysterious borders of Ravenloft unhindered, will o'mists are almost never placed in a situation requiring direct physical confrontation. Nevertheless, when combat does become necessary, they are fearsome opponents and not to be taken lightly.

Will o'mists are agile fliers who can hover in place without effort, move with sudden bursts of speed, or drift slowly, as if bobbing on the wind itself.

When in battle, will o'mists attack with a burst of electricity. Will o'mists can strike in this manner every third round, causing 2–16 (2d8) points of damage to anyone within 30' of the attacking creature. A successful saving throw vs. spell reduces this damage by half. Victims wearing metal armor have a +4 bonus to their saving throws due to the exceptional conductivity of metal and its natural grounding effects.

Physical weapons affect will o'mists normally; however, most magical attacks are useless against them. Of all known spells, only *vampiric touch* and *energy drain* work against these monsters.

Habitat/Society: Will o'mists are always encountered alone. Capable of manipulating the mists and gaining access even to a domain whose lord has sealed its borders, will o'mists have unparalleled freedom in the Land of the Mists.

Only the Vistani know the secret of summoning and commanding such creatures. It is unknown whether the ability to command will o'mists is inherited or whether the knowledge is passed from generation to generation. In fact, it is generally believed that this command of these creatures is what enables the Vistani to pass through the mists and travel freely through the domains of Ravenloft.

Ecology: As with other variants of the will o'wisp, it appears that will o'mists feed off of the electrical energy generated by human and demihuman brains. It is thought that the will o'mist in particular can only leech such energy from people when they are actually crossing the misty borders of Ravenloft. This may account for reports that some people claim to have been struck by a wave of disorientation and nausea upon stumbling out of the mists.

Since will o'mists are incapable of straying more than a few yards from the mists themselves, they must lure humans and demihumans into the mists in order to feed. It is probable that the specific energy on which will o'mists feed is the fear and disorientation felt by many travelers in the mists. It has even been theorized that such creatures are part of a bizarre network that funnels living energy into the Land, helping it to maintain itself and draw more unwitting souls across its dark borders.

Will O'Sea

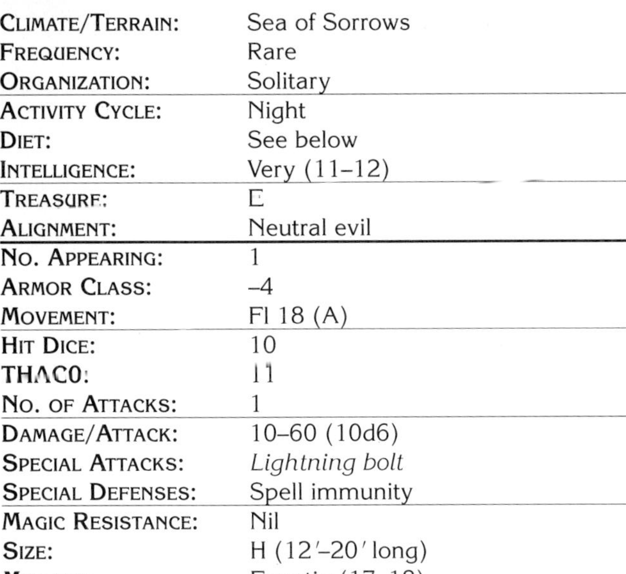

Climate/Terrain:	Sea of Sorrows
Frequency:	Rare
Organization:	Solitary
Activity Cycle:	Night
Diet:	See below
Intelligence:	Very (11–12)
Treasure:	E
Alignment:	Neutral evil
No. Appearing:	1
Armor Class:	–4
Movement:	Fl 18 (A)
Hit Dice:	10
THAC0:	11
No. of Attacks:	1
Damage/Attack:	10–60 (10d6)
Special Attacks:	*Lightning bolt*
Special Defenses:	Spell immunity
Magic Resistance:	Nil
Size:	H (12′–20′ long)
Morale:	Fanatic (17–18)
XP Value:	6,000

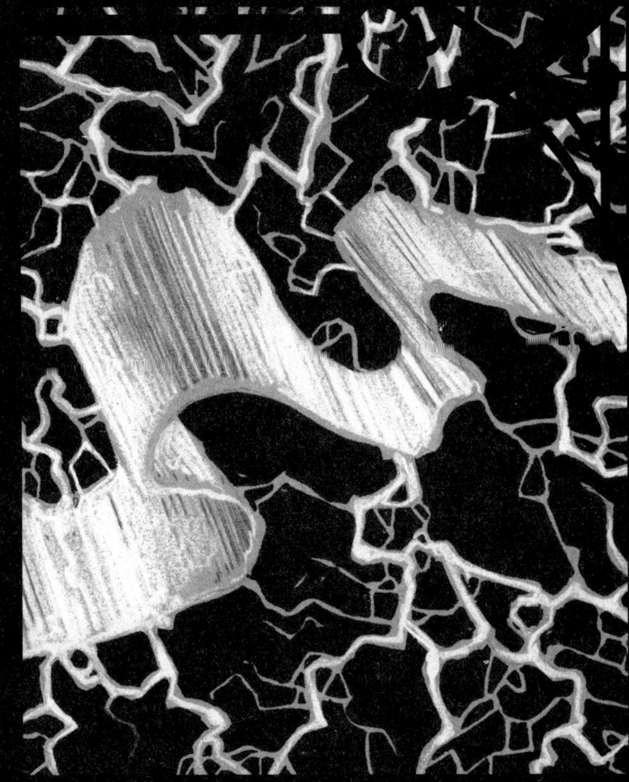

The will o'sea is a variant of the will o'wisp that makes its home on and around the seas of Ravenloft. Even more dangerous than its better known cousins, the will o'sea lures sailors to watery graves.

As beautiful as it is deadly, the will o'sea generally appears as a long, shifting cascade of glowing energy. The will o'sea is often almost indistinguishable from St. Elmo's fire, matching even the luxuriant displays of color of that mystifying phenomenon. The largest of all the will o'wisp variants, the will o'sea can alter its size and shape somewhat. These creatures have shown themselves to be adept at mimicking the shape of a ship or lighthouse. The will o'sea, unlike the will o'wisp, is unable to turn invisible, but can dampen its glow somewhat.

The will o'sea communicates with a combination of visual elements and electrical snaps, clicks, and hums. Some aged seafarers tell stories of aquatic folk who can understand this unusual dialect, but few reliable examples of this can be cited.

Combat: More aggressive than other forms of will o'wisp, the will o'sea often attempts to lure ships of all kinds into dangerous waters where they are likely to become beached or sink. The will o'sea is an extremely agile flier, capable of maneuvers ranging from hovering in place to sudden, wildly jerking flight patterns, an ability it uses well when taunting victims.

Normally, the will o'sea will not waste its energies attacking directly if it can trick its victims into crashing their ship onto rocks or an underwater reef. Appearing at dusk or in the evening, the will o'sea uses a variety of tactics to lure its intended victims into treacherous waters. One of its most common ploys is to form itself into the shape of a burning ship and then hover on top of some sharp boulders or other hazard in the hopes its intended prey will investigate. This tactic works particularly well during storms when visibility is reduced. The will o'sea may also lie beneath the surface of seaweed infested waters, attempting to lure sailors with its shimmering appearance hinting of sunken treasures.

If it appears as if the inhabitants of a vessel are going to escape with their lives, the will o'sea will take a more direct approach, using its vast energies to attack with a powerful lightning bolt. The evil entity can release such a stroke once every three rounds. The bolt does 10–60 (10d6) points of damage and has a 50% chance of setting wooden vessels alight if a saving throw vs. lightning fails.

Physical weapons affect the will o'sea normally, however most magical attacks are useless against the creature. Of all spells, only the *ice storm* and *cone of cold* spells work against this monster.

Habitat/Society: A will o'sea is always encountered alone. These creatures make their homes along almost any rough coastline, but avoid arctic waters in favor of the brilliant blue of a tropical sea. Such a creature almost always dwells amid one or more of the shipwrecks it has caused, being just as comfortable above as below the water. The will o'sea will not, however, use its lightning attack while submerged.

Will o'seas are normally found just off common sea routes, so that they can more easily find sailors to lure to their untimely ends. Whenever hunting becomes scarce, will o'seas will simply move to a more viable hunting ground.

Ecology: As with other will o'wisp variants, the will o'sea seems to feed off the electrical energy generated by human and demihuman brains. The horrified, scrambling panic of a drowning victim seems to be particularly satisfying as the creature will often go out of its way to sink a ship while itself killing as few people as possible. The will o'sea then hovers over the struggling sailors, foiling any attempts its victims make to reach land.

Ghosts and sea zombies are particularly common in the hunting grounds of a will o'sea. There have been reports of both individual spirits and entire ghost ships wandering the waters near a will o'sea's lair. The will o'sea is unaffected by such spirits, unless they keep other sailors from entering the area.

Zombie, Cannibal

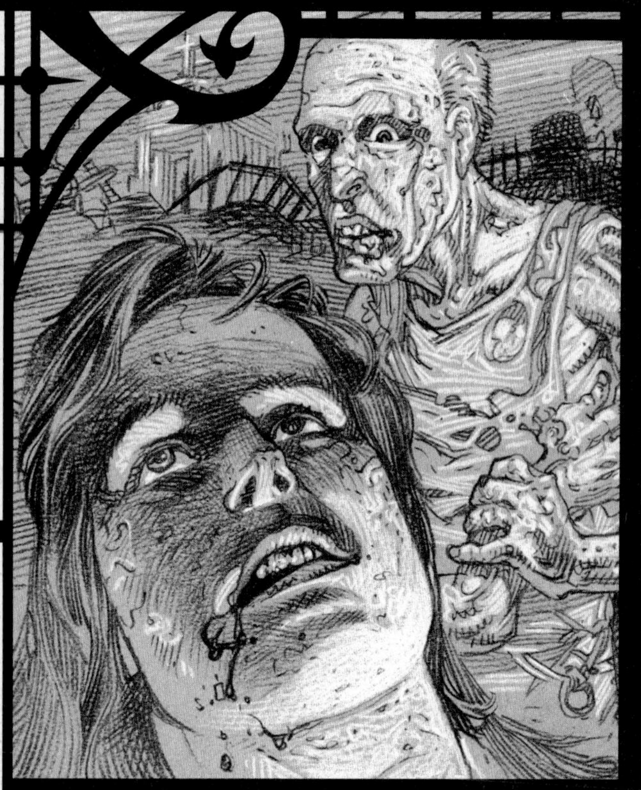

CLIMATE/TERRAIN:	Ravenloft
FREQUENCY:	Very rare
ORGANIZATION:	Pack
ACTIVITY CYCLE:	Night
DIET:	Carnivore
INTELLIGENCE:	Low (5–7)
TREASURE:	Nil
ALIGNMENT:	Chaotic evil
NO. APPEARING:	2–20 (2d10)
ARMOR CLASS:	7
MOVEMENT:	6
HIT DICE:	2+2
THAC0:	19
NO. OF ATTACKS:	1
DAMAGE/ATTACK:	1–8 or 1–2
SPECIAL ATTACKS:	Poison
SPECIAL DEFENSES:	Immune to *sleep, charm, hold,* and poison
MAGIC RESISTANCE:	Nil
SIZE:	M (6′ tall)
MORALE:	Steady (11–12)
XP VALUE:	270

Cannibal zombies shuffle through their morbid existence somewhere on the brink between the world of the living and the dark realm of the dead. These foul creatures wander about, killing many innocents and creating still more of their dread kind from victims not fortunate enough to die in their initial attack.

Cannibals appear fresher and more alive than true zombies. Still, such creatures look exceptionally haggard, with staring eyes, slack features, and ichor-dripping wounds. Their expressions only change when they actually attack, at which time they slaver and moan horribly as they claw greedily at their next meal. Cannibal zombies care nothing for clothing, and are thus most commonly dressed in fetid rags. The stench that surrounds them is a nauseating combination of rotten meat and dried blood that is noticeable up to 50 feet distant.

These pitiful creatures retain a marginal ability to communicate in the languages they knew in life. Most frequently, however, they do not pause to speak but shuffle on seeking new flesh to devour. A *speak with dead* spell or similar enchantment can force them to pause for a moment and engage in conversation. As soon as the spell lapses, however, the creature reverts to its ravenous nature.

Combat: Packs of cannibal zombies shuffle about at night in a constant search for living humans and demihumans, their preferred source of food. Most often such a pack will converge on a small household or farmstead, hammering at doors and smashing in windows, heedless of any damage done to themselves.

Once they have chosen a target, the zombies will not relent unless turned (treat as ghouls for this) or held off until sunrise. At dawn, the group will turn away with despairing moans, sometimes turning on one of their own to assuage their terrible hunger for flesh. There is, however, a 50% chance the group will return to the same household on the following evening. This remains true each evening the pack is repelled, until the zombies either succeed or change targets.

Once within range of a victim, cannibal zombies attack mindlessly, never winning initiative and thus always attacking at the end of the round. Zombies may either claw at their foes, doing 1–8 points of damage, or attempt to bite their opponents for 1–2 points of damage.

Anyone bitten by a cannibal zombie must make a saving throw vs. poison. Success indicates that the creature's poisonous saliva has had no effect. Failure means that the victim will soon become a new cannibal zombie himself unless a *cure disease* spell is cast upon him quickly. Within 2–8 (2d4) rounds after failing the saving throw the victim begins to feel a gnawing hunger. Every other round thereafter the victim must make a Constitution check. When this check fails, the victim is killed by the fast-acting poison in his veins and moves to join his new brethren in attacking the fully living. Once this happens, a *cure disease* spell will have no effect on the new zombie. A *slow poison* spell will retard the poison's onset, but this only delays the inevitable.

Cannibal zombies are immune to *sleep, charm, hold,* and all poisons. Holy water does 1–6 points of damage per flask to the monsters.

Habitat/Society: Cannibal zombies have only the most tenuous form of society. They make their homes within ruins, abandoned mausoleums, or wherever they found their last meal. Although they travel in packs, it seems this is more for convenience than for companionship, since the monsters simply fall upon each other when they cannot find sufficient living fodder. In a sense, creating more such zombies is simply a way of ensuring enough available food sources, for if a cannibal zombie does not taste flesh for three nights running, its own body will turn on itself, and the zombie will crumple into an unliving husk.

Zombie lords are able to communicate with cannibal zombies. Such lords often bribe these creatures with the promise of living flesh in return for aid in overrunning a village. This system works especially well for the zombie lord who can transform any cannibal zombies killed during the fighting into true zombies that will do the nefarious creature's bidding.

Ecology: It is not known how cannibal zombies first came into existence. It is certain, however, that such monstrosities have little to do with the natural order, although they will occasionally take part in the food chain as scavengers, feeding on carrion.

Climate/Terrain:	Har'Akir
Frequency:	Very rare
Organization:	Pack
Activity Cycle:	Night
Diet:	Nil
Intelligence:	Non- (0)
Treasure:	Nil
Alignment:	Neutral
No. Appearing:	3d6
Armor Class:	7
Movement:	9, Br 6
Hit Dice:	2
THAC0:	19
No. of Attacks:	1
Damage/Attack:	1d8
Special Attacks:	Surprise, grab
Special Defenses:	See below
Magic Resistance:	Nil
Size:	M (5′ tall)
Morale:	Fearless (19–20)
XP Value:	120

Desert zombies are animated corpses controlled by their creator, the evil mummy Senmet. In recent years, rumors have arisen that other powerful spellcasters in the domain of Har'Akir have begun to create these things, but this has yet to be proven.

A desert zombie looks like a dried-out human corpse. Unlike that of common zombies, the desiccated flesh is usually intact and does not deteriorate over time. They have brown, withered skin that clings to their bones. There is very little odor associated with desert zombies. They wear the tattered remains of whatever clothing they had on when they died. Because this clothing is subject to the ravages of time, older desert zombies may not have any garments remaining intact. Like the common zombie, they still bear whatever wounds they had in life, as well as any wounds from battles since they became zombies. Any weapons or equipment is retained, but no attempt is made to maintain it. If the zombie died holding a sword, it carries it until the weapon falls apart or rusts away.

Desert zombies have no more ability to communicate than their common peers. They are able to understand the commands of their master, but these must be limited and very direct or confusion may result.

Combat: Desert zombies move with the same halting steps as the common variety. However, they are not as slow and do not suffer the initiative penalties of normal zombies. Desert zombies roll for initiative normally. They always do the same amount of damage (1d8) regardless of the weapon they hold, or even if they are unarmed. They can be directed to use magical weapons and get any of the benefits that might be associated with them.

Like most undead, desert zombies are immune to *sleep, charm, hold,* death magic, poisons, cold (including spells), and heat (but not actual fire). The sight of a desert zombie is enough to cause a character to make a horror check. Like most situations that call for horror checks in Ravenloft, constant exposure to them makes the characters less susceptible to the horror of their existence. Thus, DMs may wish to grant experienced characters a bonus or even eliminated the need for them to make these checks.

Desert zombies can "swim" through sand. If they are close to the surface, only a few feet under, they leave furrows, like the wake of a boat on water. It can be a terrifying experience to be all alone in the desert and surrounded by unknown creatures swimming under the desert sands.

A desert zombie can reach up through the sand and grab the legs of a victim. They make a normal attack roll for the grab. The target must defend as Armor Class 10, but does get to add his Dexterity bonuses. Once held, the character has –2 penalties to his THAC0 and Armor Class.

Once grabbed, a victim will gradually be pulled beneath the desert sands. It takes three rounds for the zombie to drag the character under the sand. Each round, the character can make a Strength check to break the hold. Once under the sand, the character can survive for one round, but suffocates at the end of the second round.

Senmet directs all of the activities of the desert zombies. He can see and hear through them and control them all each round without impeding his own ability to move or attack during that round. He cannot make the zombies talk, nor are they able to pick up and use weapons or other items near them.

There are two basic strategies Senmet uses with his zombies. He has them bury themselves just under the surface of the desert where they can't be detected. When the intended victims walk over them, the zombies grab their feet and legs. Those not immediately under a character spring up out of the sand and surround the victim.

Habitat/Society: These unnatural creatures have no true society and are only an extension of their master's power. They must always be within 8 miles of Senmet. When he doesn't need them, Senmet has the zombies scatter throughout the desert and bury themselves in at least a dozen feet of sand. There they remain until they are needed once again.

Ecology: The greater mummy, Senmet, created the first desert zombies. He sacrificed all of his spell casting power to be able to create and control an army of these nightmares, as well as to take limited control over the domain of Har'Akir.

Any character who dies from the disease transmitted by the touch of the greater mummy becomes a desert zombie. It takes a full day after death for the corpse to animate. If the body is destroyed during that time, it will not be animated.

Zombie Fog

	Zombie Fog	Cadaver
CLIMATE/TERRAIN:	Ravenloft	Ravenloft
FREQUENCY:	Very Rare	Very Rare
ORGANIZATION:	Solitary	Nil
ACTIVITY CYCLE:	Night	Night
DIET:	Special	Nil
INTELLIGENCE:	Semi- (2–4)	Non- (0)
TREASURE:	Nil	Nil
ALIGNMENT:	Neutral Evil	Nil
NO. APPEARING:	1	4–40 (4d10)
ARMOR CLASS:	–1	8
MOVEMENT:	6	6
HIT DICE:	6–10	2+2
THAC0:	Varies	19
NO. OF ATTACKS:	1	1
DAMAGE/ATTACK:	special	1–6
SPECIAL ATTACKS:	*Cause despair,* control cadavers	Nil
SPECIAL DEFENSES:	+1 or better to hit, spell immunity	Spell immunity, reanimation
MAGIC RESISTANCE:	Nil	Nil
SIZE:	G (60'–100' cloud)	M (5'–6')
MORALE:	Champion (15–16)	Fearless (19–20)
XP VALUE:	6 HD: 1,400 7 HD: 2,000 8 HD: 2,000 9 HD: 3,000 10 HD: 4,000	175

The zombie fog is an evil creature that feeds on the psychic energies emitted by living creatures at the moment of their deaths. This malevolent vapor has no physical attacks of its own, relying instead upon the corpses it animates and controls to strike down any living thing that threatens it.

The zombie fog appears as a fairly dense bank of mist. Horses and dogs can sense the fog's evil nature and will attempt to avoid it at all costs. As a rule, the creature will be 25 feet in diameter for every Hit Die that it possesses. Even more noticeable are the walking corpses, or cadavers, which almost always accompany the fog. These are virtually identical to zombies, having the same shuffling gate, slack expressions, and decayed appearance as the undead.

Conventional attempts to communicate with the zombie fog or its cadavers always fail. Magical or psionic attempts that place one in direct mental contact with the creature require a madness check, but otherwise fail utterly.

Combat: The zombie fog's sole goal in battle is to engineer the deaths of as many creatures as possible within its trailing expanse. Although the zombie fog has no direct physical attacks, it can control a number of cadavers equal to its current hit points.

A zombie fog may also *cause despair* up to three times per night. When it does this, any living being within its misty tendrils must make a saving throw vs. spell. Anyone failing this roll immediately feels utterly hopeless. The despairing victim will not attack or defend himself until struck by an enemy. The first attack against such a desolate victim gains a +4 bonus to hit. In addition, the victim receives no Dexterity bonuses to his Armor Class. After this first attack, if the victim still lives, he can defend himself, but all attacks against him are made at +2, while the victim makes his attacks with a –2 penalty. Even those successfully saving against the zombie fog's attack receive a –1 on their attack rolls for the duration of the spell, due to their continuing efforts to fight off the magical despair. The despair created by the zombie fog fades away only with the coming of the dawn or the casting of a *dispel magic* on the victim.

Fortunately for the monster's foes, the zombie fog can be hit by magical weapons. Unenchanted weapons, however, do no damage to the creature.

Most magical spells have no effect upon the vaporous body of this abomination. Those that involve the creation of air currents and the like, such as the *gust of wind* spell, can injure the zombie fog, however. As a rule, any spell of this type that is used to attack the creature will inflict 1d4 points of damage per level of the spell. Thus, a 4th level *wind wall* spell would cause 4d4 points of damage to the thing.

Habitat/Society: The zombie fog is a barely sentient, nocturnal creature most often found within a day's journey of some large burial ground or other plentiful source of dead bodies. Although the sun's rays do not appear to harm the zombie fog, the misty creature is almost never active before sunset as its power to control cadavers only functions during the night.

Ecology: Each week, the zombie fog must feast on the death-energies of at least as many living creatures as it has Hit Dice. If a zombie fog is unable to feed on enough such energy in a given week, the monster will shrink in size or even die. For every week without sufficient "food," the zombie fog loses one Hit Die. Conversely, if a zombie fog feeds on twice as many deaths as necessary in a week, the monster will gain a Hit Die.

The zombie fog is believed to be related to the mist horror, but sages are uncertain as to the exact nature of this kinship.

Cadavers

Cadavers are merely dead bodies under the control of a zombie fog. They are not truly undead, and as such cannot be turned. The animating force is the zombie fog, not the negative material plane. Cadavers have no will of their own and instantly obey their animator.

As with zombies, cadavers always attack last in a round. They attack with whatever is at hand, doing 1–6 points of damage per hit. Poison, mind-affecting, *death,* and *hold* spells do not affect cadavers. They can be hit by normal weapons, however cadavers will always rise again in 1–4 rounds after being struck down. Newly risen cadavers are at full hit points. Cadavers can rise again and again. Only the death of the controlling fog or the utter destruction of the body can keep this from happening.

Zombie, Strahd

Climate/Terrain:	Barovia
Frequency:	Very rare
Organization:	Nil
Activity Cycle:	Night
Diet:	Nil
Intelligence:	Non- (0)
Treasure:	Nil
Alignment:	Neutral
No. Appearing:	1d10
Armor Class:	8
Movement:	9
Hit Dice:	4
THAC0:	17
No. of Attacks:	1–3
Damage/Attack:	1d8
Special Attacks:	Nil
Special Defenses:	Turn as mummies
Magic Resistance:	Special
Size:	M (6′ tall)
Morale:	Fearless (19–20)
XP Value:	270

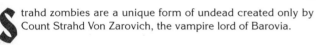

Strahd zombies are a unique form of undead created only by Count Strahd Von Zarovich, the vampire lord of Barovia.

These horrible creatures are human bodies that have been resurrected into living death. They wear the remains of the armor and clothing they wore at the time of death. Since many of them were once guards at Castle Ravenloft, 50% of these zombies wear useless, rag-tag pieces of armor. They seldom carry weapons or tools.

Strahd zombies appear fragile. Their gray-green flesh looks soft, and even their bones seem brittle. Their eyes are dark, empty pits that somehow seem to see anyway. The zombie's lips and cheeks have shrunk, revealing large, crooked teeth. Their hands end in sharp, talonlike nails that bear little resemblance to a normal person's fingernails.

Strahd zombies smell like normal zombies. In other words, they exude a rotting stench that is noticeable up to 100 feet away if it's unobstructed.

Strahd zombies can utter only two sounds. Neither vocalization causes their mouths to move discernibly. The first is a low moan, which signifies an eagerness to act. The second is a mutilated whisper of the name "Strahd." If a character declares that he wants to figure out what these creatures are hissing, he must make an Intelligence check to decipher it.

Combat: The sight of a Strahd zombie requires a horror check. If the viewer sees the vestiges of someone he once knew among the zombies, a –4 penalty is applied. Despite their fragile appearance, the negative plane energy is very strong in Strahd zombies. The power of Strahd Von Zarovich runs through them, making them as difficult to turn as mummies.

Like the common zombie, a Strahd zombie always strikes last in the round. Initially, it can attack once per round with a taloned hand. Eventually it may not have a hand to strike with, however. Any single hit of 5 points or more against a zombie severs a limb. Since they always reach out with arms extended, that usually indicates an arm. When both arms are gone, the head is the next logical target, since the zombie leans forward in an attempt to bite its victim. If an opponent attempts to hit something other than an arm or the head, he suffers a –2 penalty to his attack roll. If he rolls a natural 1, he hits an arm or the head anyway (whichever is thrust forward).

The zombie's severed head and arms can continue to move, at a rate of 1. The arms move like an inch worm, while the head rolls around. They can attack independently from the body once severed. If other body parts are severed, they flop around but cannot attack. The first time a character sees the severed limbs moving to attack, he must make another horror check. This time he gains a +2 bonus for having already stood his ground against the foul creatures.

The life force of a Strahd zombie is shared between all fallen body parts. When any body part suffers damage, the hit points are subtracted from the total of the whole. If the zombie is reduced to 0 total hit points, all body parts cease to move and attack.

Habitat/Society: Strahd zombies lurk in dungeons and graveyards, particularly around Castle Ravenloft. Being mindless undead, they have no society.

These zombies follow whatever order their master gives them. These must be a simple, no more than a single sentence of 20 words or less. They never check for morale, always following their orders until completely destroyed.

When in their native land of Barovia, Strahd zombies can "report back" to Strahd if it is a part of their orders. It takes them a full turn of inactivity to establish contact. Even then, there is a chance that Strahd may be too busy to listen. The report takes the form of a simple. Strahd receives a simple feeling of success or failure. This ability is a part of Strahd's attachment to the land of Barovia. It is not an inherent capability of the zombies.

Ecology: Strahd zombies are not a part of nature, nor are they part of the warped quality of Ravenloft. They are created with an arcane formula known only to Strahd Von Zarovich. He can create them only from the dead bodies of humans.

Zombie, Wolf

Climate/Terrain:	Forlorn
Frequency:	Very rare
Organization:	Nil
Activity Cycle:	Any (usually night)
Diet:	Nil
Intelligence:	Non- (0)
Treasure:	Nil
Alignment:	Neutral evil
No. Appearing:	2d4
Armor Class:	6
Movement:	9
Hit Dice:	2+2
THAC0:	19
No. of Attacks:	1
Damage/Attack:	1d4+1
Special Attacks:	Nil
Special Defenses:	See below
Magic Resistance:	Nil
Size:	S (2′–4′ long)
Morale:	Fearless (19–20)
XP Value:	120

Zombie wolves are not created by a wizard or a priest, but are a creation of the domain of Forlorn itself. Although originally encountered only in that grim land, there are reports that their kind have begun to spread to the other forests of Ravenloft.

Because a zombie wolf looks exactly as it did in death, these creatures often have gaping wounds and sometimes are even missing a limb. They have dirty, matted fur and a rotten stench that is noticeable up to 100 feet away.

A zombie wolf cannot howl like its living counterparts, but it does occasionally throw back its head and utter a strangled cry from rotting vocal cords (prompting a Fear Check the first time it is heard). These creatures move with a stiff-legged gait at half the speed of a living wolf.

Combat: Like all zombies, the slower speed of the zombie wolf means that it strikes last in any combat round (it automatically loses the initiative). While they can be turned and destroyed by priests, zombie wolves otherwise fight mindlessly until their intended target is dead or they are destroyed. They will break off their attack only if called off by the lord of the domain.

Zombie wolves have an Armor Class that is slightly better than that of regular wolves, due to the toughness of their dead, leathery skin. They attack by biting, just as living wolves do, inflicting 1d4+1 points of damage with a successful hit.

Like other undead, zombie wolves are immune to *charm, hold,* and *sleep* spells, as well as death magic, poison, and cold-based spells. Holy water can also damage them, inflicting 2d4 points of damage when it strikes them. They are turned as zombies, except when they are acting under the direct control or orders of the lord of Forlorn, at which time they impose a –2 penalty upon a priest or paladin's attempt to turn them.

Habitat/Society: Zombie wolves are usually found within a few miles of the spot where they were killed (and rose again to unlife). Like living wolves, they tend to form packs, but these are much smaller than normal, with no more than eight members. Under special circumstances, such as an assemblage called together by the lord of Forlorn, the pack can contain virtually every zombie wolf in the domain. It takes 1d6 hours for a pack of this size to accumulate, and anyone who sees the mass of monsters gathering is subject to both Fear and Horror Checks, even if the pack hasn't yet mobilized or chosen the viewer as its prey.

Ecology: Zombie wolves rise from the dead when the body of any regular wolf in the domain of Forlorn is not destroyed after it is killed. If this gruesome task is not carried out, the corpse of the wolf rises as a zombie 2d8 days after it has died.

It is generally thought that the creatures gain this strange form of existence from contact with the land itself, which channels energy from the Negative Material Plane. Some sages speculate that simply preventing the wolf carcass from having any contact with the ground for a full eight days will prevent it from rising as a zombie, but in the absence of any practical application of this theory, this remains unproven.